To Father

with

Joel Dec 1977.

Control System Design
by Pole-Zero Assignment

Control System Design by Pole-Zero Assignment

Based on papers presented at a
Working Party at Cambridge University
September 1974

Edited by
F. FALLSIDE
Cambridge University,
Cambridge, England

1977

ACADEMIC PRESS

LONDON · NEW YORK · SAN FRANCISCO

A Subsidiary of Harcourt Brace Jovanovich, Publishers

ACADEMIC PRESS INC. (LONDON) LTD.
24/28 Oval Road,
London NW1

United States Edition published by
ACADEMIC PRESS INC.
111 Fifth Avenue
New York, New York 10003

Library of Congress Catalog Card Number: 76-016965
ISBN: 0-12-248250-6

Text set in 10/11 pt IBM Press Roman, printed by photolithography, and bound in Great Britain at The Pitman Press, Bath

Contributors

Chow, S. G., *Department of Electrical Engineering, University of Toronto, Toronto M5S IA4, Canada*

Davison, E. J., *Department of Electrical Engineering, University of Toronto, Toronto M5S IA4, Canada*

Fallside, F., *Department of Engineering, University of Cambridge, Cambridge CB2 1PZ, England*

MacFarlane, A. G. J., *Control and Management Systems Division, Cambridge University Engineering Department, Cambridge CB2 1PZ, England*

Munro, N., *Control Systems Centre, University of Manchester Institute of Science and Technology, Manchester M60 1QD, England*

Murdoch, P., *Department of Electrical Engineering and Electronics, Brunel University, Uxbridge UB8 3PH, England*

Patel, R. V., *NASA Ames Research Centre, Moffet Field, California 94035, U.S.A.*

Porter, B., *Department of Aeronautical and Mechanical Engineering, University of Salford, Salford M5 4WT, England*

Power, H. M., *Department of Electrical Engineering, University of Salford, Salford M5 4WT, England*

Seraji, H., *Department of Electrical Engineering, Arya-Mehr University of Technology, P.O. Box 3406, Tehran, Iran*

Sridhar, B., *Dynamics Research Corporation, Wilmington, Massachusetts 01887, U.S.A.*

Wang, S. H., *Department of Electrical Engineering, University of Toronto, Toronto M5S IA4, Canada*

Wolovich, W. A., *Division of Engineering, Brown University, Providence, Rhode Island 02912, U.S.A.*

Acknowledgements

Some of the contributions in the book have been published previously in the literature in whole or in part. The Academic Press wishes to acknowledge permission to publish such contributions from: the American Institute of Aeronautics and Astronautics, pp. 136–144; the Institute of Electrical and Electronics Engineers, pp. 226–236; the International Federation of Automatic Control, pp. 16–42, pp. 51–122, pp. 136–144; and the International Journal of Control, pp. 123–135, pp. 145–165, pp. 181–195, pp. 196–225.

Preface

One of the areas of control theory which has been developing rapidly is that of linear multivariable systems. Within that area several techniques have been developed for system design using pole-zero assignment. This book is concerned with these, their relationship with other methods for linear systems and, particularly, with properties of multivariable zeros. While the subject is still developing it is hoped this book will serve a useful purpose in bringing together some of the main results in this field.

The book is based on papers presented at a Working Party on the topic at Cambridge University in September 1974. One consequence of this is that the book is not all-embracing but it is believed to be representative. A smaller consequence is that the notations used, particularly for vectors and matrices, are not uniform across the book.

It is a pleasure to acknowledge the support of the Cambridge Philosophical Society, which made the Working Party possible and Academic Press for their invaluable assistance throughout.

Cambridge, 1977 F. Fallside

Contents

Perfect Control in Linear Time-Invariant Multivariable Systems: The Control Inequality Principle*

E. J. DAVISON AND S. G. CHOW
Department of Electrical Engineering
University of Toronto
Toronto, Canada M5S 1A4

Summary. The concept of *perfect control* in linear, time-invariant, multivariable systems is formally introduced and resolved in this paper. Necessary and sufficient conditions are found for a linear, time-invariant controller to exist for a linear multivariable system, subject to a given class of external disturbances, so that perfect tracking or/and perfect regulation is achieved for a given class of reference inputs for all initial conditions in the system. Explicit controllers which accomplish this are obtained. It is also shown (the *Control Inequality Principle*) that if the system to be controlled has *more* independent control inputs than outputs to be controlled, it is *almost always possible* to achieve perfect control; if the system has equal inputs and outputs, it may or may not be possible to achieve perfect control depending on whether the system is *non-minimum phase*; if the system has more outputs than inputs, it is never possible to have perfect control.

1. Introduction

The following general servomechanism problem is considered in this paper. A system is described by the following equations:

$$\dot{x} = Ax + Bu + \sum_{i=1}^{\Gamma} (E_i, 0) \begin{bmatrix} \omega_i \\ y_i \end{bmatrix}$$

$$e = Cx + Du + \sum_{i=1}^{\Gamma} (F_i, -G_i) \begin{bmatrix} \omega_i \\ y_i \end{bmatrix} \tag{1}$$

*This work has been supported by the National Research Council of Canada under Grant No. A-4396.

where x is the n-state vector, u the m-plant input vector, $y \triangleq Cx + Du + \sum_{i=1}^{\Gamma} F_i\omega_i$ the r-output vector, $e \triangleq y - y_{\text{ref}}$ the r-error vector, where $y_{\text{ref}} \triangleq \sum_{i=1}^{\Gamma} G_i y_i^{\text{ref}}$ is the desired r-reference input vector, ω_i are n_i-disturbance vectors, which may or may not be measurable, where rank $\begin{bmatrix} E_i \\ F_i \end{bmatrix} = n_i$, and y_i^{ref} are r_i-vectors with rank $G_i = r_i \cdot A, B, C, D, E_i, F_i, G_i$ are specified constant matrices of appropriate dimensions. Without loss of generality it is assumed that the elements of the vectors ω_i and y_i, $i = 1, 2, \ldots, \Gamma$ satisfy the same differential equation:

$$\omega_i^{(p_i)} + q_{p_i}^i\, \omega_i^{(p_i-1)} + \ldots + q_2^i\, \omega_i + q_1^i \omega_i = 0 \tag{2}$$

where $Re(\tilde{\lambda}_j^i) \geqslant 0, j = 1, 2, \ldots, p_i; i = 1, 2, \ldots, \Gamma$ where $\tilde{\lambda}_j^i$ are the characteristic roots of (2). The initial conditions of (2) are assumed to be unknown for the elements of the vector ω_i and known for the elements of the vector y_i^{ref}. Without loss of generality, it is also assumed that rank $B = m$, rank $C = r$ and that the following non-redundancy condition holds:

$$\text{rank} \begin{bmatrix} E_{r_k} & E_{s_k} & E_{t_k} & \ldots \\ F_{r_k} & F_{s_k} & F_{t_k} & \ldots \end{bmatrix} = n_{r_k} + n_{s_k} + n_{t_k} + \ldots; \quad k = 1, 2, \ldots, k^* \tag{3}$$

The following problem is solved in Davison.[1]† Find a linear time-invariant controller for (1) assuming that (a) x and y are available for measurement or (b) $y_m = C_m x + D_m u + \sum_{i=1}^{\Gamma} F_i^m \omega_i$ is only available for measurement, so that $e(t) \to 0$ as $t \to \infty$, and such that the controlled system is stable for the case when ω_i is available for measurement (feedforward control) and for the case when ω_i is not available for measurement (feedback control). In addition, find a "robust controller" for the system, so that asymptotic tracking will take place independent of perturbations in the parameters of the system matrices A, B, C, D.

It is now desired to solve the above problem under the additional constraint that for all bounded initial conditions in (1) and (2) and also for all bounded initial conditions in any dynamic controllers which may be used to control (1), the performance index J given by

$$J = \int_0^{\infty} e'Qe \, d\tau, \; Q > 0$$

can be made arbitrarily small. This is called the *perfect tracking or regulation problem*. Kwakernaak and Sivan[2] have solved the above problem in the special case

† See also [7–10].

when the disturbance and reference inputs to the system (1) are all identically equal to zero.

The organization of this paper is given as follows. Section 2 defines the perfect tracking or regulation problem, section 3 (Theorems 1–3) gives necessary and sufficient conditions for there to be a solution to the problem, section 4 gives an explicit controller which enables this to be done and section 5 gives some numerical examples.

2. Mathematical Preliminaries

The following definitions are required in the development to follow:

Let $\lambda_j^i, j = 1, 2, \ldots, \bar{p}^i; i = 1, 2, \ldots, \Gamma$ denote the characteristic roots of (2) defined such that λ_j^i is repeated q_{ij} times, $j = 1, 2, \ldots, \bar{p}^i; i = 1, 2, \ldots, \Gamma$ where

$$\sum_{j=1}^{\bar{p}^i} q_{ij} = p_i, \; i = 1, 2, \ldots, \Gamma \tag{4}$$

Let H^i be a $mp_i \times mp_i$ matrix given by:

$$H^i = \begin{bmatrix} N_1^i \\ N_2^i \\ \cdot \\ \cdot \\ \cdot \\ N_{\bar{p}^i}^i \end{bmatrix}, \; i = 1, 2, \ldots, \Gamma$$

where $N_j^i, j = 1, 2, \ldots, \bar{p}^i$ is a $mq_{ij} \times mp_i$ matrix given by:

$$N_j^i = \begin{bmatrix} I & \lambda_j^i I & \lambda_j^{i^2} I & \lambda_j^{i^3} I & \ldots & \lambda_j^{i^{p_i-1}} I \\ 0 & I & \binom{2}{1}\lambda_j^i I & \binom{3}{1}\lambda_j^{i^2} I & \ldots & \binom{p_i-1}{1}\lambda_j^{i^{p_i-2}} I \\ 0 & 0 & I & \binom{3}{2}\lambda_j^i I & \ldots & \binom{p_i-1}{2}\lambda_j^{i^{p_i-3}} I \\ \cdot & \cdot & \cdot & \cdot & & \cdot \\ \cdot & \cdot & \cdot & \cdot & & \cdot \\ \cdot & \cdot & \cdot & \cdot & & \cdot \\ 0 & 0 & 0 & 0 \ldots I \ldots & & \binom{p_i-1}{q_{ij}-1}\lambda_j^{i^{p_i-q_{ij}}} I \end{bmatrix} \tag{5}$$

$$j = 1, 2, \ldots, \bar{p}^i$$

Definition. Given the system (1), assume a feedback controller $\dot{\eta} = \Lambda_2\eta + \Lambda_1 x$, $u = K_1 x + K_2\eta$ has been applied; then the *closed loop system is said to be stabilizable* if the pair $\left\{\begin{bmatrix} A & 0 \\ \Lambda_1 & \Lambda_2 \end{bmatrix}, \begin{bmatrix} B \\ 0 \end{bmatrix}\right\}$ is stabilizable.

Definition. [1, 9]. The system (1) denoted by $(A, B, C, D, E_i, F_i, G_i, \omega_i, y_{\text{ref}})$ is said to be *steady-state invertible* if:

$$\operatorname{rank}\{\Psi_{ij}\} = \operatorname{rank}\left\{\Psi_{ij} \,\middle|\, \begin{matrix} E_i & 0 \\ 0 & 0 \\ E_i & 0 \\ 0 & 0 \\ \cdot & \cdot \\ \cdot & \cdot \\ \cdot & \cdot \\ E_i & 0 \\ 0 & 0 \\ E_i & 0 \\ F_i & G_i \end{matrix}\right\}, \quad \begin{matrix} j = 1, 2, \ldots, \bar{p}^i \\ i = 1, 2, \ldots, \Gamma \end{matrix} \tag{6}$$

where $\Psi_{ij} \triangleq$

$$\begin{bmatrix}
\mathscr{A}^{q_{ij}} & \mathscr{A}^{q_{ij}-1}B & 0 & \mathscr{A}^{q_{ij}-2}B & 0 & \mathscr{A}^{q_{ij}-3}B & \ldots & 0 & B \\
C & D & 0 & 0 & 0 & 0 & \ldots & 0 & 0 \\
0 & 0 & \mathscr{A}^{q_{ij}-1} & \mathscr{A}^{q_{ij}-2}B & 0 & \mathscr{A}^{q_{ij}-3}B & \ldots & 0 & B \\
0 & 0 & C & D & 0 & 0 & \ldots & 0 & 0 \\
0 & 0 & 0 & 0 & \mathscr{A}^{q_{ij}-2} & \mathscr{A}^{q_{ij}-3}B & \ldots & 0 & B \\
0 & 0 & 0 & 0 & C & D & \ldots & 0 & 0 \\
\cdot & \cdot & \cdot & \cdot & \cdot & \cdot & \ldots & \cdot & \cdot \\
\cdot & \cdot & \cdot & \cdot & \cdot & \cdot & \ldots & \cdot & \cdot \\
\cdot & \cdot & \cdot & \cdot & \cdot & \cdot & \ldots & \cdot & \cdot \\
0 & 0 & 0 & 0 & 0 & 0 & \ldots & \mathscr{A} & B \\
0 & 0 & 0 & 0 & 0 & 0 & \ldots & C & D
\end{bmatrix}$$

$$\mathscr{A} \triangleq (A - \lambda_j^i I)$$

Definition.[3] Given the system (1), the *transmission zeros* of (1) are defined to be the set of complex numbers z which satisfy the following inequality:

$$\text{rank}\begin{bmatrix} A-zI & B \\ C & D \end{bmatrix} < n + \min(r, m) \tag{7}$$

Remark 1. It may be noted that the set of transmission zero may contain zero elements, a finite number of symmetric complex numbers, or include the whole complex plane.

Definition. The system (1) is said to be *non-minimum phase* if at least one transmission zero of (A, B, C, D) is contained in the closed right hand part of the complex plane; otherwise the system (1) is said to be *minimum phase.*

Remark 2. This definition of non-minimum phase is a generalization of the classical definition made for single-input, single-output systems.

Definition. In (1), assume that $y_m \triangleq C_m x + D_m u + \sum_{i=1}^{\Gamma} F_i^m \omega_i$ is only available for measurement and let the initial conditions of the differential equation (2) $\eta_i \triangleq (\omega_i(0), \omega_i(0), \ldots, \omega_i^{(p_i)}(0))'$ be contained in the unit sphere, i.e. let $\eta_i'\eta_i < 1, i = 1, 2, \ldots, \eta$. Then, if for any $\delta > 0$, there exists a linear, time-invariant controller C_δ.

$$C_\delta: \dot{\zeta} = \Phi(\delta)\zeta + \sum_{i=0}^{t_1} \beta_i^1(\delta) y_m^{(i)} + \sum_{i=0}^{t_2} \gamma_i^1(\delta) y_{\text{ref}}^{(i)}$$

$$u = K_0(\delta)\zeta + \sum_{i=0}^{t_1} \beta_i^2(\delta) y_m^{(i)} + \sum_{i=0}^{t_2} \gamma_i^2(\delta) y_{\text{ref}}^{(i)} \tag{8}$$

such that $J < \delta, \forall x(0) \in \{x | x'x \leqslant 1\}, \forall \zeta(0) \in \{\zeta | \zeta'\zeta \leqslant 1\}$ where J is given by

$$J = \max_{\eta_i, i = 1, 2, \ldots, \Gamma} \int_0^\infty e'Qe \, d\tau, Q > 0 \tag{9}$$

and such that the closed loop system is stable, the controller C_δ is called a *perfect controller* and the problem is called the *perfect tracking or regulation problem.*

Remark 3. Note that there is a solution to the perfect tracking or regulation problem only if there is a solution to the servomechanism problem defined previously, i.e. only if $e(t) \to 0$ as $t \to \infty$ for all disturbances and reference inputs described by (2).

3. Main Results*

Consider the system (1) with $\omega_i = 0, y_i^{\text{ref}} = 0, i = 1, 2, \ldots, \Gamma, D \equiv 0$, denoted by $(A,$

*All proofs have been omitted in the paper. They may be found in [4].

B, C); assume that (A, B) is stabilizable and (C, A) is detectable. Consider the performance index:

$$J^* = \int_0^\infty (y'Qy + \epsilon u'Ru)\, dt, \; Q > 0, R > 0, \epsilon > 0 \tag{10}$$

and let P_ϵ be the solution of the corresponding matrix Ricatti equation:

$$A'P_\epsilon + P_\epsilon A + C'QC - (P_\epsilon BR^{-1}B'P_\epsilon)\tfrac{1}{\epsilon} = 0 \tag{11}$$

then, the following lemma is a generalization of [2].

Lemma 1. Let J^*, P_ϵ be defined as given in (10), (11). Then

(i) The limit $\lim_{\epsilon \to 0} J^* = \lim_{\epsilon \to 0} x'(0)P_\epsilon x(0) \triangleq x'(0)P_0 x(0)$ exists.

(ii) If $r > m$, then $P_0 \neq 0$.

(iii) If $m \geqslant r$, then $P_0 = 0$ if and only if the transmission zeros of (A, B, C) are all in the open left hand part of the complex plane.

The following results (Theorem 1–3) are the main results of the paper. Assume for simplicity that $y_m = x$, i.e. the state x is available for measurement and that $D \equiv 0$.

Theorem 1 (The Perfect Control Theorem). Necessary and sufficient conditions that there exists a perfect controller for (1) are that the following three conditions must all hold:

(a) the system (A, B, C) is stabilizable and detectable.

(b) $m \geqslant r$.

(c) the system (A, B, C) is minimum phase.

The proof of Theorem 1 is based on a characterization result, obtained in [1, 7, 9], of all feedforward-feedback controllers which regulate (1). Theorem 1 follows by using this characterization result together with Lemma 1.

Remark 4. In the above problem formulation, there has been no restriction on the magnitude of the control inputs, nor on the magnitude of the gain parameters in the controller, and there has been no restriction placed on the number of differentiators which a controller may have. These assumptions of course are unrealistic in any practical controller. On the other hand, Theorem 1 does show the intrinsic difficulty of trying to control a system which has non-minimum phase properties, as is well known in classical control theory.

It is of interest to determine if it is possible to have a controller which is both robust and perfect, i.e. one which allows perfect regulation to occur even if the system parameters of (1) change by small amounts. The following Theorem 2 shows that this is impossible to achieve and is a fundamental result in the theory of control system design.

Definition. Given a matrix $M \in R^{n \times m}$, let $M \in \Omega_\epsilon$ where $M = \{m_{ij}\}$, denote $m_{ij} \in$

Ω_ϵ, $i = 1, 2, \ldots, n; j = 1, 2, \ldots, m$ where

$$\Omega_\epsilon = \{m_{ij} \mid |m_{ij}| < \epsilon\} \tag{12}$$

Definition. [1] Given the system (1), suppose that there exists a controller so that asymptotic regulation takes place and so that the resultant controlled system is stable. Let the plant parameters A, B and C now be perturbed, i.e. $A \to A + \delta A$, $B \to B + \delta B$, $C \to C + \delta C$ and let $\epsilon > 0$ be chosen so that the resultant closed loop system remains stable $\forall \delta A \in \Omega_\epsilon, \forall \delta B \in \Omega_\epsilon, \forall \delta C \in \Omega_\epsilon$. Then if asymptotic regulation still takes place $\forall \delta A \in \Omega_\epsilon, \forall \delta B \in \Omega_\epsilon, \forall \delta C \in \Omega_\epsilon$, the controller is said to be a *robust controller.*

Theorem 2 (The Robust Control Limitation Theorem). Assume there exists a robust controller which regulates (1) so that the controlled system is stable and so that asymptotic regulation takes place for all disturbances and reference inputs defined by (2). Then it is *impossible* for such a robust controller to ever achieve perfect control.

The proof of Theorem 2 depends on a characterization result of all robust controllers obtained in [1, 8], which states that *any* robust controller must consist of a dynamic feedback controller consisting of r unstable compensators with identical dynamics corresponding to the class of disturbance/reference inputs, connected to the error outputs of the system. This implies that the augmented controlled system *must* be non-minimum phase and hence by Theorem 1, it cannot ever have perfect control.

The following result (Theorem 3) is a very fundamental result in the general theory of control systems, and so has been called *The Control Inequality Principle*; it states that if a system to be controlled has more independent control inputs than outputs to be controlled, then it is almost always possible to achieve perfect control; if the system to be controlled has an equal number of control inputs and outputs, then the ability to achieve perfect control depends on the parameters of the system, in particular on whether the system is non-minimum phase; if the system to be controlled has more outputs than control inputs, it is never possible to achieve perfect control.

Definition. [5] Let R denote the field of real numbers. If $f = f(x_1, \ldots, x_n)$ is a polynomial in the n variables $x_1, \ldots, x_n$ with coefficients in R, then the point $\hat{x} = (\hat{x}_1, \ldots, \hat{x}_n)$ in R^n is said to be a zero of f if $f(\hat{x}_1, \ldots, \hat{x}_n) = 0$. The set of zeros of f is called the locus of f and is denoted by $V(f)$. A proper subset V or R^n is called a *hypersurface* in R^n, if it is the locus of a nonconstant polynomial.

Definition. Let $S = (A, B, C; E_1, \ldots, E_\Gamma; F_1, \ldots, F_\Gamma; G_1, \ldots, G_\Gamma)$.

Theorem 3 (The Control Inequality Principle). Given the system (1) then:
(a) If $m > r$, the class of systems S in which perfect control is not possible to achieve, lies on a hypersurface in the parameter space of S.
(b) If $m = r$, then perfect control may or may not be possible to achieve for S depending on whether (A, B, C) is minimum or non-minimum phase.
(c) If $m < r$, the class of systems S in which perfect control is possible to achieve is empty.

The proof of Theorem 3 depends on a characterization result of transmission zeros obtained in [3] together with a characterization result of steady-state invertibility conditions obtained in [1, 9].

4. The Perfect Controller

Assuming that Theorem 1 holds, the following is a description of the perfect controller which will control (1). For simplicity, assume that the disturbances ω_i are available for measurement and that rank $G_i = r, i = 1, 2, \ldots, \Gamma$ (these are not essential assumptions). Recall that it has been assumed for simplicity that $y_m = x$ and that $D = 0$.

The Perfect Controller.

$$u = Kx + \sum_{i=1}^{\Gamma} \Big\{ (G_0^i + G_1^i s + \ldots + G_{p_i-1}^i s^{p_i-1})\, \omega_i + (G_0^{i*} + G_1^{i*} s + \ldots + G_{p_i-1}^{i*} s^{p_i-1}) y_i^{\text{ref}} \Big\} \tag{13}$$

where s denotes the operator $\frac{d}{dt}(\cdot)$ and where K is a feedback gain matrix given by:

$$K = -(R^{-1}B'P_0)\frac{1}{\epsilon} \tag{14}$$

where P_0 is given by the solution of the matrix Ricatti equation:

$$A'P_0 + P_0A + C'QC - (P_0'BR^{-1}B'P_0)\frac{1}{\epsilon} = 0 \tag{15}$$

where R is any positive definite matrix, $Q > 0$ is given by the problem statement (9), and $\epsilon > 0$ is a small scalar which depends on the value of δ specified (a typical value being $\epsilon = 10^{-10}$)*. The $m \times n_i$ disturbance gain matrices [1, 7, 9] $G_j^i, j = 0, 1, \ldots, p_i - 1, i = 1, 2, \ldots \Gamma$ are given as follows:

$$\begin{bmatrix} G_0^i \\ G_1^i \\ \cdot \\ \cdot \\ \cdot \\ G_{p_i-1}^i \end{bmatrix} = \{H^i\}^{-1} \begin{bmatrix} \Lambda_1^i \\ \Lambda_2^i \\ \cdot \\ \cdot \\ \cdot \\ \Lambda_{\bar{p}i}^i \end{bmatrix} \quad i = 1, 2, \ldots, \Gamma \tag{16}$$

*The value of ϵ to be chosen depends on the degree of perfect control wished to be achieved, i.e. see remark 5.

where Λ_k^i, $k = 1, 2, \ldots, \bar{p}^i$ is a $mq_{ik} \times n_i$ matrix given as follows:

$$\Lambda_k^i = \begin{bmatrix} i\delta_k^1 \\ i\delta_k^2 \\ \cdot \\ \cdot \\ \cdot \\ i\delta_k^{q_{ik}} \end{bmatrix}, k = 1, 2, \ldots, \bar{p}^i; i = 1, 2, \ldots, \Gamma \tag{17}$$

where

$$\begin{aligned}
i\delta_k^1 &= -(iE_k^1)^\dagger \; (iD_k^1 + F_i) \\
i\delta_k^2 &= (iE_k^1)^\dagger \; (iD_k^2 + iE_k^2 i\delta_k^1) \\
i\delta_k^3 &= (iE_k^1)^\dagger \; (-iD_k^3 - iE_k^3 i\delta_k^1 + iE_k^2 i\delta_k^2) \\
i\delta_k^4 &= (iE_k^1)^\dagger \; (iD_k^4 + iE_k^4 i\delta_k^1 - iE_k^3 i\delta_k^2 + iE_k^2 i\delta_k^3) \\
&\cdot \\
&\cdot \\
&\cdot \\
i\delta_k^{q_{ik}} &= (iE_k^1)^\dagger \Big\{ (-)^{q_{ik}} iD_k^{q_{ik}} + (-)^{q_{ik}} iE_k^{q_{ik}} i\delta_k^1 + \\
&\quad + (-)^{q_{ik}-1} iE_k^{q_{ik}-1} i\delta_k^2 \ldots + iE_k^2 i\delta_k^{q_{ik}-1} \Big\} \\
k &= 1, 2, \ldots, \bar{p}^i; i = 1, 2, \ldots, \Gamma
\end{aligned} \tag{18}$$

where

$$\begin{aligned}
iE_k^\theta &\triangleq C(\lambda_k^i I - A - BK)^{-\theta} B \\
&\qquad\qquad ; \Theta = 1, 2, \ldots, q_{ik}; k = 1, 2, \ldots, \bar{p}^i \\
iD_k^\theta &\triangleq C(\lambda_k^i I - A - BK)^{-\theta} E_i
\end{aligned} \tag{19}$$

where $(iE_k^1)^\dagger = (iE_k^1)' \Big\{ (iE_k^1)\,(iE_k^1)' \Big\}^{-1}$.

The $m \times r_i$ *tracking gain matrices* [1, 7, 9] G_j^{*i}, $j = 0, 1, \ldots, p_i - 1; i = 1, 2, \ldots, \Gamma$ are equal to G_j^i, $j = 0, 1, \ldots, p_i - 1; i = 1, 2, \ldots, \Gamma$ respectively with E_i being replaced by 0 and F_i being replaced by $-G_i$.

Remarks

5. There always exists a small enough $\epsilon > 0$ in (15), so that, for a given $\delta > 0$, J given by (9) has the property that $J < \delta, \forall x(0) \in \{x \mid x'x \leq 1\}$ (assuming that the initial conditions of (2) are always contained in the unit sphere).
6. The feedback gains K and feedforward gains G_j^i, G_j^{*i} will in general have arbitrarily large norm as $\epsilon \to 0$.
7. As $\epsilon \to 0$, the poles of the closed loop system $(A + BK)$ will coincide with the transmission zeros of (A, B, C) and the remaining poles will become arbitrarily large.
8. For those systems in which condition (a), (b) of Theorem 1 hold, i.e. in which there is a solution to the servomechanism problem, [1] but in which condition (c) or/and (d) of Theorem 1 does not hold, the above controller has the property that it will minimize the performance index J^* given by (10) $\forall x(0) \in R^n$, assuming that $\omega_i \equiv 0, i = 1, 2, \ldots, \Gamma$ and $y_{\text{ref}} \equiv 0$. Thus the controller (13) can be thought of, as being the "best possible" controller which will asymptotically regulate (1).
9. The controller is unique if and only if $m = r$ and in this case:

$$(iE_k^1)^{\dagger} = (iE_k^1)^{-1}$$

In case this condition is not satisfied, the gain matrices of the controller will have minimum norm.
10. In case the disturbances ω_i cannot be directly measured, they can always be observed from the state x; [11, 4] the observer in this case consists of a differentiating network with x and u as the input and ω_i as the output.
11. It has been assumed up to the present, that the state x is available for measurement. In case, this assumption is not true the state x and some of the unmeasurable (if any) disturbances must be observed by differentiating those outputs which can be measured. This can only be done provided an observability condition is added to Theorem 1. (See [1, 4, 10] for details.)
12. It may be observed that the perfect controller is a feedforward controller [1, 7, 9] consisting of a number of differentiators in the feedforward loop and, perhaps, feedback loop if the state is not available for measurement. Since differentiation introduces noise in practical systems this implies that to get "perfect" control one should measure as many disturbances, outputs, states of the system, etc., as possible in order to minimize the number of differentiators required.

5. Numerical Examples

Two numerical examples are included to illustrate the results.

Example No. 1 (Nuclear Rocket Engine [6])

The following 4th order linearized model of a nuclear rocket engine is considered:

$$\dot{x} = Ax + Bu + E\omega \tag{20}$$

$$y = Cx$$

where $x = (n, c, T, p)'$, $u = (\delta_d, V)'$, $\omega = \delta_c$ and $y = (T, p)'$, where

n = nuclear power

c = delayed neutrons

T = thrust chamber temperature

p = thrust chamber pressure

δ_d = control drum reactivity

V = turbine power control valve

δ_c = change in flow of delayed neutrons

and A, B, C, E are given by:

$$A = \begin{bmatrix} -65 & 65 & -19.5 & 19.5 \\ 0.1 & -0.1 & 0 & 0 \\ 1.0 & 0 & -0.5 & -1.0 \\ 0 & 0 & 0.4 & -0.4 \end{bmatrix}, B = \begin{bmatrix} 65 & 0 \\ 0 & 0 \\ 0 & 0 \\ 0 & 0.4 \end{bmatrix}$$

$$E = \begin{bmatrix} 50 \\ 0 \\ -0.1 \\ 0 \end{bmatrix}, C = \begin{bmatrix} 0 & 0 & 1 & 0 \\ 0 & 0 & 0 & 1 \end{bmatrix}$$

The open loop system has eigenvalues at -64.8, -3.0×10^{-5}, $-0.603 \pm j0.52$ and a transmission zero [3] at -0.100.

It is desired to find a perfect controller for (20) for the class of constant disturbances ω and for the class of constant reference inputs y_{ref}. It is observed that (A, B) is controllable, that rank $\begin{bmatrix} A & B \\ C & 0 \end{bmatrix} = 6$, $m = r$, and that the system (A, B, C) is minimum phase so that the conditions of Theorem 1 are therefore satisfied. The control system (13) found for the case $R = \begin{bmatrix} 1 & 0 \\ 0 & 1 \end{bmatrix}$, $Q = \begin{bmatrix} 1 & 0 \\ 0 & 1 \end{bmatrix}$, $\epsilon = 10^{-9}$ is given as follows:

$$u = Kx + G_0^* y_{ref} + G_0 \omega \tag{22}$$

where

$$K = \begin{bmatrix} -30.2 & -0.999 & -3.6 \times 10^4 & 2.42 \\ 1.49 \times 10^{-2} & 6.36 \times 10^{-6} & 27.5 & -3.16 \times 10^{-4} \end{bmatrix}$$

$$G_0 = \begin{bmatrix} 2.35 \\ -1.49 \times 10^{-3} \end{bmatrix}, G_0^* = \begin{bmatrix} 3.16 \times 10^4 & 28.5 \\ -28.5 & 3.16 \times 10^4 \end{bmatrix}$$

The eigenvalues of the closed loop system $(A + BK)$ are $-1.014 \times 10^3 \pm j1.01 \times 10^3$, -1.26×10^4, -0.100. It can be observed that a pole and zero cancellation occurs at -0.100, and thus that the output response of the closed loop system will be extremely fast compared with the open loop system. The output responses of the system for the case that $\omega = 1$, $x(0) = 0$ and $y_{\text{ref}} = \begin{bmatrix} 1 \\ 0 \end{bmatrix}, \begin{bmatrix} 0 \\ 1 \end{bmatrix}$ are given in Figures 1 and 2 respectively. It can be seen that "almost" perfect tracking occurs using this controller (22).

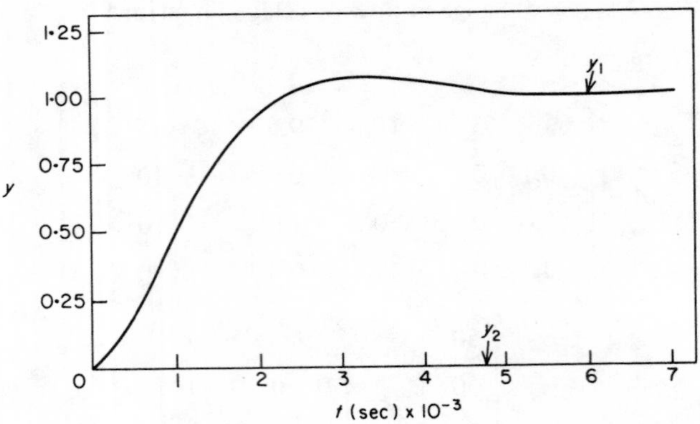

Figure 1. Output responses for example 1 for case $y_{\text{ref}} = \begin{bmatrix} 1 \\ 0 \end{bmatrix}$.

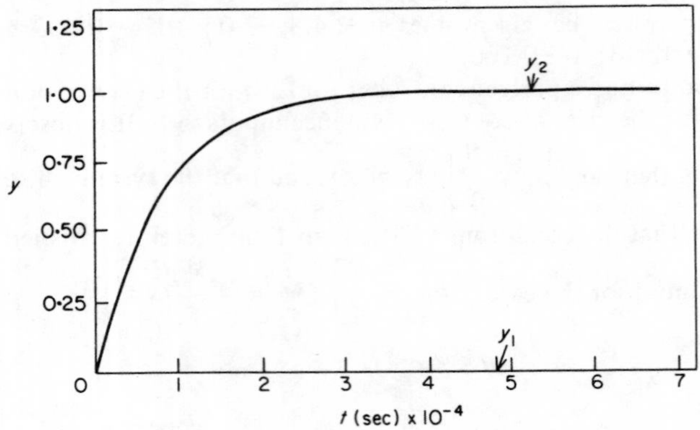

Figure 2. Output responses for example 1 for case $y_{\text{ref}} = \begin{bmatrix} 0 \\ 1 \end{bmatrix}$.

Example No. 2 (Boiler System [7])

The following 9th order linearized model of a boiler system is considered:

$$\begin{aligned} \dot{x} &= Ax + Bu + E\omega \\ y &= Cx \end{aligned} \tag{23}$$

where $y \in R^2$, $u \in R^2$, $\omega \in R^2$ and A, B, C, E are given in [7].

The dominant open-loop eigenvalues of the system are $0, -7.85 \times 10^{-3}, -8.91 \times 10^{-3}, -9.82 \times 10^{-2}, -2.38 \times 10^{-1}$, and the transmission zeros[3] of the system are $-26.4, -2.96 \pm j0.335, -0.00955, 0.749, 0.094$. It is desired to find a perfect controller for (23) for the class of constant disturbances ω and constant inputs y_{ref}. The system (23) is controllable, $\text{rank}\begin{bmatrix} A & B \\ C & 0 \end{bmatrix} = 11$, $m = r$, so that conditions (a)–(c) of Theorem 1 hold, but the system (23) is non-minimum phase so that Theorem 1 does not hold. This means that there exists no perfect controller for the system (23). However, the controller (13) will stabilize and asymptotically regulate (23) $\forall \omega \in R^2$, $\forall y_{\text{ref}} \in R^2$ and will minimize J^* given by (10) $\forall x(0) \in R^n$ assuming $\omega \equiv 0, y_{\text{ref}} \equiv 0$. Thus, it is interesting to determine how well the resultant closed loop system behaves. The control system (13) found for the case that $R = \begin{bmatrix} 1 & 0 \\ 0 & 1 \end{bmatrix}$, $Q = \begin{bmatrix} 1 & 0 \\ 0 & 1 \end{bmatrix}$, $\epsilon = 10^{-15}$ is given as follows:

$$u = Kx + G_0^* y_{\text{ref}} + G_0 \omega \tag{24}$$

where

$$K = \begin{bmatrix} 1.99 \times 10^7 & 7.72 \times 10^3 & 5.92 \times 10^3 & -1.28 \times 10^9 \\ -1.30 \times 10^4 & -1.02 \times 10^1 & -1.77 \times 10^{-1} & -1.22 \times 10^4 \end{bmatrix}$$

$$\begin{matrix} 1.11 \times 10^3 & -6.74 & -8.01 \times 10^3 & 2.41 \times 10^5 & 3.16 \times 10^7 \\ -2.01 \times 10^{-2} & -3.16 \times 10^7 & -5.04 \times 10^1 & -2.72 \times 10^1 & 4.56 \times 10^2 \end{matrix}\Bigg]$$

$$G_0^* = \begin{bmatrix} -4.57 \times 10^2 & -3.16 \times 10^7 \\ 3.16 \times 10^7 & -4.56 \times 10^2 \end{bmatrix},$$

$$G_0 = \begin{bmatrix} 7.35 \times 10^5 & 0 \\ 6.36 & -1 \end{bmatrix}$$

The eigenvalues of the closed loop system are at:

$$-5.63 \times 10^7, -1.33 \times 10^2 \pm j1.05 \times 10^2, -26.5,$$
$$-2.96 \pm j0.335, -0.749, -0.094, -0.55 \times 10^{-3}.$$

The output responses of the system for the case that $x(0) = 0$, $\omega = \begin{bmatrix} 0 \\ 1 \end{bmatrix}$, $y_{\text{ref}} = \begin{bmatrix} 1 \\ 0 \end{bmatrix}$ and $x(0) = 0$, $\omega = \begin{bmatrix} 0 \\ 1 \end{bmatrix}$, $y_{\text{ref}} = \begin{bmatrix} 0 \\ 1 \end{bmatrix}$ are given in Figures 3 and 4 respectively. It can be seen that tracking occurs, but that the output response in this case is *extremely* slow. Since the controller (24) is the optimum controller which minimizes $J^* = \int_0^\infty (e'Qe + \epsilon u'Ru)\, dt$ for the case $\omega \equiv 0, y_{\text{ref}} \equiv 0$, it can be seen that the output responses of Figures 3 and 4 are, in this sense, the best possible which can ever be achieved! Thus, it is inherently impossible to "speed up the response" of (23) without causing peaking in the outputs y; i.e. the system (23) is inherently difficult to control, which is a well known characteristic of single-input, single-output non-minimum phase systems of classical control theory.

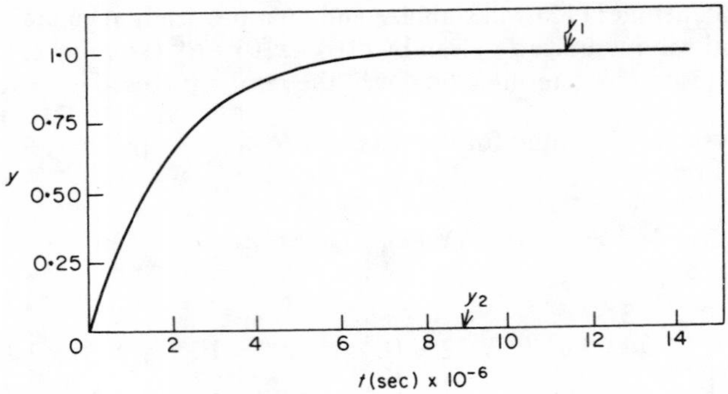

Figure 3. Output responses for example 2 for case $y_{\text{ref}} = \begin{bmatrix} 1 \\ 0 \end{bmatrix}$.

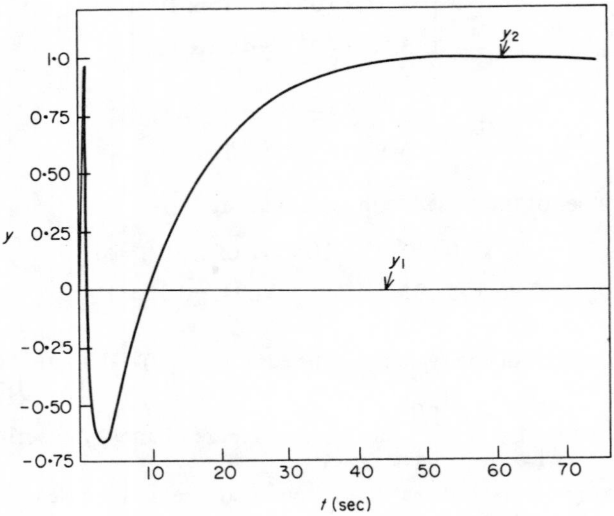

Figure 4. Output responses for example 2 for case $y_{\text{ref}} = \begin{bmatrix} 0 \\ 1 \end{bmatrix}$.

6. References

[1] Davison, E. J., "The Feedforward, Feedback and Robust Control of a General Servomechanism Problem – Parts I, II", Dept. of Electrical Engineering, University of Toronto, Control Systems Reports CS-7305, 7306, April 1973, presented at *11th Allerton Conference on Circuit and System Theory*, October 1973.

[2] Kwakernaak, H., Sivan, R., "The Maximally Achievable Accuracy of Linear Optimal Regulators with Linear Optimal Filters", *IEEE Trans. on Automatic Control*, Vol. AC-17, No. 1, 1972, pp. 79–86.

[3] Davison, E. J., Wang, S. H., "Properties and Calculation of Transmission Zeros of Linear Multivariable Systems", *Automatica*, Vol. 10, 1974, pp. 643–658.

[4] Davison, E. J., Chow, S. G., "Perfect Control in Linear Time-Invariant Multivariable Systems", Dept. of Electrical Engineering, University of Toronto, *Control Systems Report* CS-7409 April 1974, also Chow S. G., "Perfect Real Model Following in Linear Time-Invariant Systems", Ph.D. thesis, Dept. of Electrical Engineering, University of Toronto, Sept, 1976.

[5] Davison, E. J., Wang, S. H., "Properties of Linear Time-Invariant Multivariable Systems Subject to Arbitrary Output and State Feedback", *IEEE Trans. on Automatic Control*, Vol. AC-18, No. 1, 1973, pp. 24–32.

[6] Loscutoff, W. V., Schenz, R. F., "Zeros in Multivariable Systems", *JACC* 1972, pp. 899–904.

[7] Davison, E. J., "The Feedforward Control of Linear Multivariable Time-Invariant Systems", *Automatica*, Vol. 9, 1973, pp. 561–573.

[8] Davison, E. J., Goldenberg, A,, "The Robust Control of a General Servomechanism Problem: the Servo Compensator", *Automatica,* Vol. 11, 1975, pp. 461–471.

[9] Davison, E. J., "The Steady-state Invertibility and Feedforward Control of Linear Time-Invariant Systems", *IEEE Trans. on Automatic Control*, Vol. AC-21, No. 4, 1975, pp. 529–534.

[10] Davison, E. J., "Output Detectability, Steady-state Invertibility and the General Servomechanism Problem", *IEEE Conference on Decision and Control,* Dec. 1976, pp. 1250–1257.

[11] Davison, E. J., Wang, S. H., "New Results on the Controllability and Observability of General Composite Systems", *IEEE Trans. on Automatic Control,* Vol. AC-20, No. 1, 1975, pp. 123–128.

Properties and Calculation of Transmission Zeros of Linear Multivariable Systems*

E. J. DAVISON† and S. H. WANG‡
†*Department of Electrical Engineering, University of Toronto, Canada*
‡*College of Engineering and Applied Science, University of Colorado, Colorado Springs, Colorado 80907, U.S.A.*

Summary. A new definition of transmission zeros for a linear, multivariable, time-invariant system is made which is shown to be equivalent to previous definitions. Based on this new definition of transmission zeros, new properties of transmission zeros of a system are then obtained; in particular, it is shown that a system with an unequal number of inputs and outputs almost always has no transmission zeros and that a system with an equal number of inputs and outputs almost always has either $n-r$ or n transmission zeros, where n is the order of the system; transmission zeros of cascade systems are then studied, and it is shown how the transmission zeros of a system relate to the poles of a closed loop system subject to high gain output feedback. An application of transmission zeros to the servomechanism problem is also included. A fast, efficient, numerically stable algorithm is then obtained which enables the transmission zeros of high order multivariable systems to be readily obtained. Some numerical examples for a 9th order system are given to illustrate the algorithm.

1. Introduction

This paper is concerned about the properties and the numerical calculation of transmission zeros of the following system denoted by (A, B, C, D)

$$\dot{x} = Ax + Bu$$

$$y = Cx + Du \tag{1}$$

where $x \in R^n$ is the state, $u \in R^m$ is the input, $y \in R^r$ is the output and A, B, C, D are constant matrices of appropriate dimensions and $n \geqslant 1, m \geqslant 1, r \geqslant 1$, max $(r, m) \leqslant n$. It is not necessarily assumed that (1) is controllable or observable. It is to be

*This work has been supported by the National Research Council of Canada under Grant No. A4396 and by the National Aeronautics and Space Administration under Grant No. NSG 1213, and has appeared in *Automatica,* Vol. 10, 1974, pp. 643–658.

noted that the transmission zeros of a system are in general quite different from the zeros, in the conventional sense, of the various transfer functions relating inputs and outputs of the system; for single-input–single-output controllable-observable systems however, the transmission zeros are just the zeros of the transfer function of the system.

There has been considerable interest in transmission zeros recently,[1–8] Rosenbrock[1] apparently, being the first to define transmission zeros of a multivariable system. Transmission zeros of a system are important and appear in many aspects of control theory e.g. in regulation problems[2] (p. 306), decoupling theory,[3, 5] the servomechanism problem,[4, 9] and so it is desirable to have a fast, efficient algorithm which enables their numerical calculation to be reliably achieved. It is believed that this is the first time such an algorithm has been presented for the general problem described above, previous literature having dealt only with special cases of the above problem, e.g. [2, 10]. The algorithm is based on a new definition of transmission zeros[4] which is shown to be equivalent to Rosenbrock's definition [1] and others[2, 3]. Based on this definition, various new properties of transmission zeros are obtained.

Section 2 gives the new definition of transmission zeros and relates it to Rosenbrock's definition and other definitions. Section 3 deals with properties of transmission zeros and shows that a system with an equal number of inputs and outputs almost always has $n-r$ or n transmission zeros and that a system with an unequal number of inputs and outputs almost always has no transmission zeros. Section 3 also relates transmission zeros with the invertibility of a system, deals with transmission zeros of cascade systems, relates the transmission zeros to the poles of a closed loop system subject to high gain output feedback, and shows how transmission zeros are related to a general servomechanism problem. Section 4 develops two algorithms for the numerical calculation of transmission zeros. Section 5 gives a 9th order numerical example.

2. Development

The following definition, which is a generalization of that given in [4], is made:

Definition. Given the system (1), the *transmission zeros* of (1) are defined to be the set of complex numbers λ which satisfy the following inequality

$$\operatorname{rank}\begin{bmatrix} A-\lambda I & B \\ C & D \end{bmatrix} < n + \min(r, m) \tag{2}$$

in particular, *the transmission zeros are the zeros (multiplicities included) of the greatest common divisor of all* $(n+\min(r,m)) \times (n+\min(r,m))$ *minors of*

$$\begin{bmatrix} A-\lambda & B \\ C & D \end{bmatrix}.$$

Remark 1. It may be noted that the set of transmission zeros may be empty, contain a finite number of symmetric complex numbers, or include the whole complex plane.

Remark 2. Since

$$\operatorname{rank}\begin{bmatrix} A-\lambda I & B \\ C & D \end{bmatrix} = \operatorname{rank}\begin{bmatrix} T(A+BK-\lambda I)T^{-1} & TBG \\ (C+DK)T^{-1} & DG \end{bmatrix}$$

for any nonsingular $T \in R^{n \times n}$, nonsingular $G \in R^{m \times m}$ and $K \in R^{m \times n}$, it is immediately seen that the transmission zeros $\{\lambda\}$ are invariant with respect to coordinate transformations, state feedback and nonsingular input control transformations.

Definition. (A, B, C, D) is called *degenerate* if, for any specified $n + 1$ distinct scalars $\lambda_j^* \in R, j = 1, 2, \ldots, n + 1$, the following relation is true

$$\operatorname{rank}\begin{bmatrix} A - \lambda_j^* I & B \\ C & D \end{bmatrix} < n + \min(r, m), \quad j = 1, 2, \ldots, n + 1 \tag{3}$$

A degenerate (A, B, C, D) has transmission zeros which include the whole complex plane. It will in general be assumed in the rest of the development that (A, B, C, D) is *non degenerate*, i.e. that condition (3) does not hold. Note that controllable–observable systems in which rank $B = m$, rank $C = r$ may be degenerate.

Relationship of transmission zeros to Smith-McMillan form of (1)

Assume that (A, B, C, D) is controllable and observable and let the Smith–McMillan form[1] of the $r \times m$ transfer function matrix $G(s) = C(sI - A)^{-1} B + D$ be given by the $r \times m$ matrix $M(s)$ where:

$$\begin{aligned} M(s) &= \left[\operatorname{diag}\left\{ \frac{\epsilon_1(s)}{\psi_1(s)}, \frac{\epsilon_2(s)}{\psi_2(s)}, \ldots, \frac{\epsilon_r(s)}{\psi_r(s)} \right\}, 0_{r, m-r} \right], m > r \\ &= \operatorname{diag}\left[\frac{\epsilon_1(s)}{\psi_1(s)}, \frac{\epsilon_2(s)}{\psi_2(s)}, \ldots, \frac{\epsilon_r(s)}{\psi_r(s)} \right], m = r \\ &= \begin{bmatrix} \operatorname{diag}\left\{ \frac{\epsilon_1(s)}{\psi_1(s)}, \frac{\epsilon_2(s)}{\psi_2(s)}, \ldots, \frac{\epsilon_m(s)}{\psi_m(s)} \right\} \\ \\ 0_{r-m, m} \end{bmatrix}, m < r \end{aligned} \tag{4}$$

and $\epsilon_i(s)$ divides $\epsilon_{i+1}(s)$, $i = 1, 2, 3, \ldots$, $\psi_{i+1}(s)$ divides $\psi_i(s)$, $i = 1, 2, 3, \ldots$ and $\epsilon_i(s)$ and $\psi_i(s)$ are relatively prime, $i = 1, 2, \ldots, \min(m, r)$.

It will be shown that the transmission zeros of (1) for the case that (1) is controllable and observable are simply the zeros (including multiplicities) of the polynomial $\prod_{i=1}^{k} \epsilon_i(s)$, $k \triangleq \min(r, m)$.

The following result is obtained:

Theorem 1. Assume that (1) is controllable and observable; then the transmission zeros of (1) as defined by (2) are equal to the zeros (including multiplicities) of the polynomial obtained by multiplying all numerator polynomials (including any zero numerators) of the Smith–McMillan form of the transfer function matrix $C(sI - A)^{-1} B + D$.†

The following lemma is required in the proof of Theorem 1.

† Note that if this polynomial is identically equal to zero, this implies that the transmission zeros of (1) include the whole complex plane, i.e. the system (1) is degenerate.

Lemma 1. (Rosenbrock[1], p. 111). Given the controllable–observable system (1), and its system matrix

$$P(s) \triangleq \begin{bmatrix} sI - A & B \\ -C & D \end{bmatrix} \tag{5}$$

let $S_p(s)$ be the Smith form of $P(s)$. Then

$$S_p(s) = \left[\begin{array}{cc|c} I_n & 0_{n,\,r} & 0_{n,\,m-r} \\ 0_{r,\,n} & \operatorname{diag}(\epsilon_1(s), \epsilon_2(s), \ldots, \epsilon_r(s)) & 0_{r,\,m-r} \end{array}\right], \quad m > r$$

$$= \begin{bmatrix} I_n & 0_{n,\,r} \\ 0_{r,\,n} & \operatorname{diag}(\epsilon_1(s), \epsilon_2(s), \ldots, \epsilon_r(s)) \end{bmatrix}, \quad m = r$$

$$= \left[\begin{array}{cc} I_n & 0_{n,\,m} \\ 0_{m,\,n} & \operatorname{diag}(\epsilon_1(s), \epsilon_2(s), \ldots, \epsilon_m(s)) \\ \hline 0_{r-m,\,n} & 0_{r-m,\,m} \end{array}\right], \quad m < r \tag{6}$$

where $\epsilon_i(s)$, $i = 1, 2, \ldots, k$ are the invariant polynomials of the Smith–McMillan form of $G(s)$.

Proof of Theorem 1. Consider now the matrix $P(s)$ and assume that $P(s)$ has been reduced to Smith Form by the nonsingular unimodular matrices $T_1(s)$, $T_2(s)$, i.e. $S_p(s) = T_1(s)P(s)T_2(s)$ where $T_1(s)$ and $T_2(s)$ are $(n + r) \times (n + r)$ and $(n + m) \times (n + m)$ matrices respectively. In this case, it can be seen that

$$\operatorname{rank}[P(\lambda)] = \operatorname{rank}[T_1(\lambda)P(\lambda)T_2(\lambda)] = \operatorname{rank}[S_p(\lambda)] \tag{7}$$

and hence that

$$\operatorname{rank}\begin{bmatrix} A - \lambda I & B \\ C & D \end{bmatrix} < n + \min(r, m) \tag{8}$$

if and only if

$$\operatorname{rank}[S_p(\lambda)] < n + \min(r, m) \tag{9}$$

but, from lemma 1, this will occur if and only if λ is a zero of the highest order invariant polynomial $\epsilon_k(s)$ of $M(s)$, where $k = \min(r, m)$ thereby establishing the result.

Remark 3. Rosenbrock in [1], (p. 113) defined zeros of a controllable–observable system (A, B, C, D) to be the set of all zeros of the highest order invariant polynomial $\epsilon_k(s)$ of $M(s)$. It is clear that the present definition coincides with his.

Remark 4. It may be shown, [1] (p. 115) that any controllable–observable system (1) has a transfer function matrix $G(s)$ which may be written as:

where $V(s)$ and $T(s)$ are determined by $G(s)$, $T(s)$ and $V(s)$ are relatively (right) prime, $V(s)T^{-1}(s) \to 0$ as $s \to \infty$, and the Smith form of $V(s) + DT(s)$ is equal to $\text{diag}(\epsilon_1, \epsilon_2, \ldots, \epsilon_r)$ when $r = m$ where ϵ_i are the invariant polynomials of the Smith–McMillan form of $G(s)$, with corresponding changes for the case when $r \neq m$. It can be seen then, that the transmission zeros defined in (2) are just the zeros of the Smith form of $V(s) + DT(s)$ which can be thought of as being the numerator of the transfer function matrix $G(s)$. Thus, for single-input–single-output systems, the transmission zeros of $G(s)$ become simply the zeros of the corresponding transfer function of the system.

Remark 5. Kwakernaak and Sivan [2] defined zeros of a controllable–observable system with $D \equiv 0$, $m = r$ to be the zeros of the polynomial $\psi(s) \triangleq \det(sI - A) \det[C(sI - A)^{-1}B]$. Since, if $m = r$, $D = 0$,

$$\det\begin{bmatrix} A - \lambda I & B \\ C & 0 \end{bmatrix} = \det(\lambda I - A)\det[C(\lambda I - A)^{-1}B]$$

it can be seen that the present definition coincides with [2].

Remark 6. It may easily be shown that the transmission zeros defined in (2) are just the zeros of the transmission polynomial of (1) defined by Morse [3] for the special case of non degenerate systems with $D \equiv 0$. Thus a link has been made between the transmission zeros defined in [1] and [3]. In addition, Moore and Silverman [5] have discussed this connection.

3. Properties of Transmission Zeros

The following theorem shows how degenerate systems are related to invertibility.

Definition [11]. System (1) is said to be left (right) invertible if there exists a $\lambda \in R$ so that $\text{rank}\,\{C(\lambda I - A)^{-1}B + D\} = m(r)$.

Theorem 2†. A system (A, B, C, D) is left invertible if and only if the following two conditions both hold

(a) $r \geqslant m$

(b) The system (A, B, C, D) has a finite number of transmission zeros, i.e. the system (A, B, C, D) is non degenerate.

Proof. The proof follows immediately from the definition of transmission zeros, eqn. (2), on noting from [11] that $\text{rank}\,\{C(\lambda I - A)^{-1}B + D\} = k$ if and only if

$$\text{rank}\begin{bmatrix} A - \lambda I & B \\ C & D \end{bmatrix} = n + k$$

† Note that Theorem 2 is also valid if "left" is replaced by "right" and if "m" is interchanged with "r".

Remark 7. The above theorem forms the basis of a much simpler algorithm than previously reported[11, 13] for determining whether a system is invertible, i.e. it is only necessary to determine if the system is non degenerate.

3.1. Transmission zeros of arbitrary systems

The following initial result is obtained:

Theorem 3. Assume that rank $C = r$, rank $B = m$ and that (A, B, C, D) is non-degenerate; then the maximum number of transmission zeros that (1) may possess is equal to $n - \max(r, m)$ if $D \equiv 0$ and is equal to n if $D \not\equiv 0$.

Proof. The result immediately follows by equating all $(n + \min(r, m)) \times (n + \min(r, m))$ minors of

$$\begin{bmatrix} A - \lambda I & B \\ C & D \end{bmatrix}$$

equal to zero and observing that the highest order polynomial equation in λ which is possible to obtain from these minors, has order $n - \max(r, m)$ if $D \equiv 0$ and has order n if $D \not\equiv 0$.

Remark 8. For the case $r = m = 1, D \equiv 0$ the maximum number of transmission zeros that (1) may possess is equal to $n - 1$, which agrees with the well known classical result. For systems in which $\max(r, m) = n$, $D \equiv 0$ there exist no transmission zeros for the system.

The following important observation (theorems 4, 5) is now made:

Definition. Let R denote the field of real numbers. If $f = f(x_1, \ldots, x_n)$ is a polynomial in the n variables $x_1, \ldots, x_n$ with coefficients in R, then the point $\hat{x} = (\hat{x}_1, \ldots, \hat{x}_n)$ in R^n is said to be a zero of f if $f(\hat{x}_1, \ldots, \hat{x}_n) = 0$. The set of zeros of f is called the locus of f and is denoted by $V(f)$. A proper subset V of R^n is called a *hypersurface* in R^n if it is the locus of a nonconstant polynomial. Note that properties and examples of a hypersurface are given in [14].

Theorem 4. For almost all (A, B, C, D) tuples, the system (A, B, C, D) is non degenerate; i.e. the class of (A, B, C, D) systems which is degenerate must lie on a hypersurface in the parameter space of (A, B, C, D).

Proof. Let λ_i^*, $i = 1, 2, \ldots, n + 1$ be a given set of real distinct scalars. Then the system (A, B, C, D) is degenerate if and only if:

$$\text{rank} \begin{bmatrix} A - \lambda_i^* I & B \\ C & D \end{bmatrix} < n + \min(r, m), i = 1, 2, \ldots, n + 1 \qquad (10)$$

or alternately that:

$$\sum_{i=1}^{n+1} \sum_{j=1}^{\sigma_i} m_{ij}^2(A, B, C, D, \lambda_i^*) = 0 \tag{11}$$

where m_{ij} denotes the jth $(n + \min(r, m)) \times (n + \min(r, m))$ minor of

$$\begin{bmatrix} A - \lambda_i^* I & B \\ C & D \end{bmatrix}, \; 1 \leqslant j \leqslant \sigma_i,$$

and where

$$\sigma_i \triangleq \binom{n + \max(r, m)}{n + \min(r, m)}$$

which implies, since there exist (A, B, C, D) systems in which (11) is not true (in particular,

$$A = I_n, B = \begin{bmatrix} I_m \\ 0 \end{bmatrix}, C = (I_r, 0), D = 0,$$

that (A, B, C, D) must lie on a hypersurface in the parameter space of (A, B, C, D). Q.E.D.

Remark 9. Theorem 2 together with theorem 4 imply that almost all (A, B, C, D) systems are invertible, which is interesting in view of the equivalence between decoupling and right invertibility [15, 16, 17] i.e. almost all systems in which $m \geqslant r$ are decoupable.

Theorem 5. Assume that rank $C = r$, rank $B = m$; then if $m = r$, $D \equiv 0$, for almost all (A, B, C) triples, the system has $n - r$ transmission zeros, and if $m = r, D \not\equiv 0$ then for almost all (A, B, C, D) 4-tuples, the system has n transmission zeros; i.e. the class of (A, B, C) or (A, B, C, D) systems which does not have $n - r$ or n transmission zeros respectively lies on a hypersurface in the parameter space of (A, B, C) or (A, B, C, D) respectively. If $m \neq r$, then for almost all (A, B, C, D) systems there exist no transmission zeros for the system; i.e. the class of (A, B, C, D) systems which does possess a transmission zero is either empty or lies on a hypersurface in the parameter space of (A, B, C, D).

Proof. Consider the case $D \equiv 0$, $m = r$ initially; in this case, it is desired to find the set of $\{\lambda\}$ which satisfy (2) or alternately which satisfy

$$\det \begin{bmatrix} A - \lambda I & B \\ C & D \end{bmatrix} = 0 \tag{12}$$

which is a $(n - r)$th polynomial equation in λ, given by

$$c_{n-r}\lambda^{n-r} + c_{n-r-1}\lambda^{n-r-1} + \ldots + c_1\lambda + c_0 = 0 \tag{13}$$

where the coefficients $c_0, c_1, \ldots, c_{n-r}$ consist of sums of products of various terms of the matrices (A, B, C) taken together in various combinations. In order for there to exist less than $n-r$ transmission zeros for (1), it is necessary that $c_{n-r} = 0$, which implies that the elements of (A, B, C) must lie on a hypersurface in the parameter space of (A, B, C); this follows since for $c_{n-r} = 0$, it is necessary that the sums of products of various elements of the matrices (A, B, C) be equal to zero, which implies, since there exist (A, B, C) matrices in which $c_{n-r} \neq 0$ (in particular,

$$B = \begin{bmatrix} I_r \\ 0 \end{bmatrix},$$

$C = (I_r, 0), A = (0)$, that (A, B, C) must lie on a hypersurface.

In the case when $D \neq 0$, exactly the same argument as above is used to establish the result.

Consider now the case that $m \neq r$ and assume $r < m < n$. Let the hypersurface on which all degenerate (A, B, C, D) systems lie be denoted by $\mathscr{H}(A, B, C, D) = 0$ and assume that the system (A, B, C, D) is non degenerate. In this case, it is desired to find the class of $\{\lambda\}$ so that:

$$\text{rank} \begin{bmatrix} A - \lambda I & B \\ C & D \end{bmatrix} < n + r \tag{14}$$

which implies that all $(n+r) \times (n+r)$ minors of

$$\begin{bmatrix} A - \lambda I & B \\ C & D \end{bmatrix}$$

must be equal to zero, and thus that the following polynomial equations in λ must be satisfied:

$$c_q^i \lambda^q + c_{q-1}^i \lambda^{q-1} + \ldots + c_1^i \lambda + c_0^i = 0, \; i = 1, 2, \ldots, \binom{n+m}{n+r} \tag{15}$$

where it is assumed that at least one element of

$$\left\{ c_q^i, i = 1, 2, \ldots, \binom{n+m}{n+r} \right\}$$

is nonzero and where the nonzero elements of

$$c_j^i, j = 0, 1, \ldots, q; \; i = 1, 2, \ldots, \binom{n+m}{n+r}$$

are sums of products of various elements of (A, B, C, D) and $0 \leqslant q \leqslant n$. This means that for the system (A, B, C, D) to possess a transmission zero, the following inequality must be true:

$$\text{rank}\, \tilde{\Lambda} < q + 1 \tag{16}$$

where

$$\tilde{\Lambda} \triangleq \begin{bmatrix} c_q^1 & c_{q-1}^1 & & c_0^1 \\ c_q^2 & c_{q-1}^2 & \cdots & c_0^2 \\ \cdot & \cdot & & \cdot \\ \cdot & \cdot & & \cdot \\ \cdot & \cdot & & \cdot \\ c_q^{\binom{n+m}{n+r}} & c_{q-1}^{\binom{n+m}{n+r}} & \cdots & c_0^{\binom{n+m}{n+r}} \end{bmatrix}$$

or alternately that all $(q+1) \times (q+1)$ minors of $\tilde{\Lambda}$ must vanish, which implies since there exist non-degenerate (A, B, C, D) systems in which rank $\tilde{\Lambda} = q + 1$ (in particular,

$$A = \begin{bmatrix} 0 & 0 \\ I_{n-r} & 0 \end{bmatrix}, \quad B = \begin{bmatrix} I_m \\ 0 \end{bmatrix}, \quad C = (0, I_r), \quad D = 0$$

that the elements of (A, B, C, D) must lie on a hypersurface $\mathscr{H}^*(A, B, C, D) = 0$ say, in the parameter space of (A, B, C, D).

It can be seen therefore that in the case $r < m < n$ for (A, B, C, D) to possess transmission zeros, it is necessary, that either (A, B, C, D) be degenerate or that (A, B, C, D) lie on a hypersurface $\mathscr{H}^*(A, B, C, D) = 0$, or alternately, that (A, B, C, D) lie on the hypersurface $\mathscr{H}(A, B, C, D)\mathscr{H}^*(A, B, C, D) = 0$. In the case $m = n$, there exists no transmission zeros for the system as indicated in remark 8.

The same argument can be used for the case $r > m$. This proves the theorem.

Remark 10. This theorem is important because it means that *any system with more inputs than outputs* almost always has no transmission zeros and thus will almost always be solvable for any servomechanism problem,[9, 19] the "perfect control problem"[18] etc. It should be noted however that in practice, a given physical system may have a special mathematical structure which could result in the system having a different number of transmission zeros than which theorem 5 "almost always" predicts will occur; for example, it is well known that many practical single-input–single-output systems have less than $n - 1$ transmission zeros.

3.2. Transmission zeros of cascade systems

Given the two systems S_1, S_2 connected in cascade

$$\begin{aligned} S_1\colon \dot{x}_1 &= A_1 x_1 + B_1 u_1 \\ y_1 &= C_1 x_1 + D_1 u_1 \\ z &= F x_1 + G u_1 \\ S_2\colon \dot{x}_2 &= A_2 x_2 + B_2 u_2 + E v \\ y_2 &= C_2 x_2 + D_2 u_2 + H v \\ v &= K z \end{aligned} \qquad (17)$$

with $\dim u_1 = m_1$, $\dim y_1 = r_1$, $\dim u_2 = m_2$, $\dim y_2 = r_2$, let S denote the augmented system with inputs u_1, u_2 and outputs y_1, y_2. Let x_1 be a n_1-vector and x_2 be a n_2-vector. The following result is obtained:

Theorem 6†. If $m_1 = r_1$ and $m_2 = r_2$ the transmission zeros of the augmented system S are equal to the set of transmission zeros of S_1, with input u_1, output y_1, together with the set of transmission zeros of S_2, with input u_2, output y_2.

Proof. The transmission zeros of S are, by definition equal to the set of $\{\lambda\}$ which satisfy

$$\text{rank } \Lambda < n_1 + n_2 + \min(r_1 + r_2, m_1 + m_2) \tag{18}$$

where

$$\Lambda \triangleq \begin{bmatrix} A_1 - \lambda I & 0 & B_1 & 0 \\ EKF & A_2 - \lambda I & EKG & B_2 \\ C_1 & 0 & D_1 & 0 \\ HKF & C_2 & HKG & D_2 \end{bmatrix} \tag{19}$$

and since

$$\text{rank } \Lambda = \text{rank} \begin{bmatrix} A_1 - \lambda I & B_1 & 0 & 0 \\ C_1 & D_1 & 0 & 0 \\ EKF & EKG & A_2 - \lambda I & B_2 \\ HKF & HKG & C_2 & D_2 \end{bmatrix} \tag{20}$$

the result immediately follows.

Remark 11. The extension of theorem 6 to more than two systems is straightforward.

3.3 Transmission zeros in terms of a system's minimal realization

Consider the system (1) and let the Kalman Canonical Decomposition of (1) be given by

$$\dot{x} = \begin{bmatrix} A_1 & A_2 & A_3 & A_4 \\ 0 & A_5 & 0 & A_6 \\ 0 & 0 & A_7 & A_8 \\ 0 & 0 & 0 & A_9 \end{bmatrix} x + \begin{bmatrix} B_1 \\ B_2 \\ 0 \\ 0 \end{bmatrix} u$$

$$y = (0 \quad C_1 \quad 0 \quad C_2)x + Du \tag{21}$$

† Note that Theorem 6 is also valid if "$m_1 = r_1$ and $m_2 = r_2$" is replaced by "$m_1 \neq r_1$ or/and $m_2 \neq r_2$" provided "are equal to" is replaced by "are contained in". See Rosenbrock[1] for an alternate treatment of this problem.

where

$$\left\{\begin{bmatrix} A_1 & A_2 \\ 0 & A_5 \end{bmatrix}, \begin{bmatrix} B_1 \\ B_2 \end{bmatrix}\right\}$$

is controllable and

$$\left\{(C_1, C_2), \begin{bmatrix} A_5 & A_6 \\ 0 & A_9 \end{bmatrix}\right\}$$

is observable, and where (A_5, B_2, C_1, D) is defined to be the *minimal realization* of (1). The following result is obtained:

Theorem 7[†]. If $m = r$ the transmission zeros of (A, B, C, D) are equal to the transmission zeros of $(\mathbf{A}_5, \mathbf{B}_2, \mathbf{C}_1, \mathbf{D},)$ together with the eigenvalues of A_1, the eigenvalues A_7 and the eigenvalues of A_9.

Proof. After substituting (21) into (2) and simplifying, it is found that the transmission zeros of (A, B, C, D) are the set of $\{\lambda\}$ which satisfy:

$$\text{rank}\left[\begin{array}{cc:cc:c} A_5 - \lambda I & B_2 & 0 & A_6 & 0 \\ C_1 & D & 0 & C_2 & 0 \\ \hdashline 0 & 0 & A_7 - \lambda I & A_8 & 0 \\ 0 & 0 & 0 & A_9 - \lambda I & 0 \\ \hdashline A_2 & B_1 & A_3 & A_4 & A_1 - \lambda \end{array}\right] < n + \min(r, m) \qquad (22)$$

from which the result immediately follows.

3.4 Relationship of transmission zeros to poles of a closed loop system

The following section will deal with properties of the poles of a closed loop system subject to high gain output feedback.

The following lemma is required in the development to follow.

Definition. Given the polynomial equation in λ

$$c\left(\lambda^p + \sum_{i=0}^{p-1} c_i \lambda^i\right) + \epsilon\left(\sum_{i=0}^{q} \bar{c}_i(\epsilon)\lambda^i\right) = 0, \; q \geqslant p \qquad (23)$$

with real coefficients $c, c_i, \bar{c}_i$ with $c \neq 0$ such that: $\bar{c}_q(\epsilon) \neq 0$, $|\bar{c}_i(\epsilon)| < M, i = 1, 2, \ldots, q, \forall \epsilon \in [0, \infty)$, let the roots of (23) be denoted by $\lambda_j, j = 1, 2, \ldots, q$. Let the

* Note that Theorem 7 is also valid if "$m = r$" is replaced by "$m \neq r$" provided "are equal to" is replaced by "are contained in". See Rosenbrock[24] for an alternate treatment of this problem.

roots of the polynomial equation in λ:

$$c\left(\lambda^p + \sum_{i=0}^{p-1} c_i \lambda^i\right) = 0$$

be denoted by $\sigma_j, j = 1, 2, \ldots, p$.

The following lemma can easily be established from Krall[20]*:

Lemma 2. For any $(\delta, \bar{\delta})$, $\delta > 0$, $\bar{\delta} > 0$, there exists an $\epsilon^*(\delta, \bar{\delta}) > 0$ so that $\forall \epsilon \in [0, \epsilon^*)$, p roots of (23) suitably ordered, have the property that $|\lambda_j - \sigma_j| < \delta$, $j = 1, 2, \ldots, p$ and $q - p$ roots of (23) suitably ordered, have the property that $|\lambda_j| > \bar{\delta}, j = p + 1, p + 2, \ldots, q$ where the geometric mean of $\lambda_j, j = p + 1, p + 2, \ldots, q$ is proportional to

$$\left|\frac{c}{\epsilon \bar{c}_q(\epsilon)}\right|^{1/(q-p)} \quad \text{as } \epsilon \to 0.$$

Definition. Given the system (1) with $D \equiv 0$, assume that rank $C = r$, rank $B = m$. Let $\sigma(\rho)$ denote an eigenvalue of $(A + \rho BKC)$, where $K \in R^{m \times r}$ with rank $K = \min(m, r)$, $\rho \in R$, and assume that there exists a scalar $\lambda^* \in R$ with the property that for any $\epsilon > 0$, there exists $\bar{\rho}(\epsilon) > 0$ so that $|\sigma(\rho) - \lambda^*| < \epsilon$, $\forall \rho > \bar{\rho}(\epsilon)$; then λ^* is called a *finite eigenvalue* of $(A + \rho BKC)$.

Let the transmission zeros of (A, B, C) be denoted by $\lambda_i, i = 1, 2, \ldots, p, 0 \leqslant p \leqslant n\text{-max}(r, m)$. Let the finite eigenvalues of $(A + \rho BKC)$ be given by $\lambda_i^*, i = 1, 2, \ldots, q, 0 \leqslant q \leqslant n$. The following result will be proved:

Theorem 8. Given the non degenerate system (1) with $D \equiv 0$, assume that rank $C = r$, rank $B = m$, and let the output feedback control $u = \rho K y$ be applied to (1), where rank $K = \min(m, r)$ and ρ is a real scalar. Then if $r = m$, the finite eigenvalues of $A + \rho BKC$ coincide with the transmission zeros of (A, B, C), i.e. $p = q$; if $r \neq m$, then for almost all K, a subset of the finite eigenvalues of $A + \rho BKC$ coincides with the transmission zeros of (A, B, C), i.e. the class of K matrices in which a subset of the finite eigenvalues of $A + \rho BKC$ does not coincide with the transmission zeros of (A, B, C) is either empty or lies on a hypersurface in the parameter space of K.

Remark 12. This result is a generalization of the classical Root-locus result for single-input–single-output systems, in which it is well known that for high gain output feedback, the poles of the closed loop system approach the zeros of the transfer function describing the system.

Proof of Theorem 8. It will be assumed in the proof that (A, B, C) is controllable and observable, since from theorem 7, the general case immediately reduces to this special case. Now since the system (1) is controllable, it may be transformed by a coordinate transformation and a nonsingular transformation of control variables into the following form: [21]

$$\dot{x} = A^* x + B^* v$$

$$y = C^* x$$

* The authors wish to thank W. M. Wonham for bringing this reference to their attention.

where

$$
A^* \triangleq \left[\begin{array}{c|c|c}
A_1 & 0 & \cdots \quad 0 \\
e_1^1 & e_2^1 & \quad e_m^1 \\
\hline
0 & A_2 & \cdots \quad 0 \\
e_1^2 & e_2^2 & \quad e_m^2 \\
\hline
\cdot & \cdot & \cdot \\
\cdot & \cdot & \cdots \quad \cdot \\
\cdot & \cdot & \cdot \\
\hline
0 & 0 & \cdots \quad A_m \\
e_1^m & e_2^m & \quad e_m^m
\end{array}\right],
$$

$$
B^* \triangleq \left[\begin{array}{c|c|c}
b_1 & 0 & \cdots \quad 0 \\
\hline
0 & b_2 & \cdots \quad 0 \\
\hline
\cdot & \cdot & \cdot \\
\cdot & \cdot & \cdots \quad \cdot \\
\cdot & \cdot & \cdot \\
\hline
0 & 0 & \cdots \quad b_m
\end{array}\right] \tag{24}
$$

$$
C^* = (C_1, C_2, \ldots, C_m)
$$

where e_j^i, $j = 1, 2, \ldots, m$; $i = 1, 2, \ldots, m$ is a row vector, A_i is a $(n_i - 1) \times n_i$ matrix with the following structure:

$$
A_i = \begin{bmatrix}
0 & 1 & 0 & \cdots & 0 \\
0 & 0 & 1 & \cdots & 0 \\
\cdot & \cdot & \cdot & & \cdot \\
\cdot & \cdot & \cdot & & \cdot \\
\cdot & \cdot & \cdot & & \cdot \\
0 & 0 & 0 & & 1
\end{bmatrix} \tag{25}
$$

b_i is a n_i vector with the following structure $b_i = (0, 0, \ldots, 0, 1)$, and n_i, $i = 1, 2, \ldots, m$ are the *controllability indices*[21] of (A, B). Let

$$
E^i \triangleq (e_i^{1\prime}, e_i^{2\prime}, \ldots, e_i^{m\prime})', \; i = 1, 2, \ldots, m \tag{26}
$$

Then the transmission zeros of (A, B, C) are invariant under such a transformation, as noted in remark 2, and are given by the set of $\{\lambda\}$ which satisfy the condition

$$\text{rank} \begin{bmatrix} A^* - \lambda I & B^* \\ C^* & 0 \end{bmatrix} < n + \min(m, r) \tag{27}$$

which after substitution and simplification may be written as

$$\text{rank}\ \Gamma(\lambda) < \min(m, r) \tag{28}$$

where

$$\Gamma(\lambda) \triangleq \left[C_1 \begin{bmatrix} 1 \\ \lambda \\ \cdot \\ \cdot \\ \cdot \\ \lambda^{n_1 - 1} \end{bmatrix}, C_2 \begin{bmatrix} 1 \\ \lambda \\ \cdot \\ \cdot \\ \cdot \\ \lambda^{n_2 - 1} \end{bmatrix}, \ldots, C_m \begin{bmatrix} 1 \\ \lambda \\ \cdot \\ \cdot \\ \cdot \\ \lambda^{n_m - 1} \end{bmatrix} \right] \tag{29}$$

Consider now applying the feedback control $v = \rho K y$ to (22) where rank $K = \min(r, m)$. Assume for simplicity that $r = m$. Then the eigenvalues of the closed loop system are given by the set of $\{\sigma\}$ which satisfy the equation:

$$\det(A^* + \rho B^* K C^* - \sigma I) = 0 \tag{30}$$

which after substitution for A^*, B^*, C^* and considerable simplification reduces to the solution of the following $m \times m$ determinant for σ:

$$\det\left\{ \rho K \Gamma(\sigma) + \left[E^1 \begin{bmatrix} 1 \\ \sigma \\ \cdot \\ \cdot \\ \cdot \\ \sigma^{n_1 - 1} \end{bmatrix}, E^2 \begin{bmatrix} 1 \\ \sigma \\ \cdot \\ \cdot \\ \cdot \\ \sigma^{n_2 - 1} \end{bmatrix}, \ldots, E^m \begin{bmatrix} 1 \\ \sigma \\ \cdot \\ \cdot \\ \cdot \\ \sigma^{n_m - 1} \end{bmatrix} \right] - \text{diag}(\sigma^{n_1}, \sigma^{n_2}, \ldots, \sigma^{n_m}) \right\} = 0 \tag{31}$$

which becomes, on expanding the determinant of the left hand side of (31), the following:

$$\rho^m \det[K\Gamma(\sigma)] + \left\{ \sigma^n + \sum_{i=0}^{n-1} c_i(\rho) \sigma^i \right\} = 0 \tag{32}$$

where the coefficients $c_i(\rho)$ have the property that

$$\lim_{\rho\to\infty} \frac{c_i(\rho)}{\rho^m} = 0, \quad i = 0, 1, \ldots, n-1.$$

Since K is a nonsingular matrix (32) may then be written as:

$$\det[\Gamma(\sigma)] + \frac{1}{\rho^m \det K}\left\{\sigma^n + \sum_{i=0}^{n-1} c_i(\rho)\sigma^i\right\} = 0 \tag{33}$$

Now since it has been assumed that (A, B, C) is non degenerate then $\det \Gamma(\sigma)$ is a nonzero polynomial in λ, and hence from lemma 2, it follows that the finite eigenvalues of the matrix $(A + \rho BKC)$ are given by the solution of:

$$\det \Gamma(\sigma) = 0 \tag{34}$$

for σ, which means from (28), that the finite eigenvalues of $(A + \rho BKC)$ are equal to the transmission zeros of (A, B, C), thereby establishing theorem 8 for the case $m = r$.

The proof of theorem 8 for the case $r \neq m$ follows by using exactly the same argument as above. The details are omitted. Q.E.D.

3.5 An application of transmission zeros – the robust servo compensator

The following problem, which is an extension of [19], gives an illustration of the importance of transmission zeros in multivariable control system design:

Given the linear, time-invariant system

$$\begin{aligned} \dot{x} &= Ax + Bu + Ew \\ y &= Cx + Du + Fw \end{aligned} \tag{35}$$

where $x \in R^n$ is the state, $u \in R^m$ is the input, $y \in R^r$ is the output and $w \in R^\Omega$ is a disturbance vector which is unmeasurable and is assumed to satisfy the following equation:

$$\begin{aligned} \dot{z}_1 &= \mathscr{A}_1 z_1 \\ w &= \mathscr{C}_1 z_1 \end{aligned} \tag{36}$$

where $z_1 \in R^{n_1}$ and where $(\mathscr{A}_1, \mathscr{C}_1)$ is observable and $z_1(0)$ is unknown, it is desired to find a robust controller for (35) in the sense of [19] so that $y - y_{\text{ref}} \to 0$ as $t \to \infty$, $\forall x(0) \in R^n$, $\forall z_1(0) \in R^{n_1}$, for any finite perturbations in the elements of A, B, C, D which do not cause the resultant closed loop system to become unstable where y_{ref} is a specified reference† for the output given as follows:

$$\begin{aligned} y_{\text{ref}} = G\sigma,\ \dot{z}_2 &= \mathscr{A}_2 z_2 \\ \sigma &= \mathscr{C}_2 z_2 \end{aligned} \tag{37}$$

where $z_2 \in R^{n_2}$ and where $(\mathscr{A}_2, \mathscr{C}_2)$ is observable and $z_2(0)$ is known. It is assumed without loss of generality that rank $C = r$, rank $B = m$, rank $\binom{E}{F} =$ rank $\mathscr{C} = \Omega$, rank $G =$ rank $\mathscr{C}_2 = \dim \sigma$, and that the eigenvalues of $\mathscr{A}_1, \mathscr{A}_2$ are all in the

† According to standard control terminology this is equivalent to a reference input.

closed right hand part of the complex plane. It is assumed that the state x is available for measurement and for non-trivality that max (rank $\binom{E}{F}$, rank $(G)) \geqslant 1$.

Definition. Let all the zeros of the minimal polynomial of $\mathscr{A}_1$ be given by $\{\Lambda_1\}$ and let all the zeros of the minimal polynomial of $\mathscr{A}_2$ be given by $\{\Lambda_2\}$. Then define $\{\lambda_1, \lambda_2, \ldots, \lambda_q\} \triangleq \{\Lambda_1\} \cup \{\Lambda_2\}$.

Let

$$y \triangleq (y_1, y_2, \ldots, y_r)', y_{\text{ref}} \triangleq (y_{1,r}, y_{2,r}, \ldots, y_{r,r})'.$$

The following result is obtained:

Theorem 9.† A necessary and sufficient condition that there exists a robust linear time-invariant controller for (35) such that $y - y_{\text{ref}} \to 0$ as $t \to \infty$ for all unmeasurable disturbances w and all specified y_{ref} described by (36) and (37) respectively, and such that the controlled system is controllable (or stabilizable) is that the following conditions all hold:

(a) (A, B) be controllable (or stabilizable)

(b) $m \geqslant r$

(c) the transmission zeros of (A, B, C, D) not coincide with $\lambda_i, i = 1, 2, \ldots, q$.

Remark 13. In case these two conditions hold, the robust controller must be a feedback controller of order at least rq with $(y - y_{\text{ref}})$ as an input to the controller. (see [19] for a characterization of all such controllers).

Controller

The following robust controller called a *servocompensator* [19] will satisfy the requirements of theorem 9 and is of minimum order (rq):

$$u = K_0 x + \sum_{i=1}^{r} K_i \eta_i \tag{38}$$

where

$$\dot{\eta}_i = \mathscr{C}\eta_i + \begin{bmatrix} 0 \\ 0 \\ \cdot \\ \cdot \\ \cdot \\ 0 \\ 1 \end{bmatrix} (y_i - y_{i,r}), \quad i = 1, 2, \ldots, r \tag{39}$$

† See [25] for a generalization of this result.

where

$$\mathscr{C} = \begin{bmatrix} 0 & 1 & 0 & \dots & 0 \\ 0 & 0 & 1 & \dots & 0 \\ \cdot & \cdot & \cdot & & \cdot \\ \cdot & \cdot & \cdot & & \cdot \\ \cdot & \cdot & \cdot & & \vdots \\ \cdot & \cdot & \cdot & & \vdots \\ -\delta_1 & -\delta_2 & -\delta_3 & \dots & -\delta_q \end{bmatrix} \tag{40}$$

and $\delta_1, \delta_2, \dots, \delta_q$ are the coefficients of the polynomial

$$\prod_{i=1}^{q} (\lambda - \lambda_i)$$

i.e.

$$\prod_{i=1}^{q} (\lambda - \lambda_i) \triangleq \lambda^q + \delta_q \lambda^{q-1} + \delta_{q-1} \lambda^{q-2} + \dots + \delta_2 \lambda + \delta_1 \tag{41}$$

The gain matrices $K_0, K_i, i = 1, 2, \dots, r$ are found so that the closed system is stable and has satisfactory transient response by using standard methods.[19, 9]

Remark 14. In the above controller it is not necessary to know $E, F, \mathscr{C}_1, \mathscr{C}_2, \mathscr{A}_1, \mathscr{A}_2$. It is essential however to know the zeros of the minimal polynomial of $\mathscr{A}_1$ and $\mathscr{A}_2$.

Proof of theorem 9. The proof of sufficiency of theorem 9 follows immediately from [19]. The proof of necessity of the theorem and minimality of the controller follows, by using exactly the same development as in [19] on noting that the system (35)–(37) is equivalent to the following system:

$$\dot{x} = Ax + Bu + \sum_{i=1}^{\Gamma} (E_i, 0) \begin{bmatrix} \omega_i \\ \bar{y}_i \end{bmatrix} + \sum_{i=1}^{\Gamma} \sum_{k=1}^{\nu^i} ({}_kE_i, 0) \begin{bmatrix} {}_k\omega_i \\ {}_k\bar{y}_i \end{bmatrix}$$

$$y - y_{\text{ref}} = Cx + Du + \sum_{i=1}^{\Gamma} (F_i, -G_i) \begin{bmatrix} \omega_i \\ \bar{y}_i \end{bmatrix} + \sum_{i=1}^{\Gamma} \sum_{k=1}^{\nu^i} ({}_kF_i, -{}_kG_i) \begin{bmatrix} {}_k\omega_i \\ {}_k\bar{y}_i \end{bmatrix} \tag{42}$$

where rank $\begin{pmatrix} E_i & 0 \\ F_i & -G_i \end{pmatrix} \geqslant 1, i = 1, 2, \dots, \Gamma$ and where the elements of the vectors ω_i, $\bar{y}_i, i = 1, 2, \dots, \Gamma$ satisfy the following differential equation:

$$\omega^{(p_i)} + \delta^i_{p_i} \omega^{(p_i - 1)} + \delta^i_{p_i - 1} \omega^{(p_i - 2)} + \dots + \delta^i_2 \dot{\omega} + \delta^i_1 \omega = 0, p_i \leqslant q \tag{43}$$

where the initial conditions of (43) are assumed to be unknown for the elements of ω_i and known for the elements y_i, and where $(\lambda_1, \ldots, \lambda_q)$ are the zeros (multiplicities included) of the least common multiple of the Γ characteristic polynomials corresponding to (43) with $i = 1, 2, \ldots, \Gamma$. The elements of the vectors ${}_k\omega_i$, ${}_k\bar{y}_i$, $i = 1, 2, \ldots, \Gamma$ satisfy a differential equation with characteristic roots equal to those of (43) except that the multiplicity of all roots is now reduced by at least one.

4. The numerical computation of transmission zeros of a system

This section deals with an efficient numerical procedure for determining the transmission zeros of a sytem. The following lemma is required in the development:

Lemma 3. The characteristic equation of the $(n + m) \times (n + m)$ matrix

$$\begin{bmatrix} A & \gamma B \\ C & \gamma D \end{bmatrix}$$

where $A \in R^{n\times n}$, $B \in R^{n\times m}$, $C \in R^{m\times n}$ and γ is a positive scalar is given as follows:

$$P(\lambda) - \frac{\lambda}{\gamma}\left\{\left[\frac{\lambda}{\gamma}\right]^{m-1} P_m(\lambda) + \left[\frac{\lambda}{\gamma}\right]^{m-2} P_{m-1}(\lambda) + \ldots + \left[\frac{\lambda}{\gamma}\right] P_2(\lambda) + P_1(\lambda)\right\} = 0 \tag{44}$$

where

$$P(\lambda) \triangleq \det \begin{bmatrix} A - \lambda I & B \\ C & D \end{bmatrix} \tag{45}$$

is a polynomial in λ, which may be identically zero, of order p, $0 \leqslant p \leqslant n - m$ if $D \equiv 0$ and of order p, $0 \leqslant p \leqslant n$ if $D \not\equiv 0$; $P_m(\lambda)$ is a monic polynomial in λ of order n and $P_j(\lambda)$, $j = 1, 2, \ldots, m - 1$ are polynomials in λ of order $\leqslant n$.

Proof. The result is obtained by expanding the determinant

$$\det \begin{bmatrix} A - \lambda I & B \\ C & D - \frac{\lambda}{\gamma} I \end{bmatrix} \tag{46}$$

using cofactors about the last column and putting the result equal to zero. The details are omitted.

The following theorem is now obtained:

Definition. Let $S(\gamma)$ be given by:

$$S(\gamma) \triangleq \begin{bmatrix} A & \gamma B \\ C & \gamma D \end{bmatrix} \tag{47}$$

where γ is a real scalar. Let the transmission zeros of (A, B, C, D) be denoted by λ_i, $i = 1, 2, \ldots, p$.

Theorem 10. Assume that $r = m$ and that (A, B, C, D) is nondegenerate. Then for any $\epsilon > 0$, there exists a $\bar{\gamma}(\epsilon)$ so that p eigenvalues of $S(\gamma)$, suitably ordered, σ_i, $i = 1, 2, \ldots, p$, $0 \leqslant p \leqslant n$, have the property that $|\lambda_i - \sigma_i| < \epsilon$, $i = 1, 2, \ldots, p$, $\forall \gamma > \bar{\gamma}(\epsilon)$. Moreover, as $\gamma \to \infty$ the remaining $n + m - p$ eigenvalues of $S(\gamma)$ become arbitrarily large with a geometric mean proportional to $\{\gamma\}^{m/(n+m-p)}$.

Proof. From lemma 3, the characteristic equation of the matrix $S(\gamma)$ can be expressed as:

$$P(\lambda) - \epsilon\{\epsilon^{m-1}\lambda^m P_m(\lambda) + \epsilon^{m-2}\lambda^{m-1}P_{m-1}(\lambda)$$
$$+ \ldots + \epsilon\lambda^2 P_2(\lambda) + \lambda P_1(\lambda)\} = 0 \tag{48}$$

where

$$\epsilon \triangleq \frac{1}{\gamma},$$

where $\lambda^m P_m(\lambda)$ is a polynomial of order $n + m$ and $\lambda^j p_j(\lambda)$, $j = 1, 2, \ldots, m - 1$ are polynomials of order $\leqslant n + m$ and $P(\lambda)$ is a polynomial of order p given by (45). From lemma 3, it is also seen that as $\epsilon \to 0$ or alternatively as $\gamma \to \infty$, p roots of the equation (48) will become arbitrarily close to the roots of the polynomial equation $P(\lambda) = 0$ and $n + m - p$ roots will become arbitrarily large with a geometric mean proportional to

$$\left\{\frac{1}{\epsilon}\right\}^{m/(n+m-p)}.$$

This proves the theorem.

It is observed that this theorem implies, subject to certain assumptions, that as $\gamma \to \infty$, the transmission zeros of (A, B, C, D) are contained in the eigenvalues of $S(\gamma)$; this observation forms the basis of the proposed algorithm to find transmission zeros of a system. In the case when $m > r$, the following modification is now required to find transmission zeros using theorem 10:

(a) Choose a real scalar $\tilde{\lambda}$ so that

$$\text{rank}\begin{bmatrix} A - \tilde{\lambda} I & B \\ C & D \end{bmatrix} = n + r.$$

It should be noted that such a scalar always exists if the system (A, B, C, D) is non-degenerate.

(b) Find a $(m - r) \times (n + m)$ matrix (E_1, E_2) so that

$$\text{rank}\begin{bmatrix} A - \tilde{\lambda} I & B \\ C & D \\ E_1 & E_2 \end{bmatrix} = n + m \tag{49}$$

It should be noted that such a matrix (E_1, E_2) always exists since

$$\begin{bmatrix} A - \tilde{\lambda} I & B \\ C & D \end{bmatrix}$$

has rank equal to $n + r$.

It then follows from (2), that the transmission zeros of (A, B, C, D) are contained in the transmission zeros of

$$\left\{A, B, \begin{pmatrix} C \\ E_1 \end{pmatrix}, \begin{pmatrix} D \\ E_2 \end{pmatrix}\right\}$$

and the latter can be directly found by using theorem 10.

In the case that $m < r$, by duality, it follows that the transmission zeros of (A, B, C, D) are equal to the transmission zeros of (A', C', B', D') and these may be found by using theorem 10 on applying the above modification.

The case when (A, B, C, D) is degenerate means that the transmission zeros include the whole complex plane. This condition may be easily checked by using the definition given in (3).

The following algorithm is therefore obtained to find the transmission zeros of a system (A, B, C, D). Note that it has not been assumed necessarily that (1) is controllable or observable, or that rank $C = r$, rank $B = m$ or that (A, B, C, D) is non degenerate in applying this algorithm.

Algorithm I to find transmission zeros of (A, B, C, D)

(1) If $m < r$ replace the system (A, B, C, D) by (A', C', B', D'), interchange the value of m and r and go to step (2). If $m \geqslant r$ go to step (2).

(2) Choose $n + 1$ distinct real scalars λ_i^*, $i = 1, \ldots, n + 1$ and if rank

$$\text{rank}\begin{bmatrix} A - \lambda_i^* I & B \\ C & D \end{bmatrix} < n + r, \; i = 1, \ldots, n + 1$$

stop, because the system is degenerate; otherwise

$$\text{rank}\begin{bmatrix} A - \lambda_i^* I & B \\ C & D \end{bmatrix} = n + r$$

for at least one value of λ_i^*, $i = 1, \ldots, n+1$, say λ_k^*. Store λ_k^* and go to step (3).

(3) Calculate

$$N_f \triangleq \frac{\left\| \begin{pmatrix} A \\ C \end{pmatrix} \right\|}{\|(B, D)\|}$$

and choose $\gamma = 10^{15} N_f$ for example†. If $m = r$ form the matrix

$$\Lambda(\gamma) \triangleq \begin{bmatrix} A & \gamma B \\ C & \gamma D \end{bmatrix}$$

and go to step 4; otherwise, choose a $(m-r) \times (m-r)$ matrix (E_1, E_2) with

$$\|E_1\| \doteqdot \left\| \begin{pmatrix} A \\ C \end{pmatrix} \right\|, \quad \|E_2\| \doteqdot \|(B, D)\|$$

so that

$$\operatorname{rank} \begin{bmatrix} A - \lambda_k^* I & B \\ C & D \\ E_1 & E_2 \end{bmatrix} = n + m$$

(by using a pseudo-random number generator say), form the matrix

$$\Lambda(\gamma) \triangleq \begin{bmatrix} A & \gamma B \\ C & \gamma D \\ E_1 & \gamma E_2 \end{bmatrix}$$

and go to step (4).

(4) Find the eigenvalues of the matrix $\Lambda(\gamma)$. Let the eigenvalues be denoted by $\tilde{\lambda}_i$, $i = 1, 2, \ldots, n+m$.

(5) Retain those eigenvalues obtained in step (4) $\tilde{\lambda}_{ki}$, $i = 1, 2, \ldots$ which have the property that

$$\operatorname{rank} \begin{bmatrix} A - \tilde{\lambda}_{ki} I & B \\ C & D \end{bmatrix} < n + r, \quad i = 1, 2, \ldots$$

These eigenvalues, if any, are the transmission zeros of the system. Stop.

† It is assumed that double precision arithmetic is used with this value of γ. A significantly larger value than this value is not suggested because of problems of overflow. If single precision arithmetic is used, a smaller value of γ is suggested, say $\gamma = 10^8 N_f$, to minimize the effect of rounding errors on the digital computer.

Remark 15. The calculation of eigenvalues required in step (4) can be done in a computational efficient manner by using, for example, the *QR* Transformation technique.[22] The total computational time required by this algorithm only varies as n^3 [22] and hence the total computational time of the proposed algorithm also only varies as n^3, which is quite reasonable. It should be noted that provided proper scaling[22] of the matrix $\Lambda(\gamma)$ is performed, there is no problem of finding eigenvalues of $\Lambda(\gamma)$ accurately in spite of the large number γ. A typical computational time required to find the transmission zeros of a 100th order system is 4 min on an IBM 7094 digital computer.

Theorem 8 forms the basis of a new simplified algorithm which may be used, in special cases, to find the transmission zeros of a system.

4.1. Algorithm II to find transmission zeros of a system with $D \equiv 0$, rank $B = m$, rank $C = r$

It will be assumed that $D \equiv 0$, rank $B = m$, rank $C = r$ and that (A, B, C) is non degenerate in the discussion to follow.

For systems which may or may not be controllable and observable, theorem 8 gives an alternate way of calculating the transmission zeros of a system i.e. simply choose an arbitrary output gain matrix of full rank multiplied by a "large" scalar, i.e. $\rho = 10^{15}$, and find the eigenvalues of the closed loop system. In case $m = r$ the finite eigenvalues of the system will then be the transmission zeros of the system. In case $m \neq r$, the finite eigenvalues of the system which do not satisfy (2) should be discarded; the remaining finite eigenvalues are then the transmission zeros of the system.

Remark 16. It can be seen that both algorithms I and II require finding the eigenvalues of a matrix containing large elements, the size of the matrix being smaller in the case of algorithm II. Since algorithm II is somewhat simpler to use than algorithm I, it is recommended that algorithm II be used whenever applicable.

Remark 17. Reference [10] deals with an algorithm for finding transmission zeros of (1) for the special case $m = r = 1, D \equiv 0$. Ref. [2] makes two suggestions for finding transmission zeros of controllable–observable systems with $m = r, D \equiv 0$, by using the fact that substituting suitable values for s into the RHS and LHS of certain polynomial identities, will lead to a set of linear algebraic equations, whose solution will eventually give the zeros of the system. The method unfortunately may lead to ill-conditioning if satisfactory values for s cannot be found.

5. Numerical Examples

The following examples illustrate the proposed algorithms discussed in section 4 for finding transmission zeros of a system.

Example no. 1. Consider the following 9th order system which describes a boiler system[23]:

$$\begin{aligned} \dot{x} &= Ax + Bu \\ y &= Cx + Du \end{aligned} ; \quad u = \begin{bmatrix} u_1 \\ u_2 \end{bmatrix}, \quad y = \begin{bmatrix} y_1 \\ y_2 \end{bmatrix} \tag{50}$$

Where A is given in Table 1 and B, C and D are as follows:

$$B = \begin{bmatrix} 0 & 0 \\ 0 & 0 \\ 1.56 & 0 \\ 0 & -5.13 \times 10^{-6} \\ 8.28 & -1.55 \\ 0 & 1.78 \\ 2.33 & 0 \\ 0 & -2.45 \times 10^{-2} \\ 0 & 2.94 \times 10^{-5} \end{bmatrix},$$

$$C = \begin{bmatrix} 0 & 0 & 0 & 0 & 0 & 1 & 0 & 0 & 0 \\ 0 & 0 & 0 & 0 & 0 & 0 & 0 & 0 & 1 \end{bmatrix}, \quad D = 0$$

It is desired to find the transmission zeros of the system. In this case the following results were obtained using algorithm I (with $\gamma = 10^{25}$).

Transmission zeros of system

$-2.639513729 \times 10^{1}$

$-2.957771983 \pm j3.352672040 \times 10^{-1}$

$7.486064353 \times 10^{-1}$

$9.403261463 \times 10^{-2}$

$-9.546070736 \times 10^{-3}$

In order to show how the transmission zeros vary depending on γ, a complete listing of all eigenvalues of the matrix

$$\begin{bmatrix} A & \gamma B \\ C & \gamma D \end{bmatrix}$$

for Example No. 1 are now given for the case $\gamma = 10^{15}, 10^{20}, 10^{25}$ in Table 2 below. It is seen that the eigenvalues marked with an asterisk are clearly invariant with respect to γ and correspond to the transmission zeros of the system. The extraneous eigenvalues are approximately proportional to $\gamma^{\frac{2}{5}}$ as predicted.

Example No. 2. This example is the same as example No. 1 except that **C** is now:

$$\mathbf{C} = (0 \quad 0 \quad 0 \quad 0 \quad 0 \quad 0 \quad 0 \quad 0 \quad 1) \tag{51}$$

In this case, it is found that there are no transmission zeros for the system.

TABLE 1. *Matrix A*

-3.93	-3.15×10^{-3}	0	0	0	4.03×10^{-5}	0	0	0
3.68×10^{2}	-3.05	3.03	0	0	-3.77×10^{-3}	0	0	0
2.74×10^{1}	7.87×10^{-2}	-5.96×10^{-2}	0	0	-2.81×10^{-4}	0	0	0
-6.47×10^{-2}	-5.20×10^{-5}	0	-2.55×10^{-1}	-3.35×10^{-6}	3.60×10^{-7}	6.33×10^{-5}	1.94×10^{-4}	0
3.85×10^{3}	1.73×10^{1}	-1.28×10^{1}	-1.26×10^{4}	-2.91	-1.05×10^{-1}	1.27×10^{1}	4.31×10^{1}	0
2.24×10^{4}	1.80×10^{1}	0	-3.56×10^{1}	-1.04×10^{-4}	-4.14×10^{-1}	9.00×10^{1}	5.69×10^{1}	0
0	0	2.34×10^{-3}	0	0	2.22×10^{-4}	-2.03×10^{-1}	0	0
0	0	0	-1.27	1.00×10^{-3}	7.86×10^{-5}	0	-7.17×10^{-2}	0
-2.20	-1.77×10^{-3}	0	-8.44	-1.11×10^{-4}	1.38×10^{-5}	1.49×10^{-3}	6.02×10^{-3}	-1.00×10^{-10}

TABLE 2. *Variation of Eigenvalues with respect to γ for Example No. 1*

$\gamma = 10^{15}$	$\gamma = 10^{20}$	$\gamma = 10^{25}$
6.065242×10^{5}	5.675202×10^{7}	1.714906×10^{10}
$-3.028627 \times 10^{5} \pm j5.039790 \times 10^{5}$	-5.149293×10^{7}	-1.714380×10^{10}
-8.832675×10^{4}	1.594333×10^{7}	8.183266×10^{8}
8.754852×10^{4}	$-1.060120 \times 10^{7} \pm j1.535046 \times 10^{7}$	$-4.117916 \times 10^{8} \pm j7.102096 \times 10^{8}$
*-2.639514×10^{1}	*-2.639514×10^{1}	*-2.639514×10^{1}
*$-2.957772 \pm j3.352672 \times 10^{-1}$	*$-2.957772 \pm j3.352672 \times 10^{-1}$	*$-2.957772 \pm j3.352672 \times 10^{-1}$
* 7.486064×10^{-1}	* 7.486064×10^{-1}	* 7.486064×10^{-1}
* 9.403261×10^{-2}	* 9.403261×10^{-2}	* 9.403261×10^{-2}
*-9.546071×10^{-3}	*-9.546071×10^{-3}	*-9.546071×10^{-3}

* Denotes transmission zero of the system.

Example No. 3. This example is the same as example No. 1 except that **C** is now:

$$\mathbf{C} = (0 \quad 0 \quad 0 \quad 0 \quad 0 \quad 1 \quad 0 \quad 0 \quad 0) \tag{52}$$

In this case it is found that there are no transmission zeros for the system.

Remark 18. Note that the results of examples 2 and 3 agree with the observation made previously in theorem 5, i.e. that there exist no transmission zeros for almost all **(A, B, C, D)** systems in which there are an unequal number of inputs and outputs.

Example No. 4 This example is the same as example No. 1. In this case, since $D \equiv 0$, rank $B = m$, rank $C = r, r = m$, and the system (50) is nondegenerate, the algorithm II of section 4 may be applied to find the transmission zeros for the system; the following results shown in Table 3 were obtained on choosing arbitrary output gain matrices for the system.

TABLE 3. *Eigenvalues of $(A + \rho BKC)$ for Example No. 4*

$\rho = 10^{15}, K = \begin{bmatrix} 0.85992 & 5.9231 \\ 4.80780 & -1.4696 \end{bmatrix}$	$\rho = 10^{15}, K = \begin{bmatrix} -6.1048 & -0.41035 \\ 6.4977 & -3.3044 \end{bmatrix}$
8.557841×10^{15}	1.156581×10^{16}
$3.543997 \pm j2.373841 \times 10^{6}$	1.789469×10^{6}
$*-2.639514 \times 10^{1}$	-1.789337×10^{6}
$*-2.957772 \pm j3.352672 \times 10^{-1}$	$*-2.639514 \times 10^{1}$
$*\ 7.486064 \times 10^{-1}$	$*-2.957772 \pm j3.352672 \times 10^{-1}$
$*\ 9.403261 \times 10^{-2}$	$*\ 7.486064 \times 10^{-1}$
$*-9.546071 \times 10^{-3}$	$*\ 9.403261 \times 10^{-2}$
	$*-9.546071 \times 10^{-3}$

* Denotes transmission zero of the system.

The eigenvalues marked with an asterisk correspond to the transmission zeros of the system and agree with the transmission zeros obtained in Example No 1 to 7 figure accuracy.

6. Conclusions

This paper has given a new definition of transmission zeros for linear multivariable time-invariant systems, which has been shown to be equivalent to previous definitions by theorem 1. Based on this definition, new properties of transmission zeros are then described; in particular, theorem 2 shows the equivalence of the invertibility of a system with the system having a finite number of transmission zeros, theorem 3 gives the maximum number of transmission zeros which a system may have under certain mild conditions, and theorem 5 shows that a system which has an equal number of inputs and outputs almost always has $n - r$ zeros if $D = 0$ and n zeros if $D \neq 0$, and that a system which has an unequal number of inputs and outputs almost always has no transmission zeros. This later observation is extremely important; it means, for example, that a controllable system which has more inputs than outputs to be controlled almost always will have a solution to the "perfect" control problem. [18]. Transmission zeros of cascade systems are then studied in theorem 6, and theorem 7 relates the transmission zeros of a system to the system's minimal realization. Theorem 8 shows how the poles of a closed loop system subject to high gain feedback are related to the transmission zeros of a system and forms the basis of a simple algorithm to calculate transmission zeros of a system assuming that $D = 0$, rank $B = m$, rank $C = r$. An illustration of how transmission zeros arise in control system design problems is given in theorem 9 for a general servomechanism problem. A general algorithm which is fast and numerically efficient is then given, based on theorem 10, which enables the transmission zeros of large multivariable systems to be determined. A 9th order numerical example has been included to illustrate the algorithm.

7. References

[1] Rosenbrock, H. H., *State-Space and Multivariable Theory*. Nelson (1970).

[2] Kwakernaak, H. and Sivan, R., *Linear Optimal Control Systems*, pp. 41–42. Wiley-Interscience, New York (1972).

[3] Morse, A. S., Structural invariants of linear multivariable systems. *SIAM J. Control*, **11**, pp. 446–465 (1973).

[4] Wang, S. H., Davison, E. J., "Canonical forms of linear multivariable systems", *SIAM J. on Control and Optimization,* vol. 14, No. 2, 1976, pp. 236–250.

[5] Moore, B. C. and Silverman, L. M., Equivalent characterizations of zeros in multivariable systems. *I.E.E.E. Decision and Control Conference*, December (1972).

[6] Rosenbrock, H. H., The zeros of a system. *International J. Control*, **18**, pp. 297–299 (1973).

[7] Desoer, C. A. and Schulman, J. D., Zeros and poles of matrix transfer functions and their dynamic interpretation. *I.E.E.E. Trans. Circuit Theory*, **CAS-21**, pp. 3–8 (1972).

[8] Wolovich, W. A., On determining the zeros of state-space systems. *I.E.E.E. Trans. Automatic Control*, **AC-18**, 542–544 (1973).

[9] Davison, E. J., The output control of linear time-invariant multivariable systems with unmeasurable arbitrary disturbances. *I.E.E.E. Trans. Automatic Control*, **AC-17**, 621–630 (1972).

[10] Davison, E. J., A computational method for finding the zeros of a multivariable linear time-invariant system. *Automatica*, **6**, 481–484 (1970).

[11] Wang, S. H. and Davison, E. J., A new invertibility criterion for linear multivariable systems. *I.E.E.E. Trans. Automatic Control*, **AC-18**, 538–539 (1973).

[12] Sain, M. K. and Massey, J. L., Invertibility of linear time-invariant dynamic systems. *I.E.E.E. Trans. Automatic Control*, **AC-14**, 141–149 (1969).

[13] Silverman, L. M., Inversion of multivariable linear systems. *I.E.E.E. Trans. Automatic Control*, **AC-14**, 270–276 (1969).

[14] Davison, E. J. and Wang, S. H., Properties of linear time-invariant multivariable systems subject to arbitrary output and state feedback. *I.E.E.E. Trans. Automatic Control*, **AC-18**, 24–32 (1973).

[15] Silverman, L. M. and Payne, H. J., Input–output structure of linear systems with application to the decoupling problem. *SIAM J. Control*, **9**, 199–233 (1971).

[16] Wang, S. H., Relationship between triangular decoupling and invertibility of linear multivariable systems. *Int. J. Control*, **15**, 395–399 (1972).

[17] Fabian, E. and Wonham, W. M., Generic Solvability of the Decoupling Problem. Dept. of Electrical Engineering, University of Toronto, Control Systems Report No. 7301, January 1973.

[18] Davison, E. J. and Chow, S. G., Perfect control in linear time-invariant multivariable systems: the control inequality principle. *8th Annual Princeton Conference on Information Sciences and Systems*, March (1974).

[19] Davison, E. J., The robust control of a servomechanism problem for linear time-invariant multivariable systems. *IEEE Trans. on Automatic Control*, vol. AC-21, No. 1, 1976, pp. 25–34.

[20] Krall, A. M., *Stability Techniques for Continuous Linear Systems*, Theorems 6.3.9, 6.3.10. Gordon and Breach (1967).

[21] Luenberger, D. G., Canonical forms for linear multivariable systems. *I.E.E.E. Trans. Automatic Control*, **AC-12**, 290–293 (1967).

[22] Parlett, B. N. and Reinsch, C., Balancing a matrix for calculation of eigenvalues and eigenvectors. In *Linear Algebra* (editors: J. H. Wilkson and C. Reinsch). Springer-Verlag, New York (1971).

[23] Davison, E. J., The systematic design of control systems for large multivariable linear systems. *Automatica*, **9**, 441–452 (1973).

[24] Rosenbrock, H. H., Structural properties of first-order dynamic systems. *International J. Control*, (to appear).

[25] Davison, E. J., Goldenberg, A., The robust control of a general servomechanism problem: the Servo Compensator. *Automatica*, vol. 11, 1975, pp. 461–471.

Review of a Pole-Zero Assignment Design Method

F. FALLSIDE*, R. V. PATEL† and H. SERAJI‡
*Electrical Division, Cambridge University Engineering Department, England
†NASA Ames Research Center, Moffett Field, U.S.A.
‡Department of Electrical Engineering, Arya-Mehr University of Technology, Iran

1. Introduction

This paper sets out to review the development of a pole–zero assignment design method established in this Department over the last few years. Most parts of it have been published separately, the aim here is to attempt an overall view with some conclusions. It rests basically on the use of unity–rank feedback, this is one of its major restrictions but the resulting simplification in analysis and computation is demonstrated and exploited. An important feature of any design method is its ease of use. When the work started it was clear that interactive graphics techniques developed mainly for mechanical engineering design were potentially well suited to control system design by pole-assignment. This proved to be the case and considerable use was made of interactive graphics in the development of the method. This had a strong influence on the way the design algorithms were developed and led to the establishment of a number of interactive graphics design packages, employing both light-pen and keyboard interaction.

The paper begins with pole assignment for the single-input case, moves to the multi-input case, describes the design packages briefly and finally gives some extensions. A film demonstrating design using one of the interactive graphics packages will be shown during the presentation.

2. Single-Input Systems

The completely controllable and completely observable system is

$$\dot{x} = Ax + bu, \; y = Cx \qquad (1)$$

with x, y, A, b, C of respective dimensions $n, l, n \times n, n \times 1, l \times n$, and the rank of C is l ($\leqslant n$). Or in transfer-function form

$$Y(s) = W(s)U(s), \; W(s) = C(sI - A)^{-1}\, b = w(s)/F(s) \qquad (2)$$

where $F(s) = |sI - A|$ is the nth order open-loop characteristic polynomial.

2.1. Pole-assignment by feedback controllers [1–7]

The output y is now fed back via a constant l-row feedback vector k and so

$$u = v - ky \tag{3}$$

see Figure 1a, and now

$$Y(s) = \frac{w(s)}{H(s)} V(s) \tag{4}$$

where $H(s) = |sI - A + bkC|$ is the nth order closed loop characteristic polynomial. Redrawing the system in classical unity feedback configuration, Figure 1b, we see

$$\frac{Z(s)}{V(s)} = \frac{kw(s)}{F(s) + kw(s)}, \quad \frac{Y(s)}{V(s)} = \frac{w(s)}{F(s) + kw(s)} \tag{5}$$

Finally from eqns (4) and (5)

$$H(s) = F(s) + kw(s) \tag{6}$$

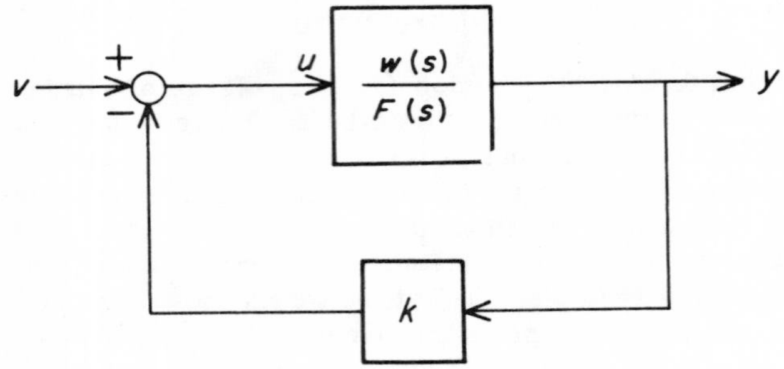

Figure 1(a).

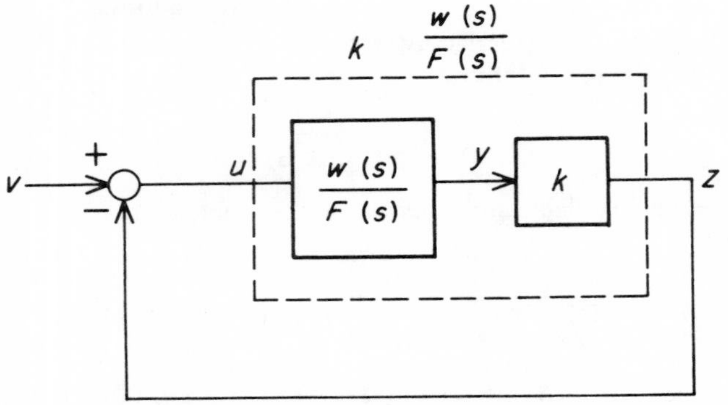

Figure 1(b).

This equation gives a very direct relationship for pole-assignment. (Eqn. (6) was originally derived, ref. [1], using a property of return-difference, the above derivation via Figure 1 was later suggested by P. C. Young.) Written in full (6) is

$$(s^n + a_n s^{n-1} + \ldots + a_1) = (s^n + d_n s^{n-1} + \ldots + d_1)$$
$$+ \{k_1(m_{11} + \ldots + m_{1n}s^{n-1}) + \ldots + k_l(m_{l1} + \ldots + m_{ln}s^{n-1})$$

Then equating the coefficients of like powers of s

$$\begin{aligned} m_{11}k_1 + \ldots + m_{l1}k_1 &= a_1 - d_1 \\ &\vdots \\ m_{1n}k_1 + \ldots + m_{ln}k_l &= a_n - d_n \end{aligned} \qquad (7)$$

or

$$M^T k^T = a - d \qquad (8)$$

There are now two cases (a) for $l = n$, i.e. as many outputs as states or for complete state feedback with $C = I$, then eqn. (8) has a unique solution $k^T = (M^T)^{-1}(a - d)$ and since M is invariant we need only calculate $(M^T)^{-1}$ once giving a fast solution for the feedback k for any desired closed-loop poles a. (b) for $l < n$ eqn. (8) represents an overdetermined set of n equations in l unknowns $k_l \ldots k_1$. Now a solution for k exists if and only if it is consistent, that the solution of l equations satisfies the remaining $(n - l)$ equations. The consistency condition is found to be linear in a, of the form $\alpha a = \beta$; implying allowable regions for the closed-loop poles in the s-plane, [2]. When a chosen set of closed-loop poles or a is unattainable several procedures are possible, in one the error function $E = \|\alpha a - \beta\|^2$ is minimized via a to establish a near set of attainable poles and the required k is calculated from eqn. (8). Alternatively a matrix pseudo-inverse approach can be used to yield results in closed form, [5] it also allows results such as that p poles can be assigned for $p \leqslant l$ etc.

This assignment technique is found to be computationally much simpler than some others, see ref. [4] for comparisons, and as such well suited to interactive computer design techniques.

2.2. Other aspects of design

This frequency domain formulation yields a number of other useful results.

2.2.1. *Stabilization* [6]

By combining the Routh-Hurwitz conditions on the coefficients a of $H(s)$ with the $(n - l)$ constraint equations $\alpha a = \beta$ there results a simple necessary condition for stabilization: that all the elements in each row of α must not have opposite signs to the corresponding element of β, and if the corresponding element is zero then all the elements in that row of α must not have the same sign. This can be used to determine which states must be fed back to stabilize an unstable system and in integrity studies.

2.2.2. *Synthesis by response fitting*[8]

For a given output y_j the closed-loop transfer function matrix eqn. (5) gives an implicit relation between the response and the feedback k

$$Y_j(s)/V(s) = w_j(s)\Big/\left\{F(s) + \sum_{i=1}^{l} k_i w_i(s)\right\} \tag{9}$$

The best choice of feedback k to fit a specified closed-loop frequency, or time, response can be calculated by setting up the deviations using eqn. (9) and then iterating on k to minimize the sum-of-squares of the deviations.

2.2.3. *Steady-state values*[9]

For an input with finite steady-state values v_{ss} then from eqn. (5) and the Final-Value theorem

$$y_{ss} = w_1(s)\, v_{ss}/(d_1 + kw_1(s)), \quad w_1(s) = w(0) \tag{10}$$

Similarly for x_{ss} and u_{ss}. This allows a very rapid computation of steady-state values as k is varied without the need for repeated matrix inversions.

2.2.4. *Optimal systems*[1, 10, 11]

A well known design difficulty in the design of optimal systems is the choice of performance index weighting elements to achieve a desirable transient response. Using a state rather than an output formulation, $X(s) = g(s)V(s)/H(s)$, the performance index to be minimized by choice of state feedback $p, u = v - px$, is

$$PI = \int_0^\infty \left(\sum_{i=1}^{n} q_{ii} x_i^2 + ru^2 \right) dt \tag{11}$$

and it can be shown[8] that there is an explicit computable relationship between the closed-loop response and the performance index via

$$H(s)H(-s) = F(s)F(-s) + \frac{1}{r} \sum_{i=1}^{n} q_{ii} g_i(s) g_i(-s) \tag{12}$$

Further the relationship between closed-loop poles and the feedback is

$$H(s) = F(s) + pg(s) \tag{13}$$

The foregoing relationships give a close link between optimality and pole-assignment, they allow the design of optimal systems for a desired response[1, 10] and the link between optimality and closed-loop pole positions.[10]

3. Multi-Input Systems

As is well known for single-input systems the zeros are invariant under feedback and for a specified set of closed-loop poles the feedback is unique. However other aspects of performance such as integrity or steady-state behaviour may not be simultaneously met by this unique feedback. For multi-input systems the situation is quite different, the zeros move in an uncontrolled way under feedback, there is no unique feedback for a given set of closed-loop poles or for a given set of steady-state input–output relationships etc. The complication is increased but degrees of freedom are introduced by non-uniqueness. An ideal design procedure would pick out the feedback matrix which satisfied all the design requirements simultaneously.

The present method is not ideal because it has the restriction of unity–rank feedback, however it has several strong advantages, the feedback is calculated from linear equations and its simplicity allows the degrees of freedom implicit in multi-input systems to be exploited.

The completely controllable and completely observable system is

$$\dot{x} = Ax + Bu, \quad y = Cx \tag{14}$$

with now u and B of dimensions m and $n \times m$ and the rank of C is l ($\leqslant n$).

3.1. Pole-assignment by feedback controllers [1, 2, 3, 13]

The outputs are now fed back via an $m \times l$ feedback matrix K such that

$$u = V - Ky \tag{15}$$

Further K is constrained to have unity–rank by defining it in the dyadic form

$$K = qk \tag{16}$$

where q and k are m-column and l-row respectively. The resulting system is shown in Figure 2a and the dyadic feedback or "gearing" is seen to effectively control the system by a scalar control μ which is applied to the m-inputs via q. This reduces the design of the multi-input system (A, B, C) to that of the much simpler "equivalent" single-input system

$$\dot{x} = Ax + (Bq)\,\mu, \quad y = Cx \tag{17}$$

Given q the vector k is then determined to assign the closed-loop poles of this "equivalent" single-input system with a feedback law $\mu = -ky$ using the method of Section 2.1. The feedback matrix for the multi-input system is then given by $K = qk$, if the equivalent single-input system (A, Bq, C) is completely controllable and completely observable, and it can be shown that this requires A to be cyclic, (if not an additional feedback K_1 is employed to render it cyclic, see Figure 2b, before the design is started).

The vector q reflects the degrees of freedom in multi-input systems. For example it can be used to weight the relative tightness of feedback to each input since

$$K = qk = \begin{bmatrix} q_1k_1 & \dots & q_1k_l \\ \cdot & & \cdot \\ \cdot & & \cdot \\ q_mk_1 & \dots & q_mk_l \end{bmatrix} \tag{18}$$

Again when there are fewer outputs than states or when incomplete state-feedback is used the constraint equation for the equivalent single-input system becomes $\alpha(q)a = \beta(q)$ allowing greater freedom in pole assignment.

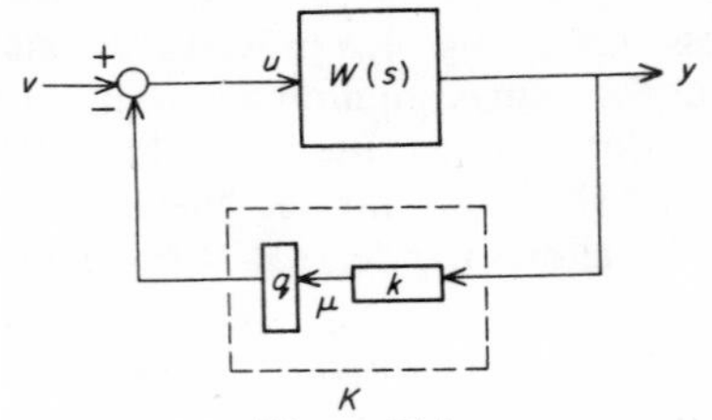

Figure 2(a).

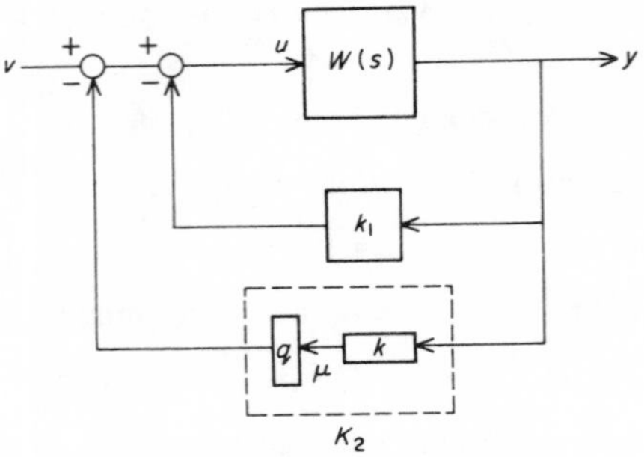

Figure 2(b).

3.2. Other aspects of design

As in the single-input case the frequency-domain formulation yields a number of other useful results, and in particular use can be made of the degrees of freedom to satisfy other aspects of design via q. The general procedure in using q is to specify an initial q, and determine K to specify the closed-loop poles, the error function $E(q)$ between another performance aspect of the closed-loop system and its desired value is then set up and q is then incremented to minimize $E(q)$ (via Powell), q is then updated and the whole procedure is repeated until the minimization of $E(q)$ is obtained. This has been applied to performance aspects additional to pole-assignment such as *zero-assignment*, steady-state characteristics, restrictions on magnitudes of feedback gains and on control inputs, sensitivity of poles, integrity, incomplete feedback and stabilization.

This method exploits to a considerable extent the degrees of freedom in multi-input systems, within the restrictions of unity-rank feedback. There are of course limits on the number of performance attributes which can be achieved simultaneously and the nature of the minimization is problem-dependent.

In addition to this minimization approach the formulation of most of these design features is simple and easily computable. Since these are in some respects generalizations of the results of Section 2.2, they are not developed here but referenced.[1, 10, 14, 15]

4. Interactive Graphics Design Packages

Design in the s-plane is well based in classical practice e.g. Guillemin, root-locus etc. and much qualitative information on response interpretation and design is available from diagrams of pole–zero locations. It was thus natural to establish an interactive graphics design technique, using the analysis of the previous Sections, based on displays of the s-plane and with designer interaction by movement of the displayed poles by light-pen or keyboard.

In addition to pole assignment and calculation of the required feedback, the previous analysis allows the provision of several other design options. These include: the attainment of other design requirements via minimization of $E(q)$, the inspection of design criteria such as integrity, sensitivity, optimality, etc., and the display of the response of the designed system to specified inputs – step, pulse, frequency response, etc.

Several such design packages for single and multi-input systems have been established and implemented, mainly on the Cambridge CAD Centre Atlas system [5, 16] and several applications have been reported.[17–20] Attention has been paid to ease of use, once the open-loop system data has been loaded all subsequent interaction is via the light-pen or keyboard. Use is made of light buttons for calling up options and entering design information. Experience has shown that closed-loop poles are good manipulatable features for interactive graphics design and that the speed of the design algorithms allow close coupling between the designer and the design.

5. Conclusions and Extensions

The development of a particular pole-assignment technique for multivariable systems and its implementation in interactive graphics design packages have been reviewed. The technique has several advantages of simplicity and computational speed. Aside from its restriction to unity–rank feedback its main limitation is with regard to zero-assignment. Several methods have been developed to overcome this. In one [27] an iterative method has been introduced and in another [22] a cascade controller is employed additionally. A further and promising application of the pole-assignment algorithm has been made to non-linear systems [23] in which a linearizing controller has been implemented which linearizes the system model over a wide range of operation and updates the feedback matrix correspondingly to ensure a response with effectively constant closed-loop pole locations over the operating range.

6. References

[1] Fallside, F. and Seraji, H., 1970, *Proc. I.E.E.*, **117(10)**, pp. 2017–2024.
[2] ———, 1971, *Proc. I.E.E.*, **118(6)**, pp. 797–801.
[3] ———, 1971, *Proc. I.E.E.*, **118(11)**, pp. 1648–1654.
[4] ———, 1972, *Int. J. Electron.*, **32(1)**, pp. 95–106.
[5] Seraji, H., 1972, *Ph.D. dissertation*, University of Cambridge.

[6] ———, 1971, Cambridge University Engineering Department Technical Report, *CUED/B-Elect/TRIO.*

[7] Davison, E. J., 1970, *I.E.E.E. Trans.*, **AC-15**, pp. 348–351.

[8] Fallside, F., Patel, R. V. and Seraji, H., 1972, *Int. J. Electron.*, **33(6)**, pp. 717–720.

[9] Fallside, F. and Seraji, H., 1971, *Electron. Lett.*, **7(8)**, pp. 197–198.

[10] ———, 1971, *Proc. 2nd IFAC Symposium on Multivariable Systems*, Dusseldorf.

[11] ———, 1970, *Electron. Lett.*, **6(22)**, pp. 721–723.

[12] Seraji, H., 1972, Cambridge University Engineering Department Technical Report, *CUED/B-Elect/TR14.*

[13] Fallside, F. and Seraji, H., 1973, To be published in *Int. J. Control.*

[14] ———, 1971, *Electron. Lett.*, **7(3)**, pp. 64–65.

[15] ———, 1972, *Electron. Lett.*, **8(2)**, pp. 42–43.

[16] Patel, R. V., 1972, *Ph.D. dissertation*, University of Cambridge.

[17] Fallside, F. and Seraji, H., 1971, Proc. 4th UKAC Convention on Multivariable Control System Design and Applications, Manchester, *I.E.E. Conf. Publ.*, **78**, pp. 87–92.

[18] Fallside, F., Patel, R. V. and Seraji, H., 1972, *Proc. I.E.E.*, **119(2)**, pp. 247–254.

[19] ———, 1972, Proc. 2nd International Computer-aided Design Conference, Southampton, *I.E.E. Conf. Publ.*, **86**, pp. 86–91.

[20] ———, 1973, Proc. CACSD Conf., Cambridge, *I.E.E. Conf. Publ.*, **96**, pp. 101–112.

[21] Fallside, F. and Patel, R. V., 1972, *Electron. Lett.*, **8(13)**, pp. 324–325.

[22] Seraji, H., 1973, Proc. CACSD Conf., Cambridge, *I.E.E. Conf. Publ.*, **96**, pp. 94–100.

[23] Fallside, F. and Thompson, J. M., "Linearising feedback controllers for certain non-linear systems". In preparation.

Relationships Between Recent Developments in Linear Control Theory and Classical Design Techniques

A. G. J. MACFARLANE
Control Group, Engineering Department,
University of Cambridge, Cambridge, England

Summary. A comprehensive survey is given of recent work on the use of matrix-valued functions of a complex variable for the analysis and design of linear multivariable feedback systems. Several emerging design techniques are outlined and a simple illustrative design example given showing how such methods may be used in practice.

1. Introduction

Classical methods[1] for the design of simple single-input single-output feedback systems, which are based on the Nyquist frequency-locus technique[2, 3] and the Evans root-locus technique,[4] are constructed round the basic properties of scalar functions of a complex variable. The purpose of this survey is to deal with the applications of matrix functions of a complex variable to the analysis and design of multivariable feedback systems, and to show how the fundamental concepts of the classical theory – transfer function, poles, zeros and frequency-responses – can be generalized and related to the state space methods on which so much of recent work in control theory has concentrated. In preparing it I have drawn heavily on the fundamentally important researches carried out by Rosenbrock,[5–9, 26] Wonham and Morse,[10, 11] Desoer and Schulman,[12, 13] Bengtsson[14, 15] and Kouvaritakis.[28]

The layout of the survey is as follows. Section 2 is concerned with the state–space model description of input–output coupling, and uses a dyadic generalization of the basic convolution relationship for single-input single-output systems. A similar form of dyadic operator decomposition is used in the later frequency-response treatment. The concept of a multivariable system zero is discussed at length in Section 3. It is the satisfactory generalization to the multivariable case of the concept of a zero which is the key to an integrated treatment of state space and frequency-response treatments of the general feedback problem. Section 4 discusses how multivariable system zeros can be related to the geometrical structures associated with the state space model, and Section 5 attempts to explain the physical significance of the multivariable zero. The remainder of the survey is concerned with the use of techniques based on the properties of matrix-valued functions of a complex variable to extend classical design techniques to the multivariable case.

The whole treatment is based on the theory of linear vector spaces; excellent texts giving the required mathematical background are those by Halmos[17] and Fano.[18]

2. States, Characteristic Frequencies and Poles

The essential feature of the response of a dynamical system to an input is that its present behaviour is influenced by its past history. Dynamical system behaviour cannot therefore be specified simply in terms of "instantaneous" relationships between a set of input and a set of output variables. An extra set of variables is required whose purpose is to take into account the past history of the system; these variables are called the *state variables* of the dynamical system. The basic form of description of a dynamical system is therefore comprised of sets of relationships between three sets of system variables: *input, output* and *state* variables.[16] The state variables are *functionals* of the input variables and of themselves; that is they associate numbers, the values of the state variables, with sets of functions of time which define the past behaviour of the inputs and of the states themselves. Thus if $\{u_1(t), u_2(t), \ldots, u_l(t)\}$ is a set of input variables and $\{x_1(t), x_2(t), \ldots, x_n(t)\}$ a set of state variables, and if we take the simplest possible functional relationship, namely integration, the ith state variable will be expressed in the form

$$x_i(t) = \int_{-\infty}^{t} f_i(x_1, \ldots, x_n; u_1, \ldots, u_l; t)\,\mathrm{d}t \quad i = 1, 2, \ldots, n$$

where the set of functions f_i define the nature of the dynamical system behaviour. This implies that the state variables satisfy the set of first order differential equations

$$\frac{\mathrm{d}x_i}{\mathrm{d}t} = f_i(x_1, \ldots, x_n; u_1, \ldots, u_l; t) \quad i = 1, 2, \ldots, n \tag{2.1}$$

Such a model of dynamical system behaviour is completed by stating how a set of output variables $\{y_1(t), \ldots y_m(t)\}$ is obtained from the set of input and state variables:

$$y_j(t) = \phi_j(x_1, \ldots, x_n; u_1, \ldots, u_l; t) \quad j = 1, 2, \ldots, m \tag{2.2}$$

This form of description, the state space model, is nowadays taken as the standard form on which most dynamical system theory is based.[16] It is important to appreciate the implications of the simplicity of the assumptions which underlie it. More complicated forms of functional relationships are appropriate for some kinds of dynamical system and have been for example investigated by Volterra[19] in studying certain forms of biological system.

In what follows we will restrict ourselves to the simplest general form of dynamical model specified in terms of a set of first order differential equations. An intuitively-appealing picture of the operation of such a model is that the state variables can be regarded as defining the operation of an internal mechanism which is influenced by the input variables and whose operation is observed via the output variables. In historical terms, the internal mechanism of the first forms of dynamical model to be studied was that of the storage, dissipation and conversion of energy, and the input variables defined the supply of power to the energetic mechanism; it is often convenient to appeal to such a picture for intuitive purposes.

The supreme advantage of the basic form of state–space model, particularly for linear sytems, is that it enables one to describe system behaviour in *geometrical* terms; the unifying thread running through the whole of the subsequent discussion given here is that of a geometrical approach. The input, state and output variables are assembled as the components of three vectors: an input vector $u(t)$ living in an input space U, a state vector $x(t)$ in a state space X, and an output vector $y(t)$ in an output space Y. Thus the behaviour of the basic model is defined in terms of the set of four mappings between these spaces shown in Figure 1. When the system is linear and time-invariant the state–space model then assumes the special form: [16]

$$\frac{dx}{dt} = Ax + Bu \qquad (2.3)$$

$$y = Cx + \phi(u)$$

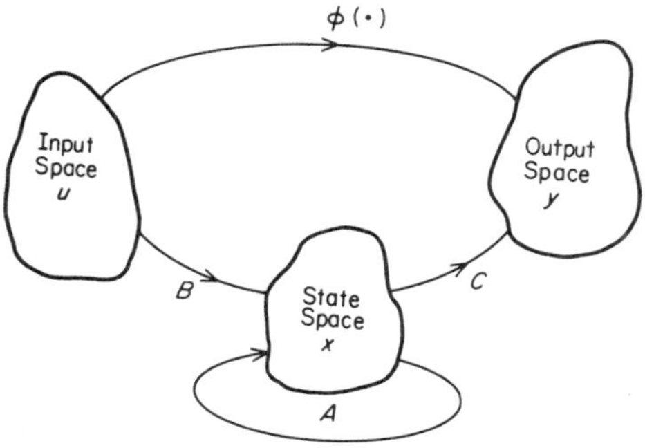

Figure 1. Set of mappings.

where A, B and C are appropriate constant–coefficient matrices and $\phi(u)$ represents some direct "non-dynamic" coupling between input and output. In what follows we will usually assume that no term $\phi(u)$ is present, and thus that the whole propagation of input into output variables takes place via the dynamical mechanism associated with the state.

2.1. Convolution form of description of input–output coupling

In describing the structure of operators representing the dynamical behaviour of multivariable systems, one is dealing with the mapping of spaces into spaces. The state mechanism involves the mapping of the state space into itself. Any detailed description of the state transition mechanism therefore makes use of the standard decomposition of an operator in terms of invariant subspaces.[16, 46]

Suppose A is a matrix associated with the linear state space model of eqn. (2.3). Further *suppose that A has a set of distinct eigenvalues* $\{\lambda_1, \lambda_2, \ldots, \lambda_n\}$ with a corresponding set of eigenvectors $\{u_1, u_2, \ldots, u_n\}$. From these we can form a matrix U whose columns are the eigenvectors of A so that

$$U = [u_1 \quad u_2 \quad \ldots \quad u_n]$$

Since the eigenvectors are, by assumption, linearly independent, U may be inverted to get a matrix V

$$U^{-1} = V = \begin{bmatrix} v_1^t \\ v_2^t \\ \cdot \\ \cdot \\ \cdot \\ v_n^t \end{bmatrix}$$

whose rows $\{v_1^t, v_2^t, \ldots, v_n^t\}$ must be such that

$$v_i^t u_j = \delta_{ij} \tag{2.4}$$

where δ_{ij} is 1 if $i = j$, otherwise zero. The eigenvector set $\{u_1, u_2, \ldots, u_n\}$ is a *basis* for the state space; this means that any vector in the state space can be expressed as a linear combination of the eigenvectors. The vector set $\{v_1, v_2, \ldots, v_n\}$ is called the corresponding *dual basis* and these two bases are used to give a geometrical description of the operator A in the following way. Suppose we wish to express some state vector x as a linear combination of the vector set $\{u_i\}$, that is to find a set of co-ordinates $\{\alpha_1, \alpha_2, \ldots, \alpha_n\}$ such that

$$x = \sum_{j=1}^{n} \alpha_j u_j \tag{2.5}$$

Multiplying both sides of this expression on the left by v_i^t and using (2.4) gives that

$$v_i^t x = \sum_{j=1}^{n} \alpha_j v_i^t u_j = \alpha_i$$

and so

$$x = \sum_{i=1}^{n} [v_i^t x] u_i \tag{2.6}$$

This shows how the dual basis is used to project any given vector into a given basis.

Now consider the operation of the matrix A on a state vector x which has been expressed as a linear combination of eigenvectors. We have

$$Ax = A \sum_{i=1}^{n} u_i [v_i^t x]$$

$$= \sum_{i=1}^{n} A u_i v_i^t x$$

$$= \sum_{i=1}^{n} \lambda_i u_i v_i^t x$$

since, from the definition of an eigenvector

$$Au_i = \lambda_i u_i \quad i = 1, 2, \ldots, n \tag{2.7}$$

This simple argument shows that the operator A can be written in the *dyadic form*

$$A = \sum_{i=1}^{n} \lambda_i u_i v_i^t \tag{2.8}$$

Since dyadic decompositions play an important part in the forms of operator descriptions discussed later, it is worthwhile briefly explaining their geometrical significance at this point. Suppose A, expressed in this dyadic form, acts on some state vector x so that we have

$$Ax = \sum_{i=1}^{n} \lambda_i u_i v_i^t x \tag{2.9}$$

In order to interpret this form of operator decomposition it is helpful to note that:

(i) $v_i^t x$ is the coordinate of x along the ith eigenvector u_i;
(ii) the action of A on any eigenvector u_i is simply to multiply it by the corresponding eigenvalue λ_i.

Hence eqn. (2.9) exhibits the action of A on a state vector in the following geometrical way:

(i) the state x is projected into the eigenvector basis $\{u_i\}$ via the dual basis set v_i^t;
(ii) the corresponding coordinates are acted on by the simple scalar multiplication by λ_i characteristic of the action of the operator on its ith eigenvector;
(iii) the result is reassembled as an appropriate sum of eigenvectors.

Against this background, let us now consider the convolution form of description of the linear state–space model

$$\dot{x} = Ax + Bu$$

$$y = Cx \tag{2.10}$$

This relates the input vector $u(t)$ and the output vector $y(t)$ in the form

$$y(t) = C\exp(At)\,x(0) + C\int_0^t \exp A(t-\tau)Bu(\tau)\,d\tau \tag{2.11}$$

where $x(0)$ is an initial value of the state vector at time $t = 0$. If A is expressed in the dyadic form of eqn. (2.8) it follows directly that $\exp(At)$ can be expressed in the form

$$\exp(At) = \sum_{i=1}^{n} [\exp \lambda_i t]\, u_i v_i^t \tag{2.12}$$

It follows that

$$y(t) = C\sum_{i=1}^{n} u_i[\exp \lambda_i t]\, v_i^t x(0) + C\int_0^t \sum_{i=1}^{n} u_i[\exp \lambda_i(t-\tau)]\, v_i^t Bu(\tau)\,d\tau$$

$$= \sum_{i=1}^{n} \gamma_i[\exp \lambda_i t]\, v_i^t x(0) + \sum_{i=1}^{n} \gamma_i \int_0^t [\exp \lambda_i(t-\tau)]\, \beta_i^t u(\tau)\,d\tau \tag{2.13a}$$

where $\{\gamma_1, \gamma_2, \ldots, \gamma_n\}$ are the columns of the matrix CU and $\{\beta_1^t, \beta_2^t, \ldots, \beta_n^t\}$ are the rows of the matrix VB. Finally, using the symbol * to denote convolution we may write this in the form:

$$y(t) = \sum_{i=1}^{n} \gamma_i[\exp \lambda_i t]\, v_i^t x(0) + \sum_{i=1}^{n} \gamma_i[\exp \lambda_i t] * \beta_i^t u(t) \tag{2.13b}$$

This dyadic form of description is rather different from the simple form used to describe the action of A on the state space. Here the row vectors β_i^t and the column vectors γ_i are associated with *different* spaces; furthermore, these spaces will generally be of different dimensions. Dyadic representations of this kind can conveniently be thought of in terms of pairing a set of vectors in one space with a corresponding set of vectors in another space. Associated with the r-dimensional input space there is a set of n row vectors $\{\beta_1^t, \ldots, \beta_n^t\}$, and associated with the output space there is a set of n column vectors $\{\gamma_1, \ldots, \gamma_n\}$. The row vectors β_i^t are the rows of VB and so represent the coupling between the inputs and the eigenvectors of the A matrix, which characterize motion in the state space. The column vectors γ_i are the columns of CU and so represent the coupling between the eigenvectors in the state space and the output space. All possible motions in the state space may be expressed as a sum of characteristic motions associated with eigenvectors; these characteristic motions are called *modes*.[16] A system input $u(t)$ is coupled into the ith mode by forming an inner product $\beta_i^t u(t)$. This component function of time $\beta_i^t u(t)$ is then convoluted with the characteristic exponential motion associated with the ith mode to get another component function of time $\exp \lambda_i t * \beta_i^t u(t)$. The output is then assembled as a sum of motions along the output–space vector set γ_i as

$$\text{output} = \sum_{i=1}^{n} \gamma_i[\exp \lambda_i t] * \beta_i^t u(t) \tag{2.14}$$

One of the constituent dyadic elements of this decomposition is shown in signal–flow graph form in Figure 2.

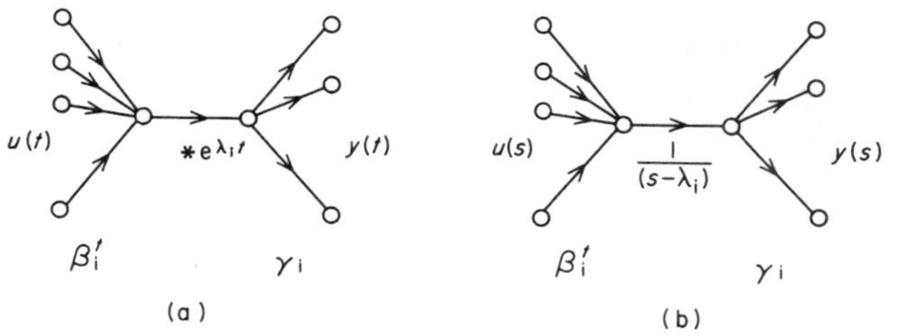

Figure 2. Component dyads.

2.2. Transform description of input–output coupling; controllability and observability

For zero initial conditions, the input and output transform vectors of the system described by the linear state space differential equations

$$\dot{x} = Ax + Bu$$

$$y = Cu$$

are related by

$$y(s) = G(s)u(s) \tag{2.15}$$

where $y(s)$ and $u(s)$ are vectors whose elements are the Laplace transforms of the elements of the output vector $y(t)$ and the input vector $u(t)$ respectively, and

$$G(s) = C(sI - A)^{-1}B$$

is the transfer function matrix relating input and output transform vectors.

Putting

$$A = U \Lambda V$$

where

$$\Lambda = \text{diag}\,[\lambda_1, \lambda_2, \ldots, \lambda_n]$$

and again assuming for simplicity that all the eigenvalues of A are distinct, we get

$$G(s) = CU(sI - \Lambda)^{-1}VB$$

$$= \sum_{i=1}^{n} \frac{\gamma_i \beta_i^t}{(s - \lambda_i)} \tag{2.16}$$

This dyadic form of representation of the transfer function matrix gives a clear picture of the way in which inputs are coupled into modes, and modes into outputs. The column vector set $\{\gamma_i: i = 1, 2, \ldots, n\}$ and the row vector set $\{\beta_i^t: i = 1, 2, \ldots, n\}$ have the following interpretations.

(i) The vectors $\{\gamma_1, \gamma_2, \ldots, \gamma_n\}$ represent the modal vectors $\{u_1, u_2, \ldots, u_n\}$ when "seen through" the output matrix C; that is

$$\gamma_i = Cu_i \quad i = 1, 2, \ldots, n \tag{2.17}$$

Thus if any of the column vectors γ_i vanishes, there will be no coupling between the output and the ith mode and the characteristic frequency λ_i will not appear in the overall transfer function matrix. If γ_i vanishes the ith mode is said to be *unobservable*;[16,20] if γ_i does not vanish, the ith mode is said to be *observable*. If all the modes are observable, the system is said to be completely observable.

(ii) The row vectors $\{\beta_1^t, \beta_2^t, \ldots, \beta_n^t\}$ represent the dual modal vectors $\{v_1^t, v_2^t, \ldots, v_n^t\}$ when "seen through" the input matrix B; that is

$$\beta_j^t = v_j^t B \quad j = 1, 2, \ldots, n \tag{2.18}$$

Thus if any of the row vectors β_j^t vanishes, there will be no coupling between the jth mode and the input, and the characteristic frequency λ_j will not appear in the overall transfer function matrix. If β_j^t vanishes, the jth mode is said to be *uncontrollable*;[16,20] if β_j^t is not a zero row vector, the jth mode is said to be *controllable*. If all the modes are controllable, the system is said to be completely controllable.

2.3. Poles and characteristic frequencies

Equation (2.16) can be written in the form

$$G(s) = \sum_{i=1}^{n} \frac{G_i}{(s - \lambda_i)} \tag{2.19}$$

and it can be shown, using arguments based on the Sylvester interpolation formula, [46] that

$$G_i = \operatorname*{limit}_{s \to \lambda_i} [(s - \lambda_i)G(s)] \tag{2.20}$$

Contour integrals of matrix-valued functions of a complex variable can be defined in terms of their elements as follows. If

$$G(s) \text{ has elements } g_{ij}(s)$$

then

$$\int_\Gamma G(s)\, ds \text{ has elements } \int_\Gamma g_{ij}(s)\, ds$$

where Γ is a specified contour in the complex plane. Since g_{ij} is the residue of $g_{ij}/(s - \lambda_i)$ at the pole λ_i, it is natural to extend the residue calculus to matrix-valued integrals and thus to call G_i the *residue matrix* for $G(s)$ at the pole λ_i, now regarded as a pole of the matrix-valued function of a complex variable $G(s)$. This leads naturally to the following definition.

Pole: A complex number p is called a pole of order n of a matrix-valued function of a complex variable s if and only if some element of $G(s)$ has a pole of order n at p, and no element has a pole of larger order than n at p.

Since

$$G(s) = C(sI - A)^{-1}B = \frac{C\,\mathrm{adj}[sI - A]B}{\det(sI - A)} \tag{2.21}$$

we see that the set of poles of $G(s)$ is a subset of the set of eigenvalues of A. The eigenvalues of A will be called the *characteristic frequencies* of the system when, as in discussing controllability and observability, it is necessary to distinguish between the set of poles of $G(s)$ and the set of eigenvalues of A.

2.4. Complex frequency interpretation of complex variables

It is of considerable interest to use eqn. (2.13b) to study how exponential signals are propagated through a linear dynamical system. The key point to note in this context is that the result of convoluting two exponential signals is to generate a waveform proportional to the difference of the exponentials divided by the difference of their exponents.[21] Suppose then that we feed in to a linear dynamical system an input of exponential type of the form

$$u(t) = a \exp(vt)\, 1(t) \tag{2.22}$$

where a is a constant vector. Then we will have that the output is given by

$$\begin{aligned} y(t) &= \sum_{i=1}^{n} \gamma_i [\exp \lambda_i t]\, v_i^t x(0) + \sum_{i=1}^{n} \gamma_i \exp \lambda_i t * \beta_i^t\, a \exp vt \qquad \text{for } t > 0 \\ &= \sum_{i=1}^{n} \gamma_i \exp \lambda_i t v_i^t x(0) + \sum_{i=1}^{n} \gamma_i \frac{\beta_i^t a}{(v - \lambda_i)} [\exp(vt) - \exp(\lambda_i t)] \end{aligned} \tag{2.23}$$

Inspection of this expression shows that the forced response consists of terms containing the input exponential together with a sum of modal terms similar to those associated with the free motion. Since we can always choose an appropriate initial condition such as to exactly cancel any required combination of modal terms, this means that, for an input of the form (2.20) we can always choose an appropriate set of initial conditions so that the output response is given by

$$\begin{aligned} y(t) &= \sum_{i=1}^{n} \frac{\gamma_i \beta_i^t}{(v - \lambda_i)}\, a \exp(vt) \qquad \text{for } t > 0 \\ &= G(v)u(t) \end{aligned} \tag{2.24}$$

This shows that, assuming an appropriate initial condition vector is chosen, the response to an exponential input of the form (2.20) is associated with a constant transmittance matrix found by substituting $s = v$ in the system transfer function matrix. From this point of view the transfer function matrix $G(s)$ may be regarded as defining the system response to an exponential input of exponent s, and the complex variable s can be regarded as a *complex frequency variable* as in the single-input single-output case.[21]

3. Zeros[6, 13, 14, 26, 27, 28, 45]

In the single-input single-output system case, a zero of a scalar transfer function $g(s)$ is simply a value of the complex frequency s for which the transfer function $g(s)$ vanishes. In the general multivariable system case, where we have a transfer function matrix $G(s)$, a zero of $G(s)$ is not some value of s such that $G(s)$ becomes a zero matrix, but is one at which its rank is locally reduced.[13] The rank of a matrix function $G(s)$ is a function of s which is computed by substituting a specific value of s, say s_0, to get a complex matrix $G(s_0)$ whose rank may then be determined. For almost all values of s this will be a quantity which is called the *normal rank* of $G(s)$; for a finite number of specific values of s the rank computed in this way may be less than the normal rank. Such an exceptional value is called the *local rank* of $G(s)$ for that specific value of s.

The physical significance of the relationship between zeros and rank, and the intimate relationship between zeros and feedback, can best be demonstrated by considering a simple basic multivariable feedback arrangement. Suppose we have a system with the same number of inputs and outputs so that we may connect all the outputs directly back to the correspondingly-numbered inputs to get the archetypal feedback situation shown in Figure 3a. Now the essential feature of a set of feedback connections of this sort is that one set of variables has forcibly been made the same as another set of variables, and so the difference between the two sets of variables must vanish identically. An inspection of Figure 3b shows that the operator which generates the difference between input and output vectors, when operating on the input vector, is obviously

$$F(s) = I_m - Q(s) \tag{3.1}$$

where $Q(s)$ represents the system forward transmittance. Since the feedback connections force the difference between input and output to be identically zero, any non-

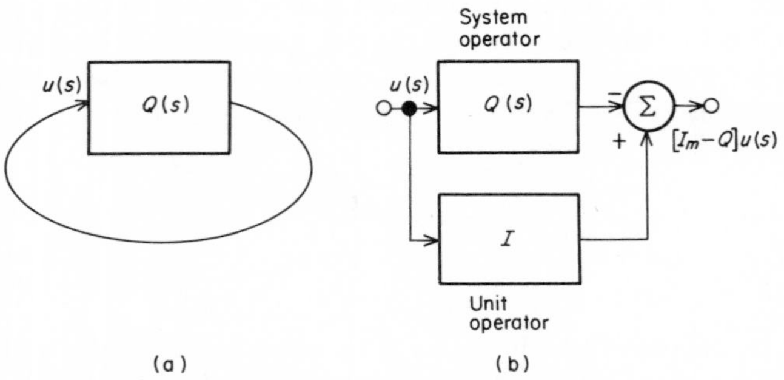

Figure 3. Return-difference.

zero input signal transform vector which exists under these feedback conditions must be such that

$$F(s)u(s) = 0 \tag{3.2}$$

As we are considering the free motion of a linear system, the components of $u(s)$ will consist of the transforms of exponential modal functions, and we can thus associate the set of values of s for which this relationship holds directly with the system closed-loop characteristic frequencies. Equation (3.2) shows that the appropriate values of s are those for which the columns of $F(s)$ become linearly dependent and thus such that (since in this particular situation $F(s)$ is a square matrix)

$$\det F(s) = 0 \tag{3.3}$$

Hence the closed-loop system characteristic frequencies are the zeros of the return-difference matrix $F(s)$.

Since the poles of the matrices $Q(s)$ and $F(s)$ are obviously the same, we see that the poles of the return-difference operator $F(s)$ are associated with the system open-loop characteristic frequencies and its zeros are associated with the system closed-loop characteristic frequencies. A detailed study of this situation in fact shows that [22]

$$\det F(s) = \frac{CLCP(s)}{OLCP(s)} \tag{3.4}$$

where $CLCP(s)$ and $OLCP(s)$ are respectively the closed-loop and open-loop system characteristic polynomials.

We will proceed shortly to discuss how the zeros of a given transfer function matrix can be determined. If we assume for the moment, for simplicity of argument alone since the assumptions are *not* generally true, that we are dealing with square matrices, and that the zeros may then be taken as those values of s for which the corresponding determinant vanishes, then we may exhibit another vital link between zeros and feedback.

Suppose we have a system, as shown in Figure 4, with a forward transfer function

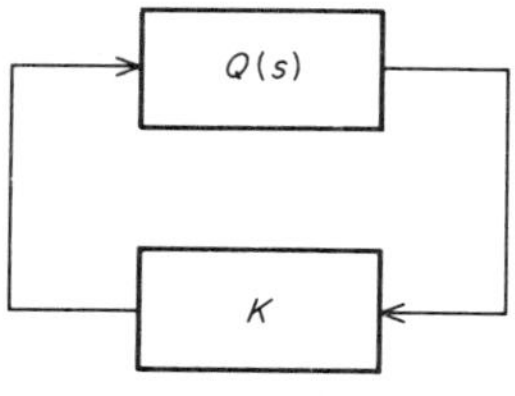

Figure 4. High-gain feedback.

matrix $Q(s)$ whose output is feedback connected to its input through a set of high-gain elements represented by a matrix of real elements K. For this configuration it may be shown that

$$\det[I + KQ(s)] = \frac{CLCP(s)}{OLCP(s)} \tag{3.5}$$

where $CLCP(s)$ and $OLCP(s)$ are the system closed-loop and open-loop characteristic polynomials, and I is a unit matrix of appropriate order. The return-difference determinant on the left-hand side of this equation can be expanded as

$$\det[I + KQ(s)] = 1 + \text{trace}(KQ) + \ldots + \det(KQ) \tag{3.6}$$

Now let all the elements of K become arbitrarily large in such a way that $\|K\|$ (the norm of K, a measure of its "size") tends to infinity. We will then have, *for finite values of s*, that

$$\frac{CLCP(s)}{OLCP(s)} \to \det KQ = [\det K]\,[\det Q] \tag{3.7}$$

From this we reach the important conclusion that, as the amounts of feedback gain imposed on the system become arbitrarily large, those closed-loop system characteristic frequencies which remain finite tend to the zeros of the open-loop transmittance matrix $Q(s)$. In other words, the zeros of transmittance operators in multivariable systems play exactly the same role in high-gain feedback situations as the scalar transfer function zeros play in the familiar root-locus method of studying the behaviour of single-loop feedback systems.

3.1. Calculation of poles and zeros via Smith-McMillan form

One of the standard ways of calculating the poles and zeros associated with a general transfer function matrix $G(s)$ is via a canonical form of representation for matrices whose elements are rational functions in s called the Smith-McMillan form. This is a straightforward development of the Smith form for polynomial matrices [6, 24] which we will therefore introduce first.

Smith form: If all the elements of a matrix are polynomials in s, it is called a polynomial matrix. Such matrices may be put into a standard form, called the Smith form, by a series of elementary row and column operations and using only polynomials. If $A(s)$ is an m by l polynomial matrix of normal rank r, then $A(s)$ may be transformed via a sequence of elementary row and column operations using only polynomials into a matrix $S(s)$ having the form:

$$S(s) = \begin{bmatrix} S^*(s)_{r,r} & O_{r,l-r} \\ O_{m-r,r} & O_{m-r,l-r} \end{bmatrix} \tag{3.8}$$

where

$$S^*(s) = \text{diag}\,\{S_1(s), S_2(s), \ldots, S_r(s)\} \tag{3.9}$$

and the polynomials $\{S_i(s); i = 1, 2, \ldots, r\}$ have the property that

$$S_1(s) \mid S_2(s) \mid \ldots \mid S_r(s)$$

where $S_i(s) \mid S_j(s)$ denotes that $S_i(s)$ divides $S_j(s)$ without remainder. The sequence of elementary row and column operations involved in transforming a given polynomial matrix $A(s)$ to Smith form may be represented by pre- and post-multiplication by appropriate polynomial matrices so that

$$S(s) = L(s)A(s)R(s) \tag{3.10}$$

Furthermore, since the determinant of each elementary operation involved in the transformations is a constant, it follows that both the $m \times m$ matrix $L(s)$ and the l by l matrix $R(s)$ must be *unimodular* polynomial matrices (that is ones having a constant value of determinant independent of s).

Smith-McMillan form: A çanonical form for rational function matrices, the Smith-McMillan form, is a direct consequence of the Smith form for polynomial matrices. Any rational function matrix $G(s)$ of order $m \times l$ and of normal rank r can be written in the form

$$G(s) = \frac{1}{\mathrm{d}(s)} N(s) \tag{3.11}$$

where $N(s)$ is a polynomial matrix and $\mathrm{d}(s)$ is the least common denominator of all the elements of $G(s)$. If $N(s)$ has a Smith form $S(s)$ then

$$N(s) = L^{-1}(s)S(s)R^{-1}(s) \tag{3.12}$$

where $L^{-1}(s)$ and $R^{-1}(s)$ are appropriate unimodular matrices. The Smith-McMillan form of $G(s)$ is then defined as [24]

$$M(s) = \frac{1}{\mathrm{d}(s)} S(s) \tag{3.13}$$

where in the $m \times l$ matrix $M(s)$ all possible numerator–denominator cancellations are assumed to have been carried out. Thus

$$M(s) = L(s)G(s)R(s) \tag{3.14}$$

where $M(s)$ has the form

$$M(s) = \begin{bmatrix} M^*(s) & O_{r,\, l-r} \\ O_{m-r,\, r} & O_{m-r,\, l-r} \end{bmatrix} \tag{3.15}$$

with

$$M^*(s) = \mathrm{diag}\left\{\frac{\epsilon_1(s)}{\psi_1(s)}, \frac{\epsilon_2(s)}{\psi_2(s)}, \ldots, \frac{\epsilon_r(s)}{\psi_r(s)}\right\} \tag{3.16}$$

Since in the elements of the diagonal block in $S(s)$ each $S_i(s)$ divides all $S_{i+j}(s)$, it follows that in the diagonal block $M^*(s)$ of the Smith-McMillan form each $\epsilon_i(s)/\psi_i(s)$ must divide all $\epsilon_{i+j}(s)/\psi_{i+j}(s)$. Therefore we have in the Smith-McMillan form that

(i) $\epsilon_1(s) | \epsilon_2(s) | \ldots | \epsilon_r(s)$

(ii) $\psi_r(s) | \psi_{r-1}(s) | \ldots | \psi_1(s)$

(As a mnemonic rule: the numerators divide up and the denominators divide down.)

As an example of the Smith-McMillan form we have that for

$$G(s) = \begin{bmatrix} \dfrac{1}{(s+1)(s+2)} & \dfrac{-1}{(s+1)(s+2)} \\ \dfrac{(s^2+s-4)}{(s+1)(s+2)} & \dfrac{(2s^2-s-8)}{(s+1)(s+2)} \\ \dfrac{(s^2-4)}{(s+1)(s+2)} & \dfrac{(2s^2-8)}{(s+1)(s+2)} \end{bmatrix}$$

$$M(s) = \begin{bmatrix} \dfrac{1}{(s+1)(s+2)} & 0 \\ 0 & \dfrac{(s-2)}{(s+1)} \\ 0 & 0 \end{bmatrix}.$$

Kalman's classic study [47] of the derivation of minimal-order state-space realizations of a given transfer function matrix showed that the zeros of the set of polynomials $\{\psi_i(s): i = 1, 2, \ldots, r\}$ are the characteristic frequencies associated with any minimal realization of $G(s)$, and must therefore appear as poles of any transmittances associated with $G(s)$. This leads to the following definition of the poles of $G(s)$. [6]

Poles of $G(s)$: The zeros of the set of polynomials $\{\psi_i(s): i = 1, 2, \ldots, r\}$, taken all together, are defined to be the *poles* of $G(s)$. In what follows the poles of a matrix $G(s)$ will usually be denoted by $\{p_1, p_2, \ldots, p_n\}$ and we will put

$$p(s) = (s - p_1)(s - p_2) \ldots (s - p_n) \tag{3.17}$$

where $p(s)$ is conveniently referred to as the *pole polynomial* of $G(s)$ and is given by

$$p(s) = \prod_{i=1}^{r} \psi_i(s) \tag{3.18}$$

Since the transformation matrices $L(s)$ and $R(s)$ used in forming the Smith-McMillan decomposition are unimodular, they are of full rank for all values of s; thus we see that the values of s for which the local rank of $G(s)$ is less than its normal rank are precisely those values of s for which the polynomials $\{\epsilon_i(s): i = 1, 2, \ldots, r\}$ vanish. Hence we have the following definition.

Zeros of $G(s)$: The zeros of the set of polynomials $\{\epsilon_i(s): i = 1, 2, \ldots, r\}$, taken all together, are defined to be the zeros of the matrix $G(s)$. In what follows the zeros of a matrix $G(s)$ will usually be denoted by $\{z_1, z_2, \ldots, z_k\}$ and we will put

$$z(s) = (s - z_1)(s - z_2) \ldots (s - z_k) \tag{3.19}$$

where $z(s)$ is conveniently called the *zero polynomial* of $G(s)$ and is given by

$$z(s) = \prod_{i=1}^{r} \epsilon_i(s) \tag{3.20}$$

It follows from these definitions that

$$\det M^*(s) = \frac{z(s)}{p(s)} \tag{3.21}$$

In the particular case that $G(s)$ is a non-identically-singular square matrix we will have that

$$\begin{aligned}\det G(s) &= \det [L(s)M(s)R(s)]\\ &= \alpha \det M^*(s)\\ &= \alpha \frac{z(s)}{p(s)}\end{aligned} \tag{3.22}$$

where α is a scalar quantity independent of s. It is important to remember however that $z(s)$ and $p(s)$ are *not necessarily relatively prime*. Thus, since cancellations of common factors between $z(s)$ and $p(s)$ are possible in evaluating the determinant, eqn. (3.22) should *not* in general be used to find or define the zeros and poles of a square matrix $G(s)$. For a simple example of such a situation consider

$$G(s) = \begin{bmatrix} \dfrac{(s-1)}{(s+1)(s+2)} & 0 \\ 0 & \dfrac{1}{(s-1)} \end{bmatrix}$$

which has poles at -1, $+1$ and -2 and a zero at $+1$ yet has:

$$\det G(s) = \frac{1}{(s+1)(s+2)}$$

3.2. Calculation of poles and zeros from transfer function matrix $G(s)$

For the calculation of the poles and zeros of a transfer function matrix, the route via the Smith-McMillan form is not very convenient, particularly if the calculation is being done by hand. Alternative methods are therefore required which obtain these quantities from $G(s)$ in a more direct manner. The most straightforward approach is via the minors of $G(s)$ and uses the following simple results.[25]

(i) The pole polynomial $p(s)$ is the least common denominator of all non-identically-zero minors of all order of $G(s)$.

(ii) The zero polynomial $z(s)$ is the greatest common divisor of the numerators of all minors of $G(s)$ of order r, where r is the normal rank of $G(s)$, provided that these minors have all been adjusted in such a way as to have the pole polynomial $p(s)$ as their common denominator.

For example, consider the matrix

$$G(s) = \frac{1}{(s+1)(s+2)(s-1)} \begin{bmatrix} (s-1)(s+2) & 0 & (s-1)^2 \\ -(s+1)(s+2) & (s-1)(s+1) & (s-1)(s+1) \end{bmatrix}$$

The minors of order 2 are

$$G^{1,2}_{1,2} = \frac{1}{(s+1)(s+2)} \qquad G^{1,2}_{2,3} = \frac{2}{(s+1)(s+2)}$$

$$G^{1,2}_{2,3} = \frac{-(s-1)}{(s+1)(s+2)^2}$$

so that, considering the minors of all orders we get

$$p(s) = (s+1)(s+2)^2(s-1)$$

On adjusting the denominators of all the minors of order 2 to be $p(s)$ we have

$$\bar{G}^{1,2}_{1,2} = \frac{(s-1)(s+2)}{p(s)} \qquad \bar{G}^{1,2}_{1,3} = \frac{2(s-1)(s+2)}{p(s)}$$

$$\bar{G}^{1,2}_{2,3} = \frac{-(s-1)^2}{p(s)}$$

and so

$$z(s) = (s-1)$$

This can be checked by calculating the Smith-McMillan form which turns out to be

$$M(s) = \begin{bmatrix} \dfrac{1}{(s+1)(s+2)(s-1)} & 0 \\ 0 & \dfrac{(s-1)}{(s+2)} \end{bmatrix}$$

Consideration of this example, in which $z(s)$ and $p(s)$ have a common factor, shows that the adjustment of the minors to have a common denominator, before taking the greatest common divisor of their numerators, is what "puts back" any common factors cancelled when forming the determinants involved.

3.3. Decoupling zeros

The finite zeros of a transfer function matrix $G(s)$ will be called *transmission zeros* of the associated dynamical system. It is often convenient to regard any system characteristic frequencies which do not appear in the transfer function matrix as associated with poles which have been cancelled by an appropriate set of zeros. This idea led Rosenbrock to introduce the concept of *a decoupling zero*.[6, 26]

3.3.1. *Output decoupling zeros*

A system mode will be unobservable if the corresponding eigenvector of A lies in the kernel of the operator represented by the matrix C, that is if there exists a vector w and a complex number s such that

$$[sI - A]w = 0 \quad \text{and} \quad Cw = 0$$

Since these two equations can be combined into

$$\begin{bmatrix} sI - A \\ C \end{bmatrix} w = 0 \tag{3.23}$$

this is equivalent to saying that the characteristic frequencies corresponding to those system modes which are unobservable are the zeros of the matrix

$$P_0(s) = \begin{bmatrix} sI - A \\ C \end{bmatrix} \tag{3.24}$$

These zeros are called system *output decoupling* zeros. It can be shown that the existence of an output decoupling zero implies the presence of a common polynomial matrix factor between $(sI - A)$ and C which cancels when the system transfer function matrix is formed; in this way the output decoupling zeros can be shown to remove unobservable characteristic frequencies by cancellation in an exact generalization of the scalar transfer function situation.

3.3.2. *Input decoupling zeros*

A system mode will be uncontrollable if there exists a complex number s and a row vector v^t such that

$$v^t [sI - A] = 0 \text{ and } v^t B = 0$$

Since these two equations can be combined into

$$v^t [sI - A \quad B] = 0 \tag{3.25}$$

this is equivalent to saying that the characteristic frequencies corresponding to those modes which are uncontrollable are the zeros of the matrix

$$P_c(s) = [sI - A \quad B] \tag{3.26}$$

These zeros are called *input decoupling* zeros. Their existence implies the presence of a common polynomial factor between the matrices $(sI - A)$ and B which is cancelled on forming the system transfer function matrix, thus removing the characteristic frequencies corresponding to uncontrollable modes by cancellation.

3.3.3. *Input–output decoupling zeros*

A system mode can be both uncontrollable and unobservable. Corresponding to such modes are a set of input–output decoupling zeros, which may be defined as those output decoupling zeros which disappear when all the input decoupling zeros are eliminated (by removing the uncontrollable part of the system).

3.3.4. *Relationship to standard state space tests*

The number of input decoupling zeros can be shown to be the rank defect of the matrix

$$[B \quad AB \quad A^2B \quad \ldots \quad A^{n-1}B]$$

and the number of output decoupling zeros to be the rank defect of

$$[C^t \quad A^tC^t \quad \ldots \quad (A^t)^{n-1}C^t]$$

3.4. System zeros[26]

Both the transmission zeros and the decoupling zeros for a system can be obtained from the single matrix function

$$P(s) = \begin{bmatrix} sI - A & B \\ -C & 0 \end{bmatrix} \tag{3.27}$$

which is one form of Rosenbrock's system matrix. It is obvious how zeros of this matrix are decoupling zeros of the system. In order to gain some insight into its wider properties consider the special case of a system having a square transfer function matrix $G(s)$. Using the Schur formula for the evaluation of a partitioned determinant we have:

$$\det P(s) = \det G(s) \det (sI - A)$$

$$= \frac{z(s)}{p(s)} \det (sI - A) \tag{3.28}$$

where $z(s)$ and $p(s)$ are the zero and pole polynomials of $G(s)$. This shows how transmission zeros associated with $G(s)$ are included among the zeros of $P(s)$. It also shows how any characteristic frequency factors of $\det (sI - A)$ not included among the poles of $G(s)$ become zeros of $P(s)$.

The basic reason why $P(s)$ in general can be used to define both forms of system zero is because the minors of $P(s)$ and those of $G(s)$ are related by

$$G^{i_1, i_2, \ldots, i_k}_{j_1, j_2, \ldots, j_k} = \frac{P^{1, 2, \ldots, n, n+i_1, n+i_2, \ldots, n+i_k}_{1, 2, \ldots, n, n+j_1, n+j_2, \ldots, n+j_k}}{\det (sI - A)} \tag{3.29}$$

where $G^{i_1, i_2, \ldots, i_k}_{j_1, j_2, \ldots, j_k}$ denotes the minor formed from G by deleting all rows except rows $i_1, i_2, \ldots, i_k$ and all columns except columns $j_1, j_2, \ldots, j_k$.

The set of transmission zeros plus decoupling zeros has been called by Rosenbrock the set of *system zeros.*[26] He has[27] defined them in the following way. For the system matrix $P(s)$ consider all minors formed from rows $1, 2, \ldots, n, n + i_1, n + i_2, \ldots, n + i_k$ and columns $1, 2, \ldots, n + j_1, n + j_2, \ldots, n + j_k$. Let p satisfying $0 \leqslant p \leqslant \min (l, m)$ be the largest value of k for which there is a minor of this form not identically zero. Let $\phi(s)$ be the monic greatest common divisor of all these minors

$$P^{1,2, \ldots, n, n+i_1, n+i_2, \ldots, n+i_k}_{1, 2, \ldots, n, n+j_1, n+j_2, \ldots, n+j_k}$$

having $k = p$ which are not identically zero. Then the zeros of $\phi(s)$ are defined to be the *system zeros*. The zeros of $\det (sI - A)$ are defined to be the *system poles.*

With these definitions, the following relationships can be established: [26]

{system zeros} = {input decoupling zeros, output decoupling zeros, transmittance zeros}
− {input–output decoupling zeros}

{system poles} = {input decoupling zeros, output decoupling zeros, transmittance poles}
− {input–output decoupling zeros}

If output feedback is applied through a real matrix, then it can be shown that: [26]

{closed-loop system zeros} = {open-loop system zeros}
{closed-loop input decoupling zeros} = {open-loop input decoupling zeros}
{closed-loop output decoupling zeros} = {open-loop output decoupling zeros}
{closed-loop input–output decoupling zeros} = {open-loop input–output decoupling zeros}
{closed-loop transmittance zeros} = {open-loop transmittance zeros}

3.5. Desoer–Schulman treatment of zeros

In order to maintain the closest possible analogy to the scalar transfer function case, Desoer and Schulman [13] define transfer function matrix zeros in terms of a general factorization of a matrix $G(s)$ into the product of a polynomial matrix and the inverse of another polynomial matrix:

$$G(s) = D_l(s)^{-1}N_l(s) \tag{3.30}$$

or

$$G(s) = N_r(s)D_r(s)^{-1} \tag{3.31}$$

If $G(s)$ is an $m \times l$ matrix then the polynomial matrices $N_l(s)$ and $N_r(s)$ are $m \times l$ and the polynomial matrices $D_l(s)$ and $D_r(s)$ are $m \times m$ and $l \times l$ respectively. Furthermore

$$N_l(s) \text{ and } D_l(s) \text{ are left coprime,}$$

and

$$N_r(s) \text{ and } D_r(s) \text{ are right coprime.}$$

The pair of matrices $N_l(s)$ and $D_l(s)$ are left coprime if and only if there exist polynomial matrices $P(s)$ and $Q(s)$ such that

$$N_l(s)P(s) + D_l(s)Q(s) = I_m \tag{3.32}$$

for all complex numbers s. The pair of matrices $N_r(s)$ and $D_r(s)$ are right coprime if and only if there are polynomial matrices $P(s)$ and $Q(s)$ such that

$$P(s)N_r(s) + Q(s)D_r(s) = I_l \tag{3.33}$$

for all complex numbers s. Algorithms have been described [6, 48] for carrying out the factorizations (3.30) and (3.31); Desoer and Schulman point out that the Smith–McMillan factorization is a special case of this form of factorization. They treat the case in which $m \geqslant l$ separately from that in which $m \leqslant l$ and we will therefore quote their definitions and results in a similar way.

3.5.1. *Systems for which* $m \geqslant l$

In this case the number of outputs is larger than or equal to the number of inputs.

They rule out the case where the normal rank of $N_l(s)$ is smaller than l, the number of inputs on the grounds that this would imply that the system had less than l effective inputs. The zero of $G(s)$ is defined as follows.

Zero of $G(s)$ when $m \geq l$: The complex number z is a zero of $G(s)$ if and only if the rank of $N_l(z)$ is less than l.

Using this approach they give the following results which relate these zeros to the transmission of exponential signals through the system. In particular, they show how the zero is related to the *complete blocking* of the transmission of some input proportional to $\exp(zt)$ where z is a zero.

Transmission-blocking property 1: If z is a zero of $G(s)$, then there exists a complex vector g of dimension l and a polynomial $\sum_\alpha m_\alpha s^\alpha = m(s)$ such that for the input

$$u(t) = 1(t)\exp(zt)g + \sum_\alpha m_\alpha \delta^{(\alpha)}(t) \tag{3.34}$$

and with zero initial value of state, the system output is identically zero for all $t > 0$. Here $1(t)$ denotes the Heaviside unit step function and $\delta^{(\alpha)}(t)$ the Dirac impulse function of order α (that is the αth generalized derivative of the unit impulse function $\delta(t)$).

Exponential-propagation property 1: If v is neither a zero nor a pole of $G(s)$ then for all non-zero complex vectors k of dimension l there is a polynomial $m(s)$ such that the input

$$u(t) = 1(t)k\exp(vt) + \sum_\alpha m_\alpha \delta^{(\alpha)}(t) \tag{3.35}$$

produces the zero-state response with exponential output form

$$y(t) = G(v)k\exp(vt) \quad \text{for all } t > 0 \tag{3.36}$$

3.5.2. *Systems for which $m \leq l$*

Here the number of outputs is less than or equal to the number of inputs. In this case if $m < l$ and there are at least $(m + 1)$ columns in $G(s)$ which are not identical to zero, then for *any* complex number z there will exist an l-dimensional complex vector g such that the input

$$u(t) = 1(t)g\exp(zt) + \sum_\alpha m_\alpha \delta^{(\alpha)}(t) \tag{3.37}$$

produces an identically zero output for $t > 0$. It is this situation which leads Desoer and Schulman to separate treatments of the two cases. If $m \leq l$ they assume that the normal ranks of $N_l(s)$ and $N_r(s)$ are both equal to m, the number of outputs. If the normal rank of $N_l(s)$ were less than m this would imply that the system would have less than m effective outputs.

Zero of $G(s)$ when $m \leq l$: The complex number z is called a zero of $G(s)$ if and only if the rank of $N_l(z)$ is less than m.

Transmission-blocking property 2: If $m \leqslant l$ then if z is a zero but not a pole of $G(s)$ there exists a linear combination $\psi(t)$ of the components of the zero-state response that

$$\psi(t) = c^t D_l(z) y(t) = 0 \quad \text{for all } t > 0 \tag{3.38}$$

for all inputs of the form

$$u(t) = 1(t) g \exp(zt) + \sum_{\alpha} m_{\alpha} \delta^{(\alpha)}(t) \tag{3.39}$$

where g is an arbitrary complex vector of dimension l and the m_{α} are appropriate vectors which depend on g.

Exponential-propagation property 2: A similar result to the one quoted under the heading "exponential-propagation property 1" may be established. However if $m \leqslant l$ it may happen that the output can be identically zero for some vector k. In this case the more general result given by Desoer and Schulman is the following. For all complex vectors b of dimension m, there is some complex vector h of dimension l and some vectors m_{α} such that

$$\begin{aligned} \psi(t) &= b^t y \\ &= b^t G(v) h \exp(vt) \neq 0 \quad \text{for } t > 0 \end{aligned} \tag{3.40}$$

when

$$u(t) = h \exp(vt) + \sum_{\alpha} m_{\alpha} \delta^{(\alpha)}(t) \tag{3.41}$$

3.5.3. *Characterization of poles*

For the matrix $G(s)$ with factorization (3.31), (3.32), Desoer and Schulman show that a complex number p is a pole of $G(s)$ if and only if there is an input

$$u(t) = \sum_{\alpha} u_{\alpha} \delta^{(\alpha)}(t) \tag{3.42}$$

such that the corresponding output, with zero initial value of state, has the form

$$y(t) = r \exp(pt) \quad \text{for all } t > 0 \tag{3.43}$$

where r is a non-zero vector. Put simply, p is a pole of $G(s)$ if and only if some input composed of generalized impulse functions exists which puts the system into such a state at $t = 0+$ that an output results which is of the purely exponential form (3.43) with the pole as exponent.

4. State Space Geometrical Treatment of Zeros

In order to closely tie together the state-space and frequency-response approaches to system analysis one needs a state-space characterization of system zeros. This may be developed using geometrical ideas introduced by Wonham and Morse.[10,

11, 14] The intuitive ideas underlying this geometrical theory of zeros are as follows: for simplicity of argument we consider a fully observable and controllable system with d distinct transmission zeros. We know that a real output feedback matrix exists for such a system, of arbitrarily high norm, which is such that a set of system poles is moved arbitrarily close to the d transmission zeros. Furthermore, these poles must correspond to a set of closed-loop modes which, in the limit, is unobservable since:

(i) arbitrarily large changes in gain only produce infinitesimal shifts in those poles arbitrarily close to the transmission zeros;
(ii) we cannot make modes uncontrollable by feedback action.

Since what can be achieved by output feedback can, a fortiori, be achieved by state feedback, we thus see intuitively that there exists a state feedback which makes d poles coincide with the d transmission zeros in such a way that the corresponding closed-loop modes are unobservable. This therefore implies the existence of a d-dimensional subspace of the state space spanned by closed-loop eigenvectors and lying within the kernel of the output map C. Furthermore there cannot be any higher-dimensional subspace spannable by closed-loop eigenvectors and lying within the kernel of C, since this would imply the existence of yet another unobservable closed-loop mode which would have to be associated with a pole in proximity with a transmission zero, which in turn implies a contradiction since there are by assumption only d transmission zeros.

Such considerations lead to the following technique, exploited by Bengtsson,[14] for computing transmission zeros from state space model parameters:

(i) choose a state feedback matrix L_M to make the maximal possible set of closed-loop eigenvectors lie within the kernel of the output map C;
(ii) form the corresponding closed-loop matrix $(A + BL_M)$;
(iii) compute the eigenvalues of $(A + BL_M)$ which are associated with those eigenvectors of $(A + BL_M)$ which lie within the kernel of C; these are the system transmission zeros.

The key to this method of relating transmission zeros to state space structure lies in the use of an important set of geometrical concepts used by Wonham and Morse in their studies of the decoupling problem;[10] these concepts are essentially associated with the study of all possible sets of closed-loop system eigenvectors under state feedback.

4.1. *A*-invariant and (*A*, *B*)-invariant Subspaces

A subspace ν of the state space is said to be A-invariant if

$$A\nu \subset \nu$$

Roughly speaking, an A-invariant subspace is spanned by the characteristic vectors of A.

If we can choose a state feedback matrix L such that

$$(A + BL)\nu \subset \nu$$

then ν is said to be an (A, B)-invariant subspace. Such a subspace is invariant under the closed-loop matrix $(A + BL)$; roughly speaking it is spanned by the characteristic vectors of $(A + BL)$.

In an important theorem which is crucial to the calculations which follow, it has been shown by Wonham and Morse that a given subspace ν is (A, B)-invariant if and only if

$$A\nu \subset \nu + \beta$$

where β denotes the range of the operator B. That is to say there will exist a matrix L such that

$$(A + BL)\nu \subset \nu \tag{4.1}$$

if and only if

$$A\nu \subset \nu + \beta \tag{4.2}$$

The necessity of condition (4.2) is fairly obvious. To show the sufficiency, one has to demonstrate that (4.2) implies the existence of a feedback matrix L such that (4.1) is true.

Let the state space $\mathcal{X}$ be the direct sum of ν and a subspace $\mathcal{X}_1$ so that

$$\mathcal{X} = \mathcal{X}_1 \oplus \nu \tag{4.3}$$

and let Q be the operator which projects $\mathcal{X}$ on $\mathcal{X}_1$ along ν. Let V be a basis matrix for ν.

Then

$$Q(A\nu) \subset Q(\nu) + Q(\beta) \tag{4.4}$$

and

$$Q(\nu) = 0 \tag{4.5}$$

so that

$$Q(A\nu) \subset Q(\beta) \tag{4.6}$$

If we now use the same symbol Q to denote the corresponding matrix representation for the operator Q, this means in matrix notation that the columns of the matrix QAV must be expressible as linear combinations of the columns of the matrix QB so that the set of equations

$$QAV = QBZ \tag{4.7}$$

has a solution Z. Since V is a basis matrix, it is of full rank and we may derive from Z a further matrix L such that

$$Z = -LV \tag{4.8}$$

Hence we have that

$$\begin{aligned} 0 &= QAV - QBZ \\ &= QAV + QBLV \\ &= Q(A + BL)V \end{aligned} \tag{4.9}$$

This implies that

$$(A + BL)\nu \subset \eta(Q) \tag{4.10}$$

where $\eta(Q)$ denotes the null space of Q. It then follows directly from the definition of Q that

$$(A + BL)\nu \subset \nu \tag{4.11}$$

and so the sufficiency is satisfied.

4.2. Maximal (*A*, *B*)-invariant subspaces

Consider the class of (A, B)-invariant subspaces which are contained in some given subspace $\mathscr{D}$ of X. Since this class is nonempty and closed under vector space summation, it must contain a unique maximal element ν^m. It has been shown by Wonham and Morse that this maximal subspace can be obtained by the following sequence:

$$\nu_0 = \mathscr{D} \tag{4.12}$$

$$\begin{aligned} \nu_i &= \mathscr{D} \cap A^{-1}(\nu_{i-1} + \beta) \\ &= \nu_{i-1} \cap A^{-1}(\nu_{i-1} + \beta) \quad i = 1, 2, \ldots, n \end{aligned} \tag{4.13}$$

If k is the first integer such that

$$\nu_{k+1} = \nu_k$$

then

$$\nu^m = \nu_k \tag{4.14}$$

and the sequence converges after at most p steps where p is the dimension of the subspace $\mathscr{D}$.

The subspace of this type which is central to the geometrical theory of transmission zeros is the maximal (A, B)-invariant subspace contained in the kernel of C, which will be denoted by $\nu_c^{\max}$.

4.3. Calculation of transmission zeros from state space model[14]

It is suggested by the intuitive argument presented at the beginning of this section that if a completely controllable and observable system has d transmission zeros

$$\dim[\nu_c^{\max}] = d$$

A full and careful treatment of this whole approach has been given by Bengtsson.[14]

Let the columns of a matrix M form a basis for $\nu_c^{\max}$, the maximal (A, B)-invariant subspace contained in the kernel of C. Then since

$$A\nu_c^{\max} \subset \nu_c^{\max} + \beta \tag{4.15}$$

the columns of the matrix AM must be linear combinations of the matrices M and B. To relate the matrix AM to the columns of M and B we may put

$$AM = [M \quad B]\, S \tag{4.16}$$

where the matrix S will be given by

$$S = [M \quad B]^{\dagger} AM \tag{4.17}$$

where $[M \quad B]^{\dagger}$ denotes the generalized inverse of the matrix $[M \quad B]$. Let $[M \quad B]^{\dagger}$ be partitioned as

$$[M \quad B]^{\dagger} = \begin{bmatrix} N \\ Y \end{bmatrix} \tag{4.18}$$

where N and Y are suitably conformable for M and B. Then we may rewrite the statement (4.15) in matrix notation as

$$AM = [M \quad B] \begin{bmatrix} N \\ Y \end{bmatrix} AM \tag{4.19}$$

from which we obtain

$$AM = MNAM + BYAM$$

which may be rearranged to give

$$(A - BYA)M = MNAM \tag{4.20}$$

If we put

$$-YA = L \tag{4.21}$$

and

$$NAM = \bar{A} \tag{4.22}$$

this takes the form

$$(A + BL)M = M\bar{A} \tag{4.23}$$

This argument shows that the state feedback matrix given by

$$L_M = -YA \tag{4.24}$$

is such that

$$(A + BL_M)\nu_c^{\max} \subset \nu_c^{\max} \tag{4.25}$$

and is thus the state feedback matrix which generates $\nu_c^{\max}$ as an invariant subspace of the closed-loop system operator. Furthermore the eigenvalues of the matrix $\bar{A}$ must be those closed-loop system eigenvalues which correspond to the set of closed-loop eigenvectors which lie in the kernel of C. It then follows directly from this that the eigenvalues of the matrix NAM are the transmittance zeros of the system, by virtue of the fact that those closed-loop poles corresponding to the unobservable modes contained in the kernel of C must cancel the transmittance zeros.

To sum up, the transmittance zeros of a completely controllable and observable system may be calculated from its state–space representation A, B and C matrices in the following way.

(i) Find a basis matrix M for the maximal (A, B)-invariant subspace contained in the kernel of C.

(ii) Find N and Y where

$$[M \quad B]^{\dagger} = \begin{bmatrix} N \\ Y \end{bmatrix}$$

(iii) then the system transmittance zeros are given by the eigenvalues of NAM.

Bengtsson has also shown how this approach can be extended to the general case where uncontrollable and unobservable modes are present. Since no uncontrollable mode eigenvectors usually lie in the kernel of C and since all unobservable mode eigenvectors lie in the kernel of C, the above procedure applied in the general case will give a characteristic polynomial for the restriction of $(A + BL_M)$ to $\nu_c^{\max}$ which has for zeros both the transmission zeros and the (unobservable) output decoupling zeros of the system. These output decoupling zeros can be removed by dividing by another polynomial associated with the restriction of $(A + BL_M)$ to another of the maximal subspaces introduced by Wonham and Morse, the maximum controllability subspace contained in the kernel of C.

4.4. Alternative approach to geometrical characterization of transmission zeros[28]

For systems with the same number of inputs and outputs a much more direct approach may be made to the geometrical characterization of transmission zeros which has been studied by Kouvaritakis.[28] If we apply output feedback to a system through a real matrix K then the closed-loop system A-matrix becomes

$$A_{Cl} = A + BKC \tag{4.26}$$

Suppose that, as is normally the case in practice, there are more states than outputs. Then BKC will not have full rank and will thus have some zero eigenvalues. It is a direct consequence of this that some of the eigenvalues of $(A + BKC)$ will remain finite as $\|K\| \to \infty$. These finite limiting values will be transmission zeros of the system and this forms the basis of a method by which they may be calculated.

For simplicity of exposition in deriving this state space characterization of zeros we will take $K = kI$, where I is a unit matrix of appropriate order, and let $k \to \infty$; their location is critically dependent on the spectral decomposition of the matrix BC. Assume, for reasons referred to later, that CB has full rank, and let BC have the spectral decomposition

$$BC = U_{BC}\Lambda_{BC}V_{BC} \tag{4.27}$$

where Λ_{BC} is a diagonal matrix of eigenvalues of BC and U_{BC} and V_{BC} are appropriate model and reciprocal-modal matrices, and assume that BC does not have full rank. Then some of the eigenvalues of BC will be zero so that the matrix Λ_{BC} can be partitioned

$$\Lambda_{BC} = \left[\begin{array}{c:c} \Lambda'_{BC} & 0 \\ \hdashline 0 & 0 \end{array}\right] \tag{4.28}$$

where Λ'_{BC} is a diagonal matrix of non-zero eigenvalues. Corresponding to this form for Λ_{BC} we have a conformable partitioning of the modal matrix U_{BC} as

$$U_{BC} = [X \;\vdots\; M] \tag{4.29}$$

where the columns of the sub-matrix M consist of those eigenvectors of BC corresponding to zero eigenvalues. When V_{BC} is correspondingly partitioned as

$$V_{BC} = \begin{bmatrix} Y \\ \hline N \end{bmatrix} \tag{4.30}$$

we get BC in the form

$$BC = [X \;\vdots\; M] \left[\begin{array}{c:c} \Lambda'_{BC} & 0 \\ \hdashline 0 & 0 \end{array}\right] \begin{bmatrix} Y \\ \hdashline N \end{bmatrix} \tag{4.31}$$

Suppose we now carry out a change of basis in the state space, taking as the new basis the eigenvectors of BC (which are assumed to form a linearly independent spanning set). Eigenvalues are invariant under this change of basis, and the effect of k on the eigenvalues of $(A + kBC)$ can most easily be seen by inspecting the transformed form of $(A + kBC)$ appropriate to this change of basis, which is

$$V_{BC}(A + kBC)U_{BC} = \left[\begin{array}{c:c} YAX + k\Lambda'_{BC} & YAM \\ \hdashline NAX & NAM \end{array}\right] \tag{4.32}$$

It follows immediately from this that, as $k \to \infty$, those eigenvalues of $(A + kBC)$ which remain finite are the eigenvalues of NAM.

This approach is restricted in the following ways:

(i) it only works for systems with the same number of inputs and outputs; and
(ii) it breaks down when CB does not have full rank.

The first restriction may be overcome by exploiting the fact that the zeros of a general matrix can be expressed as an intersection of zeros of a set of sub-systems with equal numbers of inputs and outputs. In the general case where CB does not have full rank, Kouvaritakis has shown that the system zeros are given by the roots of

$$\det[sNM - NAM] = 0 \tag{4.33}$$

where the columns of M span the null space of BC and N has an appropriate dual vector set to the columns of M as its rows.

Using synthesis results based upon this approach, Kouvaritakis [28] has generated an algorithm for choosing output matrices to achieve specified locations for system zeros.

5. Role of Multivariable Zeros in Feedback Systems Analysis

The use of matrix-valued functions of a complex variable provides a powerful and flexible tool for the analysis and design of linear feedback systems, and gives the possibility of extending the familiar ideas of classical design techniques to the general multivariable feedback situation. It is useful at this point to try to give as clear a picture as possible of the physical significance of the poles and zeros which are associated with such functions. Although only a very limited class of systems has an internal state-defining mechanism which can be completely described in terms of energy storage and power dissipation, we may consider such a restricted class of system for the purposes of intuitive insight. In this case, the various aspects of system behaviour can be associated with the concepts of energy, power and information. The three state–space model defining matrices can then, as illustrated in Figure 5, be regarded as representing:

(i) an energy-transformation map, associated with A;
(ii) a power-injection map, associated with B;
(iii) an information-extraction map, associated with C.

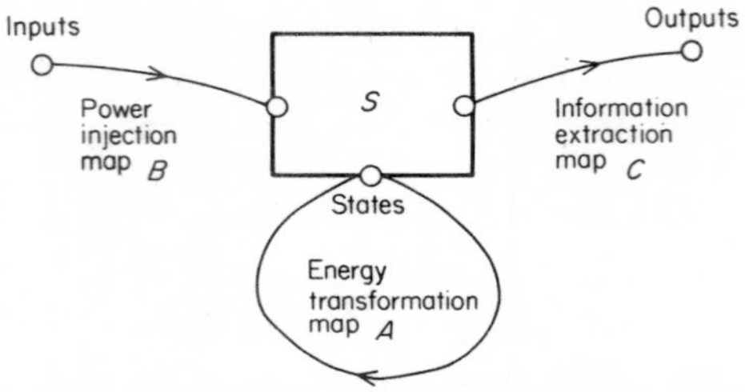

Figure 5. Physical interpretation of matrix operators A, B and C.

The matrix A represents the internal mechanism by which energy is dissipated and converted within the system. A subset of its eigenvalues forms the transmittance poles. These eigenvalues have the physical dimensions of an inverse time constant, and represent ratios of modal power to twice modal stored energy. [29]

The matrix B represents the input coupling between the information represented by the applied input signals and the power available for injection into the system states.

The matrix C represents the output coupling between the energy in the system states and the information in the available output signals.

It is obvious that the poles represent those characteristic internal energetic transformation processes of the system which are coupled to input and output. To see what the zeros represent it will be helpful to consider a trivial illustrative example. Suppose we have a system with one input, one output and two states. Let the eigenvalues of the A-matrix be λ_1 and λ_2 and assume $\lambda_1 \neq \lambda_2$. Let $\{u_1, u_2\}$ and $\{v_1^t, v_2^t\}$ be the eigenvectors and dual eigenvectors of A respectively. Let $C = c^t$, a row vector, and $B = b$, a column vector. Then a straightforward calculation shows that this system has one zero given explicitly by the formula

$$\text{zero} = \frac{c^t[u_1 v_1^t \lambda_2 + u_2 v_2^t \lambda_1]\, b}{c^t b} \tag{5.1}$$

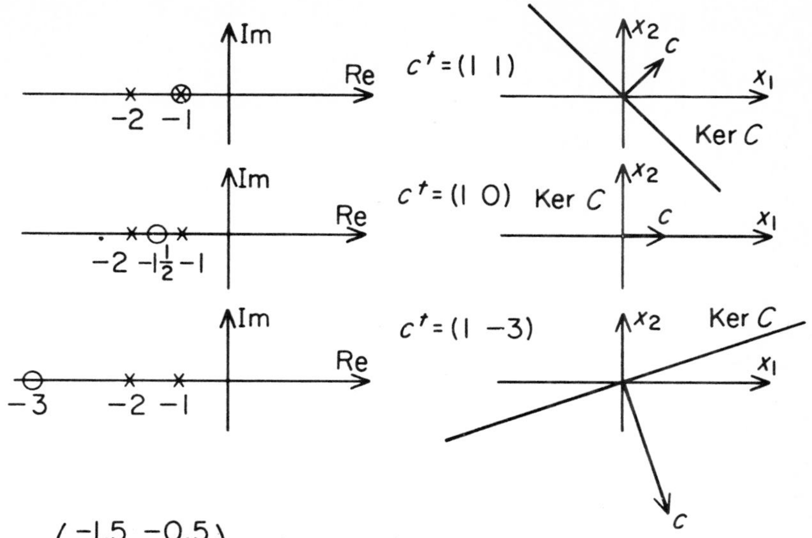

$$A = \begin{pmatrix} -1.5 & -0.5 \\ -0.5 & -1.5 \end{pmatrix} \qquad \lambda_1 = -1 \quad \lambda_2 = -2$$

$$u_1 = \begin{pmatrix} 1 \\ -1 \end{pmatrix} \quad u_2 = \begin{pmatrix} 1 \\ 1 \end{pmatrix} \qquad C = c^t$$

$$v_1^t = (0.5 \;\; -0.5) \qquad B = b = \begin{pmatrix} 1 \\ 0 \end{pmatrix}$$

$$v_2^t = (0.5 \quad 0.5)$$

Figure 6. Variation of zero with C.

Figures 6 and 7 show how the zero varies for a range of choices of the kernel of C and the range of B. It is obvious that, by a suitable variation of either of these subspaces, the zero can be placed at any point on the real axis in the complex plane. This illustrates that *zeros represent the couplings between the system's modes and its external environment*. By suitable choices of input and output couplings, system zeros can be placed at any possible locations in the complex plane. The transfer function matrix for a system represents the way information is propagated through the system. This propagation has two aspects:

(i) coupling into and out of the internal energetic processes, represented by the zeros; and
(ii) the action of the internal energetic processes themselves, represented by the poles.

Difficulties in the feedback control of a system simply arise from limitations of power or of information. Different arrangements for coupling power into the system and for extracting information from it, lead to different patterns of system zeros;

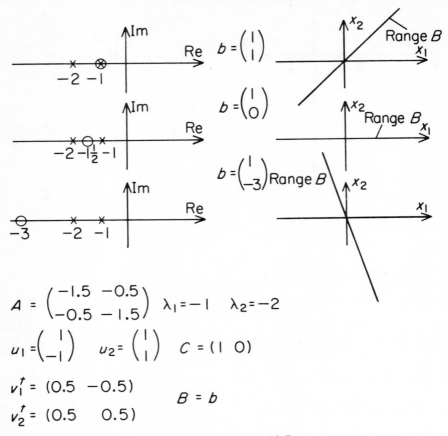

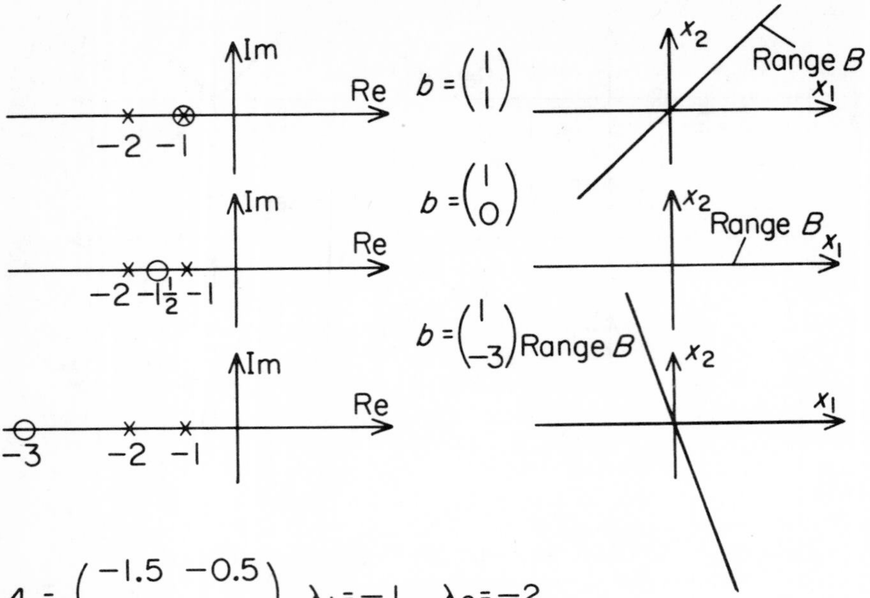

$$A = \begin{pmatrix} -1.5 & -0.5 \\ -0.5 & -1.5 \end{pmatrix} \quad \lambda_1 = -1 \quad \lambda_2 = -2$$

$$u_1 = \begin{pmatrix} 1 \\ -1 \end{pmatrix} \quad u_2 = \begin{pmatrix} 1 \\ 1 \end{pmatrix} \quad C = (1 \;\; 0)$$

$$v_1^t = (0.5 \;\; -0.5) \qquad B = b$$

$$v_2^t = (0.5 \;\; 0.5)$$

Figure 7. Variation of zero with *B*.

the number and location of these zeros gives an immediate indication of the difficulty of imposing feedback control. The only way to change the pattern of zeros and hence, implicitly, to change the nature of the feedback control problem, is to change the arrangements for output measurements and/or power inputs. It has been shown by Bengtsson[14] that the addition of extra outputs or extra inputs can always be carried out in such a way as to remove unwanted zeros. Right-half plane zeros represent particularly unfortunate forms of input and/or output coupling which result in severe control difficulties. Since, from one point of view, zeros result from an irrecoverable loss of information about states associated with an output mapping having a null space, no amount of serial dynamic compensation can recover this information, and the only cure for a system with right-half-plane zeros is the modification of the system itself by taking a fresh set of outputs and/or inputs. Suitably placed left-half-plane zeros represent acceptable locations for closed-loop poles under high-gain feedback. The combination of suitable sets of outputs in forming multivariable feedback loops should therefore be done in such a way as to create an appropriate set of left-half-plane zeros for a loop transmission matrix. A synthesis technique for this purpose has been devised by Kouvaritakis.[28] Zeros are the primary design tool for the selection of variables in the formation of feedback loops, and their systematic use could prove particularly helpful in the early stages of system development when freedom still exists to choose what sets of variables are to be manipulated and what sets are to be measured for control purposes. It could well be that the future use of feedback theory will be more concerned with selecting variable sets for measurement and manipulation in such a way that subsequent control is easy to achieve than with devising elaborate compensation schemes for systems whose structure has previously been arbitrarily fixed.

In many state–space based approaches to the feedback design problem, a priori knowledge of the system in the form of a model is used to generate approximations to system variables which cannot be directly measured. For deterministic problems such signal-reconstruction devices are called observers;[30, 31] in stochastic problems they are usually called Kalman–Bucy filters;[32] From the point of view pursued here such signal-reconstructing dynamical systems create an augmented state space, and thus provide an extra set of measurements which may be used in combination in forming feedback loops. The extra poles introduced by the signal-reconstructing system can be placed at suitably-chosen points in the complex plane. The extra zeros which are introduced by suitably combining the extra set of measurements can then be placed in the complex plane in such a way as to provide suitable phase properties for the characteristic loci of suitable multivariable feedback system loops. Thus the use of observers can be regarded from the point of view of multivariable phase compensation. In general there seems every possibility of looking at many of the classical and recent feedback design procedures from a simple common viewpoint.

6. Generalized Frequency-Response Techniques

The classical Fourier approach to the analysis of linear system behaviour[21] is to express an input function of time as a sum of sinusoidal functions and then to synthesize the response to the input as a sum of the responses to its component sinusoids. This method can again be used in the general multivariable case;[22] here however we must resolve vector functions of time $u(t)$ into a sum of vector sinusoidal functions of time. These in turn are represented in a suitable way by a complex vector, which is operated on by an appropriate matrix representing the action of the system. When such a matrix representation is available it is then a natural step to seek to decompose it into a characteristic dyadic form which is a function of frequency.

6.1. Vector sinusoids and vector phasors

In classical single-input single-output frequency-response analysis, sinusoidal functions of time are represented by complex numbers, usually then called phasors. For multiple-input multiple-output systems, the appropriate generalization of this standard approach is the representation of vector sinusoidal functions of time by complex vectors.

Vector sinusoids: A vector sinusoid, $s(t)$ say, is any vector-valued function of time t defined on the interval $(-\infty, \infty)$ and having components of the form

$$s_i(t) = \alpha_i \sin(\omega t + \theta_i)$$

The algebraic sum of any number of vector sinusoids is a vector sinusoid, and thus vector sinusoids form a linear vector space over the complex number field.

If a is a complex vector having components

$$a_i = \alpha_i \exp(j\theta_i)$$

then it is easily verified that

$$s(t) = Im\,[a \exp(j\omega t)]$$

where $Im\,[-]$ denotes the imaginary part of the expression in the bracket. Now consider a linear multivariable system having a transfer function matrix $G(s)$. If all the poles of $G(s)$ are in the open left-half plane, then the response to a vector input

$$u(t) = a \exp(j\omega t)$$

as $t \to \infty$ is given by

$$y(t) = \left[(s - j\omega)\, G(s)\, a\, \frac{1}{(s - j\omega)}\right]_{s = j\omega} \exp(j\omega t)$$

$$= G(j\omega)\, a \exp(j\omega t)$$

A similar procedure gives that the response to an input

$$u(t) = a^c \exp(-j\omega t)$$

where a^c is the conjugate of a, is given by

$$y(t) = G(-j\omega)\, a^c \exp(-j\omega t)$$

Then since

$$Im\,[a \exp(j\omega t)] = \frac{1}{2j}\,[a \exp(j\omega t) + a^c \exp(-j\omega t)]$$

we have that the system response to a vector sinusoid

$$u(t) = s(t) = Im\,[a \exp(j\omega t)]$$

is given by

$$y(t) = \frac{1}{2j}\,[G(j\omega)\, a \exp(j\omega t) + G(-j\omega)\, a^c \exp(-j\omega t)]$$

$$= Im\,[G(j\omega)\, a \exp(j\omega t)]$$

Vector phasors: The complex vector a will be called the *vector phasor* representing the vector sinusoid $s(t)$.

The above analysis shows that the familiar scalar technique for representing scalar sinusoids by phasors (which are scalar complex numbers having a modulus and phase which define the amplitude and phase of the sinusoid they represent) generalizes in a very natural way to the vector case. Since $G(j\omega)a$ is the vector phasor representing the output vector sinusoid when an input vector sinusoid is applied which is represented by the vector phasor a, we deduce that:

(i) complex phasor vectors may be used to represent vector sinusoids when calculating the response of a linear system to a vector sinusoidal input;
(ii) $G(j\omega)$ is the matrix operator which generates output phasor vectors from input phasor vectors.

6.2. Characteristic transfer functions [22, 23, 33]

The Nyquist approach to stability [1, 2] is essentially concerned with the frequency response of loop transmittance functions; in the multivariable case one is simply dealing with sets of loop transmittances. Since one always simultaneously creates a pair of input and output points whenever a loop is broken, loop transmittances can always be discussed in terms of operators having the same number of inputs and outputs. Such operators are represented by square matrices for which eigenvalues can be defined. If a plant has a different number of inputs and outputs, say more outputs than inputs, then some outputs will have to be combined (or ignored) in forming the feedback loops. The way in which such outputs can be combined was briefly referred to in Section 5. In this section it is assumed that such selection or combination of outputs as is required has already been carried out, and the discussion is therefore confined to systems having equal numbers of inputs and outputs.

Suppose we have an $m \times m$ matrix $G(j\omega)$ which represents the frequency-response of a system with m inputs and m outputs. Since this matrix can be spectrally decomposed at each frequency ω, we can compute a frequency-dependent dyadic decomposition of the form

$$G(j\omega) = \sum_{i=1}^{m} g_i(j\omega)w_i(j\omega)v_i^t(j\omega) \tag{6.1}$$

It is then natural to regard the set of scalar frequency response functions $\{g_i(j\omega): i = 1, 2, \ldots, m\}$ as a set of *characteristic frequency responses* and, in turn, to associate these with the imaginary axis evaluation of a set of *characteristic transfer functions* $\{g_i(s): i = 1, 2, \ldots, m\}$. The purpose of this section is to consider how such entities can be properly defined; their interpretation and usefulness will emerge later.

$G(s)$ is a matrix-valued function of a complex variable. If $G(s)$ is square and det $G(s)$ vanishes for every value of s, then $G(s)$ is said to be identically singular. If $G(s)$ is not identically singular, it will have a set of eigenvalues which are functions of the complex variable s, none of which will be identically zero, and a set of corresponding eigenvectors which will be vector-valued functions of the complex variable s.[33] The eigenvalues of s, for any specific value of s, are determined by the solution of the characteristic equation

$$\det[G(s) - \lambda I_m] = 0 \tag{6.2}$$

where I_m is a matrix of order m.

Let

$$\Delta(s, \lambda) = \det[G(s) - \lambda I_m] \tag{6.3}$$

Then $\Delta(s, \lambda)$ is a polynomial in λ whose coefficients are proper rational functions of s; for simplicity of exposition we will assume that $\Delta(s, \lambda)$ is irreducible. $\Delta(s, \lambda)$ defines an *algebraic function* [35, 36] of the complex variable s. For each value of $s = s_0$ say we have, except for a finite number of points (called critical points and further discussed below), an mth degree polynomial which has m distinct roots $s_0^{(1)}$, $s_0^{(2)}, \ldots, s_0^{(m)}$ say. These m roots depend continuously on s and thus (excluding critical points) define m distinct continuous single-valued functions $g_1(s), g_2(s), \ldots, g_m(s)$ which we will call the *branches* of an algebraic function $g(s)$, the *characteristic transfer function* of $G(s)$.

The critical points occur when $\Delta(s_0, \lambda)$ has a multiple root. Since a multiple root of $\Delta(s, \lambda)$ involving λ is also a root of $\partial\Delta(s, \lambda)/\partial\lambda$ it follows that the critical points of $\Delta(s, \lambda)$ are solutions of the systems of equations

$$\Delta(s, \lambda) = 0$$

$$\frac{\partial\Delta(s, \lambda)}{\partial\lambda} = 0 \tag{6.4}$$

These critical points are the roots of a polynomial in s called the discriminant of $\Delta(s, \lambda)$. The discriminant is the Sylvester eliminant of $\Delta(s, \lambda)$ and $\partial\Delta(s, \lambda)/\partial\lambda$; this is a determinant formed from the pair of polynomials $\Delta(s, \lambda)$ and $\partial\Delta(s, \lambda)/\partial\lambda$. Since these coefficients are functions of s, it follows that we can calculate the discriminant as a function of s. [35]

If a non-self-intersecting polygonal path L is drawn connecting the critical points $c_1, c_2, \ldots, c_r$ and ∞, then m distinct single-valued analytic functions $g_1(s), g_2(s), \ldots, g_m(s)$ are determined in the s-plane along L. The singularities of the functions $g_i(s)$ at the critical points are all poles or algebraic branch points. By analytic continuation over suitable paths crossing the cut L, each $g_j(s)$ can be continued into any other $g_k(s)$. Thus the algebraic function $g(s)$ has associated with it a Riemann surface which is an m-sheeted covering of the Riemann sphere, which has only a finite number of algebraic branch points, and which is compact. [36]

6.3. Generalized Nyquist stability criterion

Nyquist's stability theorem plays a central role in classical frequency-response design techniques; consequently it is of considerable importance to see how this frequency-locus concept can be extended to the multivariable case. [22, 34]

We have seen how a square transmittance operator $Q(s)$ has associated with it an algebraic function $q(s)$ having m branches $q_1(s), \ldots, q_m(s)$, whose m values can be determined along any specified path in the s-plane. If we choose for the specified path a portion of the imaginary axis, by putting $s = j\omega$ with an appropriate range of variation of the frequency variable ω, then we can compute a set of loci corresponding to the values of the branches $q_1(j\omega), \ldots, q_m(j\omega)$ in the following way.

(i) Select a value of angular frequency ω, say ω_a.
(ii) Compute the complex matrix $Q(j\omega_a)$.
(iii) Use a standard computer program (say an appropriate version of the Double *QR* Algorithm) to compute the eigenvalues of $Q(j\omega_a)$, which are a set of complex numbers denoted by $\{q_i(j\omega_a)\}$.

(iv) Plot the numbers $q_i(j\omega_a)$ on the complex plane.
(v) Repeat with further angular frequencies $\omega_b, \omega_c, \ldots$ etc.

This procedure gives a set of loci in the complex plane which we will call the set of *characteristic loci* of $Q(s)$ and denote by $\{q_i(j\omega): i = 1, 2, \ldots, n\}$. In practice such a set of loci can be rapidly computed and displayed using a computer-driven graphics display unit. For example the matrix

$$Q(s) = \begin{bmatrix} \dfrac{1 + 0.5s}{1 + 0.6s + s^2} & \dfrac{0.4 + 4s}{1 + 0.6s + s^2} \\ \dfrac{2.5 + 0.3s}{1 + 0.6s + s^2} & \dfrac{4 + 3.2s}{1 + 0.6s + s^2} \end{bmatrix}$$

has the set of characteristic loci shown in Figure 8.

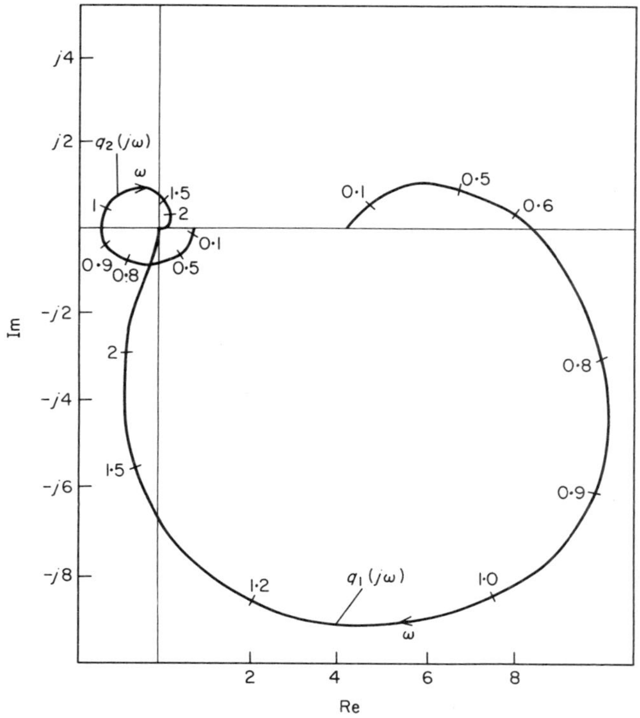

Figure 8. Example characteristic loci.

On contemplating sets of frequency-response loci such as those shown in Figure 8, one is immediately led to consider whether some natural generalization of the standard Nyquist stability criterion might apply to them which will enable us to infer what the effect on the closed-loop stability of a system will be of closing a set of loops whose transfer function matrix has a known set of characteristic loci. It turns out that such a generalization is indeed possible; however, before stating what it is, we have to consider carefully the ways in which such loci differ from the familiar single-variable Nyquist loci. One trivial difference is that the characteristic loci need not start from the real axis of the complex plane for $s = 0$, since it is possible for a matrix all of whose elements are real to have complex eigenvalues. The fundamentally important difference however arises from the fact that the Nyquist criterion normally involves mapping the closed Nyquist contour shown in Figure 9 into closed-contours in the complex plane, and then counting the number

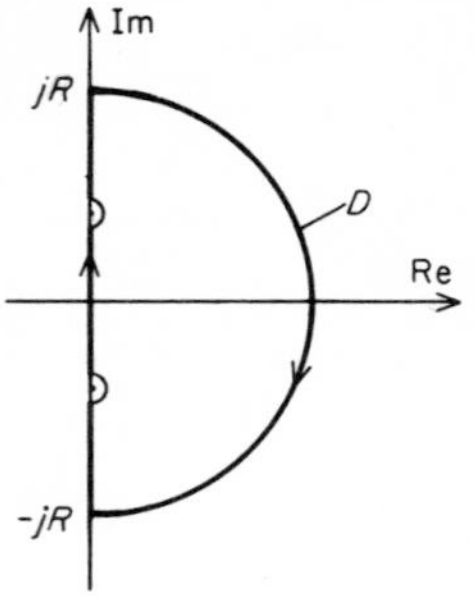

Figure 9. Nyquist's contour.

of times such contours encircle the point $(-1 + j0)$ in the complex plane. In feedback analysis this is often called the critical point in the complex plane and we will therefore call the roots of the discriminant function associated with the algebraic function $Q(s)$ the *branch points* of $q(s)$ to avoid any possible confusion. If there are any branch points in the right-half s-plane, then the characteristic loci corresponding to a mapping of the closed Nyquist contour *will not be closed loci*, because of the multiple-valued nature of the algebraic function. One cannot then simply talk about encirclements of the critical point $(-1 + j0)$ by any individual characteristic locus. However the *complete set* of loci can be joined up to give a set of closed locus curves which can be used to define an unambiguously-specified number of encirclements of the critical point.

The basic frequency-response form of stability relationships for the class of feedback systems being considered may be derived from the fundamental relationship quoted in Section 3:

$$\det F(s) = \frac{CLCP(s)}{OLCP(s)} \tag{6.5}$$

where $CLCP(s)$ and $OLCP(s)$ are the characteristic polynomials for the systems with the set of feedback loops being considered closed and open respectively and $F(s)$ is the return-difference matrix, evaluated at an appropriate break point, for the set of feedback loops being investigated.

It is fairly obvious, from an inspection of eqn. (6.5), that a straightforward form of Nyquist-type stability criterion can be obtained for the determinant of an appropriate return-difference matrix for any set of feedback loops being considered. Such an extension is of only limited interest compared to that developed below, where it is shown that the characteristic loci of the return-ratio matrix for the set of loops being considered form a natural generalization of the Nyquist diagrams of classical frequency-response theory. Nevertheless, it is convenient to first consider this simple determinant frequency-response case.

Suppose then that a set of feedback connections is made to some system within the class of systems being considered. Let D be the usual Nyquist contour in the complex plane shown in Figure 9 described clockwise, and consisting of that part of the imaginary axis from $-jR$ to $+jR$ together with a large semi-circle of radius R centred at the origin and traversing the right-half-plane. Let R be chosen sufficiently large so as to enclose within D all finite poles and zeros of det $F(s)$ lying in the right-half-plane. Furthermore, as shown in Figure 9, let the contour D be indented to exclude any poles and zeros of det $F(s)$ lying on the imaginary axis. Then, if det $F(s)$ maps D into the locus Γ_f encircling the origin in the complex plane n_f times clockwise, and if p_0 and p_c are respectively the number of right-half-plane zeros of the open-loop and closed-loop characteristic polynomials, it follows from an application of the Principle of Argument that

$$n_f = p_c - p_0 \tag{6.6}$$

where clockwise encirclements are counted as positive. Requiring p_c to be zero for absolute stability gives the encirclement relationship

$$n_f = -p_0 \tag{6.7}$$

to be necessary and sufficient for closed-loop stability.

Thus we have the basic result that a multivariable feedback system will be stable with a set of feedback loops closed if and only if a complex plane mapping of the Nyquist contour D under det $F(s)$, where $F(s)$ (of order $m \times m$) is an appropriate return-difference matrix corresponding to the loop set being investigated, encircles the origin as many times as there are right-half-plane zeros in the open-loop characteristic polynomial, and in a direction opposite to that taken in traversing the D-contour.

This result can now be extended to get an equivalent result in terms of characteristic loci. Suppose again that a set of feedback connections is made to some system and that $F(s)$ is an appropriate return-difference matrix, of order $m \times m$, evaluated at a suitable break point for the set of loops being considered. Let $\{f_i(s): i = 1, 2, \ldots, m\}$ be the m branches of the characteristic transfer function $f(s)$. We then have that

$$\det F(s) = \prod_{j=1}^{m} f_j(s) \tag{6.8}$$

Consider first the simple case where $f(s)$ *has no branch points in the right-half complex plane.* Suppose then that each branch $f_j(s)$ maps the Nyquist contour D into a locus $\Gamma_{fj}, j = 1, 2, \ldots, m$. Since we have specifically assumed that $f(s)$ has no branch points in the right-half plane, each locus Γ_{fj} will be a closed curve in the complex plane; let each Γ_{fj} encircle the origin in the complex plane n_{fj} times clockwise. It then follows from eqn. (6.8) that

$$\sum_{j=1}^{m} n_{fj} = n_f \tag{6.9}$$

where n_f, as defined previously, is the number of times Γ_f, the map of D under det $F(s)$, encircles the origin of the complex plane in a clockwise direction, and where $\sum_{j=1}^{m} n_{fj}$ is the *net* sum of origin encirclements of the characteristic loci $\{f_j(s)$: s on D; $j = 1, 2, \ldots, m\}$. Combining this with the encirclement result of the previous section then gives that the system, when all the feedback loops are closed, is stable if and only if

$$\sum_{j=1}^{m} n_{fj} = -p_0 \tag{6.10}$$

In the general case where $f(s)$ has branch points in the right-half plane, some of the individual characteristic loci will not be closed curves. The complete set of loci however can be juxtaposed in such a way as to form a family of closed curves, and Barman and Katzenelson [34] have shown how in this case the number of encirclements associated with any suitable family of closed curves formed in this way can be unambiguously defined, and used to form the required general form of stability criterion. The closed-loop system is then stable if and only if the number of critical point encirclements of this set of closed curves is equal to $-p_0$.

Normally it is a loop gain quantity which is measured in any practical situation, and consequently it is convenient to cast the final result in a form which involves loop gain matrices. Furthermore, most practical applications of feedback will involve the imposition of *negative* feedback loops, so that it is also normal to work with a negative-feedback convention. Consider therefore the situation shown in Figure 10.

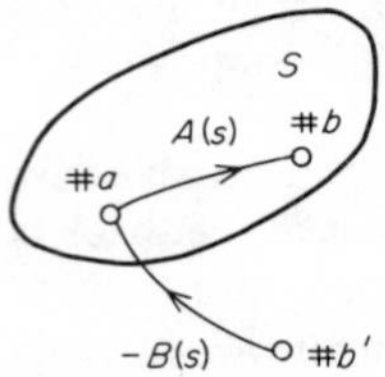

Figure 10. Feedback arrangement.

Suppose a negative-feedback transmittance matrix $-B(s)$ is feedback connected across a forward transmittance matrix $A(s)$, between a pair of vertex sets a and b on some system S. The corresponding loop gain and return-difference matrices are

$$T(s) = -A(s)B(s) \tag{6.11}$$

and

$$\begin{aligned} F(s) &= I_m + A(s)B(s) \\ &= I_m - T(s) \end{aligned} \tag{6.12}$$

Let $\{t_j(s)$: $j = 1, 2, \ldots, m\}$ be the branches of the characteristic transfer function of $T(s)$. Since $F(s)$ is a simple matrix function of $T(s)$, both will have the same characteristic signal directions, $\{w_j(s)$: $j = 1, 2, \ldots, m\}$ say, and their characteristic transfer function branches will be related by

$$f_j(s) = 1 - t_j(s) \quad j = 1, 2, \ldots, m \tag{6.13}$$

The quantity normally measured in a practical investigation is

$$A(s)B(s) = -T(s) \tag{6.14}$$

the negative of the loop gain operator for the set of loops being considered, since it is usually implicitly understood that negative feedback will ultimately be applied, often via a differencing device acting as an error detector. The final result will therefore be phrased in terms of the characteristic transfer function branches $\{-t_j(s): j = 1, 2, \ldots, m\}$ of the negative of the loop gain operator $-T(s)$. This is what is meant in following frequency-response treatments by the term: negative-feedback convention.

Collecting all of this together leads to the following result, which is basic to frequency response treatments of the multivariable feedback problem.

Generalized Nyquist stability criterion for multivariable feedback systems

Suppose a set of negative feedback connections is made to some system, and that $-T(s)$ is the negative of an appropriate $m \times m$ loop-gain matrix. Let s vary continuously round the Nyquist contour, and let the m branches of the characteristic transfer function $\{-t_j(s): j = 1, 2, \ldots, m\}$ map into a *set of closed loci* $\{\Gamma_{tk}: k = 1, 2, \ldots, r; r \leqslant m\}$. Let each closed locus Γ_{tk} encircle the critical point $(-1 + j0)$ n_{tk} times in a clockwise direction. Then the closed-loop system is stable if and only if

$$\sum_{k=1}^{r} n_{tk} = -p_0$$

where p_0 is the number of right-half-plane zeros of the open-loop system characteristic polynomial, and $\sum_{k=1}^{r} n_{tk}$ is the number of encirclements of the critical point by the *family of closed loci* Γ_{tk} taken in the clockwise direction.

The result follows from eqn. (6.13). In the remainder of this survey the phrase "set of closed characteristic loci" is to be taken to mean the set of closed-loci obtained by suitable juxtapositioning of the characteristic loci required, should right-half-plane branch points be present.

6.3.1. *Application to standard multivariable feedback configuration*

Figure 11 shows a standard multivariable feedback configuration. Here $G(s)$, $K(s)$ and $-H(s)$ represent plant, controller and negative feedback connections respectively.

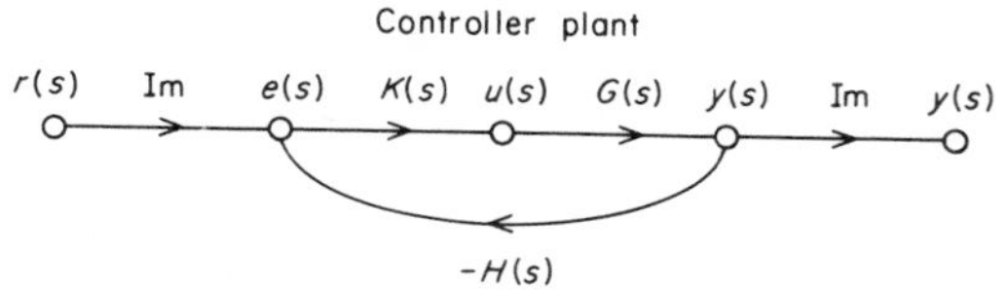

Figure 11. Standard multivariable feedback configuration.

If p_0 is the number of right-half-plane zeros for the open-loop system, then closed loop stability requires that the net sum of critical point encirclements of the closed characteristic loci of $G(s)K(s)H(s)$ or $H(s)G(s)K(s)$ or $K(s)H(s)G(s)$ be counterclockwise and equal in number to p_0. The different loop gain matrices correspond to different choices of the loop break points; which particular one is used to test for stability can be shown to be a matter of convenience.

6.3.2. *Example of generalized Nyquist criterion*

As an illustrative example suppose one has the standard multivariable feedback configuration with

$$G(s) = \frac{1}{1.25(s+1)(s+2)} \begin{bmatrix} (s-1) & s \\ -6 & (s-2) \end{bmatrix}$$

$$H(s) = -I_2 \quad \text{and} \quad K(s) = \begin{bmatrix} k_1 & 0 \\ 0 & k_2 \end{bmatrix}$$

The open-loop system is obviously stable so that

$$p_0 = 0$$

There are no right-half-plane branch points and the characteristic loci for this system are as shown in Figure 12. A gain-space diagram illustrating the stable regions of

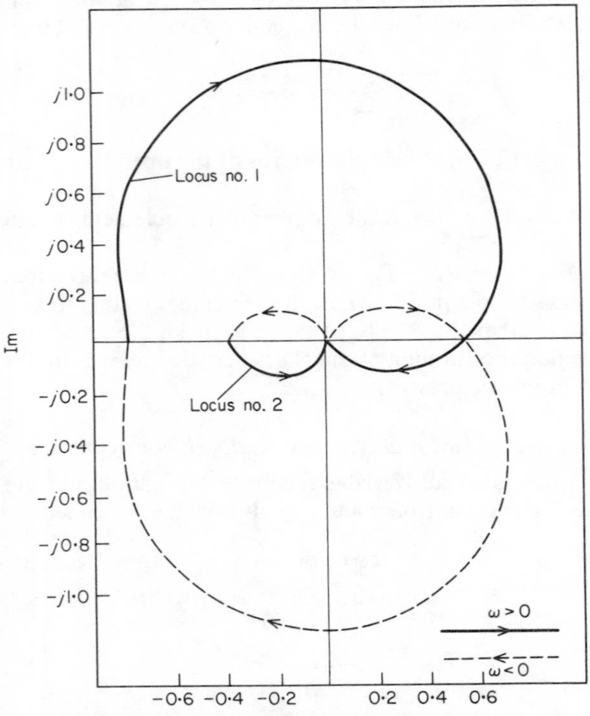

Figure 12. Stability criterion example.

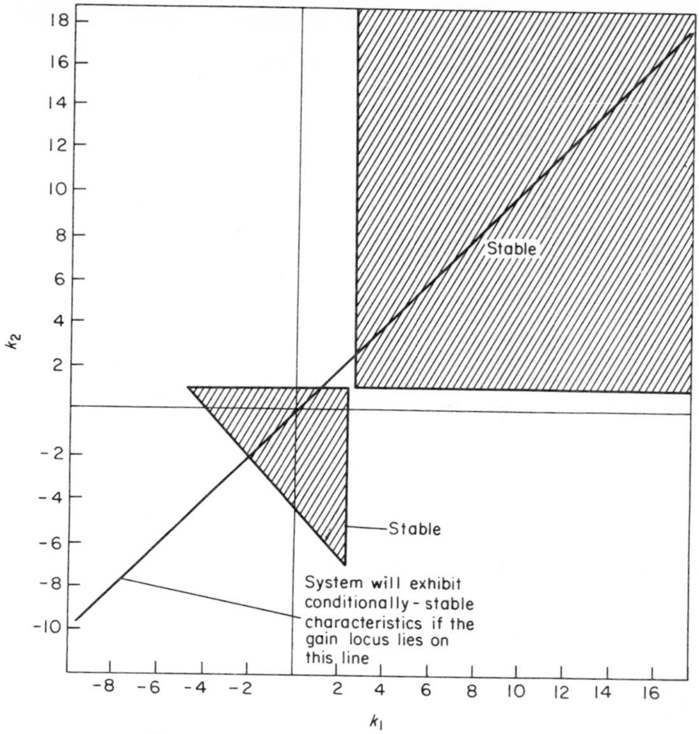

Figure 13. Gain space stability regions.

operation is shown in Figure 13. This diagram is interesting in that it shows conditionally-stable characteristics, arising from the form of the characteristic loci. To illustrate this aspect of closed-loop system behaviour, consider the simple case when

$$k_1 = k_2 = k$$

so that we can consider the diagram of Figure 12 with a critical point $(-1/k, 0)$. Examination of the characteristic loci then shows that the following conditions hold:

(i) For $0 \leqslant k \leqslant 1.25$ there are no encirclements, and the system is closed-loop stable in this region.

(ii) For $1.25 \leqslant k \leqslant 2.5$, locus No. 1 makes one clockwise encirclement while locus No. 2 makes no encirclement. Then the system is closed-loop unstable in this region.

(iii) For $2.5 < k < +\infty$ one has the interesting situation that both loci encircle the critical point once, but in opposite directions, so that the system is closed-loop stable in this region, as there are no net encirclements.

(iv) For $-\infty < k \leqslant -1.88$ the locus No. 1 encircles the critical point two times clockwise, while locus No. 2 makes no encirclement. This system is thus closed-loop unstable in this region.

(v) For $-1.88 < k \leqslant 0$ there are no encirclements and the system is closed-loop stable.

6.3.3. *Unitary space analysis of multivariable feedback system performance*

Let $Q(s)$ be the $m \times m$ open-loop transfer function matrix of the standard multivariable feedback configuration, so that

$$Q(s) = G(s)K(s) \tag{6.15}$$

Suppose $Q(s)$ has a set of characteristic transfer function branches $\{q_i(s): i = 1, 2, \ldots, m\}$. Let Γ be a specified contour in the complex plane and suppose that the set of vectors $\{w_i(s)\}$ are a basis for m-dimensional complex space for all values of s on Γ.

By definition, one has that

$$Q(s)w_i(s) = q_i(s)w_i(s) \quad i = 1, 2, \ldots, m \tag{6.16}$$

Now suppose one has an arbitrary vector $e(s)$ which is expressed as a linear combination of the frame set $w_i(s)$ by

$$e(s) = \sum_{i=1}^{m} \epsilon_i(s)w_i(s) \tag{6.17}$$

The operation of $Q(s)$ on $e(s)$ can then be represented in the form

$$Q(s)e(s) = \sum_{i=1}^{m} \epsilon_i(s)Q(s)w_i(s)$$

$$= \sum_{i=1}^{m} \epsilon_i(s)q_i(s)w_i(s)$$

$$= \sum_{i=1}^{m} [v_i^t(s)e(s)]\, q_i(s)w_i(s) \tag{6.18}$$

on using the usual Projection Rule derived in Section 2, where $\{v_i^t(s)\}$ is the dual frame to $\{w_i(s)\}$. Re-arranging this then gives that

$$Q(s)e(s) = \sum_{i=1}^{m} [w_i(s)q_i(s)v_i^t(s)]\, e(s)$$

from which one sees that the operator $Q(s)$ may be expressed in the dyadic form

$$Q(s) = \sum_{i=1}^{m} w_i(s)q_i(s)v_i^t(s) \tag{6.19}$$

This is a sum of outer products of the form: scalar times $w_i(s)v_i^t(s)$; as in Section 2 these outer products are called dyads. Since

$$w_i(s)q_i(s)v_i^t(s)e(s) = q_i(s)\epsilon_i(s)w_i(s) \tag{6.20}$$

where

$$\epsilon_i(s) = v_i^t(s)e(s) \tag{6.21}$$

the geometrical meaning of the dyadic form of operator is clear: it projects any given vector into the frame specified by the left-hand vector set $\{w_i(s)\}$, and the associated scalar then operates directly on the coordinate so obtained. Thus eqn. (6.19) clearly shows how the action of the operator $Q(s)$ on a general vector may be synthesized from its known action on the associated characteristic direction set $\{w_i(s)\}$. The arbitrary vector is projected into the characteristic direction frame, and thus expressed as a linear combination of characteristic directions. In each characteristic direction, the action of the operator is simply to multiply by the corresponding scalar characteristic transfer function. Finally, the results are added together to give the required output vector.

If $W(s)$ and $V(s)$ are as defined as respectively having columns and rows which are eigenvectors and dual eigenvectors of $Q(s)$ respectively, then it is easily verified that eqn. (6.19) may be written in matrix form as

$$Q(s) = W(s)[\text{diag}\,\{q_i(s)\}]\ V(s) \tag{6.22}$$

For unity feedback in the standard multivariable feedback configuration, with $H(s) = I_m$, the closed-loop transfer function matrix is given by

$$R(s) = [I_m + Q(s)]^{-1}Q(s)$$

from which it is readily shown that

$$R(s) = W(s)\left[\text{diag}\left(\frac{q_i(s)}{1+q_i(s)}\right)\right]V(s) \tag{6.23}$$

for which the appropriate dyadic form is

$$R(s) = \sum_{i=1}^{m}\left[\frac{q_i(s)}{1+q_i(s)}\right]w_i(s)v_i^t(s) \tag{6.24}$$

Thus, in the unity feedback case, the characteristic transfer functions of the open-loop and closed-loop configurations are

$$q_i(s) \quad \text{and} \quad \frac{q_i(s)}{1+q_i(s)}$$

respectively. The characteristic directions are the same for both open-loop and closed-loop configurations, namely $\{w_i(s)\}$. Equation (6.24) is a natural and intuitively-satisfying extension of the standard relationship between open-loop and closed-loop transferences for single-input single-output feedback systems. It shows clearly why characteristic transfer functions are the natural medium for a generalization of the Nyquist stability criterion to the multivariable case.

6.3.4. *Unitary-space geometrical picture of vector frequency-response of standard multivariable feedback configuration*

Let the contour Γ, used to define the values of s involved in the discussion, now be confined to the imaginary axis on the complex plane; this will be explicitly demonstrated by putting $s = j\omega$ where ω is the angular frequency variable. Consider the standard multivariable feedback configuration, and let $r(j\omega)$ be the phasor vector corresponding to a reference input vector sinusoid applied to the closed-loop system. Then, using eqn. (6.24), one has that the corresponding output phasor vector for the closed-loop system is given by

$$y(j\omega) = \sum_{i=1}^{m} \left[\frac{q_i(j\omega)}{1+q_i(j\omega)}\right] w_i(j\omega) v_i^t(j\omega) r(j\omega)$$

$$= \sum_{i=1}^{m} [v_i^t(j\omega) r(j\omega)] \left[\frac{q_i(j\omega)}{1+q_i(j\omega)}\right] w_i(j\omega) \tag{6.25}$$

This expression gives a clear geometrical picture of the way in which the system works, which is illustrated by Figure 14. The terms

$$[v_i^t(j\omega) r(j\omega)]$$

give the coordinates of the reference input phasor vector $r(j\omega)$ in the frame of the characteristic direction vectors $\{w_i(j\omega)\}$. The action of the closed-loop system may thus be described in the following way.

(i) The reference input phasor vector $r(j\omega)$ is split up into a sum of components

$$[v_i^t(j\omega) r(j\omega)] \; w_i(j\omega)$$

directed along the characteristic vector set $\{w_i(j\omega)\}$.

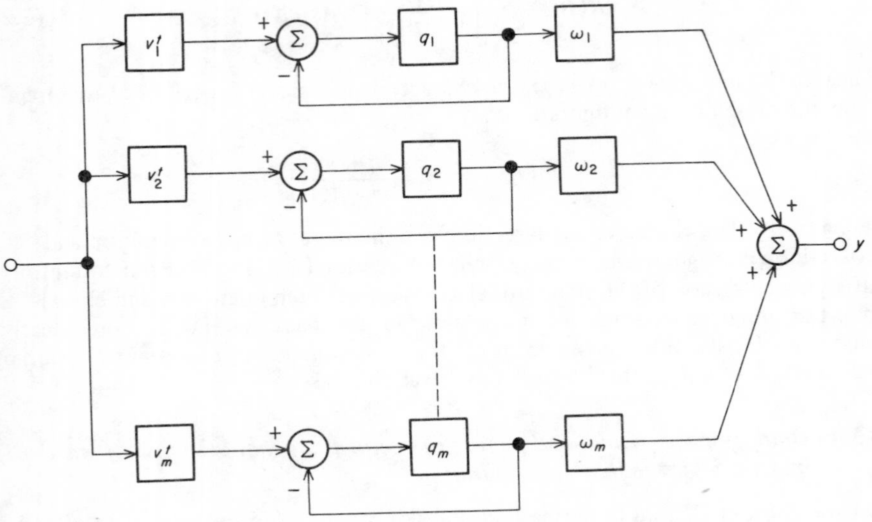

Figure 14. Action of multivariable feedback system.

(ii) The ith component coordinate $v_i^t(j\omega)r(j\omega)$ is acted upon by a scalar "characteristic feedback control system" of open-loop gain $q_i(j\omega)$ given by the characteristic locus corresponding to the ith characteristic transfer function $q_i(s)$.

Thus, after projection into the characteristic frame, the resulting coordinate is "tracked" by a "coordinate-positioning" control system with closed-loop transference

$$\frac{q_i(j\omega)}{1 + q_i(j\omega)}$$

to produce the corresponding ith component of the output phasor vector as

$$(i\text{th output component coordinate}) = \left[\frac{q_i(j\omega)}{1 + q_i(j\omega)}\right] \times (i\text{th input component coordinate}) \tag{6.26}$$

(iii) The output phasor vector $y(j\omega)$ is then assembled as a sum of component phasor vectors lying along the characteristic phasor directions $\{w_i(j\omega)\}$, and of amounts determined by the outputs of the coordinate-positioning characteristic control systems:

$$\text{output phasor} = \sum_{i=1}^{m} \left[\frac{q_i(j\omega)}{1 + q_i(j\omega)}\right] [v_i^t(j\omega)r(j\omega)]\ w_i(j\omega) \tag{6.27}$$

This simple geometrical picture immediately shows, in an intuitively-satisfying way, the physical meaning of the generalized Nyquist stability criterion: the multivariable closed-loop system is stable if all the "coordinate-position" characteristic controllers, with open-loop frequency-response characteristics $q_i(j\omega)$, are stable. Its real importance however is that it shows how the closed-loop system *performance*, as well as the stability, may be analysed in geometrical terms via the spectral decomposition into characteristic quantities.

6.3.5. *Interaction*

Consider the simple closed-loop block-diagram representation shown in Figure 15. In general, if some specific reference input demand $r_i(s)$ is imposed, some form of response $\{y_j(s): j = 1, 2, \ldots, m\}$ will result from all the closed-loop system outputs. Naturally, one will usually want one specific output $y_i(s)$ to respond to $r_i(s)$, and all

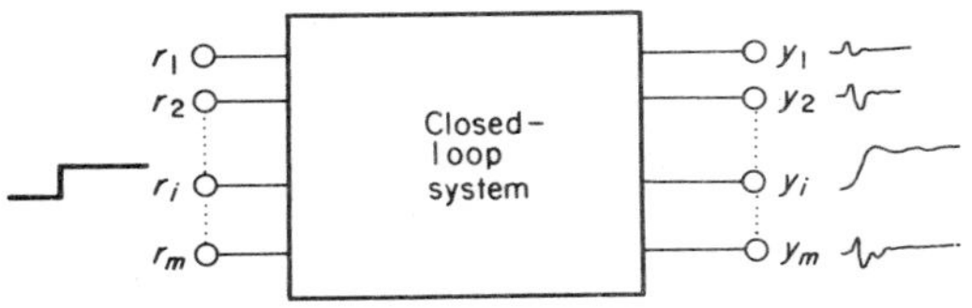

Figure 15. Interaction.

other outputs $\{y_j(s): j \neq i\}$ to remain, in some suitably-defined sense, small. By the general term interaction is simply meant the body of relationships influencing the way in which an input $r_i(s)$ affects the set of outputs $\{y_j(s): j \neq i\}$.

It follows from the discussion given in the previous section that interaction at low frequencies can in principle be suppressed to any required degree by simply ensuring that the moduli of the characteristic loci are sufficiently large at the frequency concerned. At high frequencies however, one cannot deploy arbitrarily large moduli of the characteristic loci in order to suppress interaction, because the characteristic loci must all satisfy a stability criterion of Nyquist type, and so must necessarily have small moduli at high frequencies. Furthermore, for all practical forms of plant transfer function matrix, the elements of the transfer function matrix and hence of the characteristic loci, will all tend to zero as the modulus of s tends to infinity. Suppose, therefore, that at some specific high value of angular frequency, ω_h say, all the characteristic loci of $Q(s)$ have arbitrarily small modulus. Then

$$I_m + Q(j\omega_h) \to I_m$$

and so

$$R(j\omega_h) \to Q(j\omega_h) \tag{6.28}$$

One thus reaches the following general conclusion regarding high-frequency interaction: the high-frequency cross-couplings in $R(j\omega)$ are essentially the same as those in $Q(j\omega)$, and are not therefore influenced by any feedback action. Thus, in general terms, *the only way to remove high-frequency interaction in the closed-loop system is by some suitable modification to the forward-path transference $Q(j\omega)$.*

A useful approach to the problem of high-frequency interaction is *via the characteristic direction set* of the operators involved. Consider the unity-feedback situation with $H(s) = I_m$. In this case, the characteristic direction set $\{w_i(j\omega): i = 1, 2, \ldots, m\}$ is the same for both open and closed-loop operators $Q(j\omega)$ and $R(j\omega)$. When one says that there must be little closed-loop interaction, this simply means that only the ith output of $R(j\omega)$ must respond to the ith input. This, in turn, simply means that one of the standard basic vectors e_i where

$$e_1 = \begin{bmatrix} 1 \\ 0 \\ 0 \\ \vdots \\ 0 \end{bmatrix} \quad e_2 = \begin{bmatrix} 0 \\ 1 \\ 0 \\ \vdots \\ 0 \end{bmatrix} \quad \ldots \quad e_m = \begin{bmatrix} 0 \\ 0 \\ \vdots \\ 0 \\ 1 \end{bmatrix}$$

must be a characteristic direction vector of $R(j\omega)$, and therefore of $Q(j\omega)$. It then follows that a necessary and sufficient condition for a small amount of high-frequency interaction is that the characteristic direction set of $Q(j\omega)$ must approach the standard basis direction set at high frequencies. Thus one may take as a convenient measure of interaction at high frequencies the angle between the vectors $w_i(j\omega)$ and the standard basis directions e_i for $i = 1, 2, \ldots, m$. This can be measured in terms of the angular misalignment between these vectors, given by

$$\cos \theta_i(j\omega) = \frac{|(w_i(j\omega), e_i)|}{\| w_i(j\omega) \|} \tag{6.29}$$

In summary then, interaction is determined at low frequencies by the moduli of the characteristic loci of the open-loop operator, and at high frequencies by the angular misalignment between the standard basis set and the characteristic direction set of the open-loop operator. Thus a convenient way to handle interaction over the whole required frequency range is via a *pair* of graphical plots showing:

(i) moduli of $q_i(j\omega)$ versus ω;
(ii) the misalignment angles $\theta_i(j\omega)$, as given by eqn. (6.29), versus ω.

An obvious alternative way of handling the reduction of high-frequency interaction is to make $Q(j\omega)$ of diagonal form at high frequencies. This is usually a much more severe restriction than that associated with a calculation of misalignment angles, since quasi-diagonalization is a poor indicator of alignment. This is illustrated by the system

$$Q(s) = \frac{1}{0.99\,(s+1)} \begin{bmatrix} 9 & 9 \\ -9 & 99.9 \end{bmatrix}$$

having

$$q_1 = \frac{10}{(s+1)} \quad \text{and} \quad q_2 = \frac{100}{(s+1)}$$

with

$$w_1 = \begin{bmatrix} 1 \\ 0.1 \end{bmatrix} \quad \text{and} \quad w_2 = \begin{bmatrix} 0.1 \\ 1 \end{bmatrix}$$

Despite the fact that $Q(j\omega)$ is far from diagonal at *any* frequency, the characteristic direction set is closely aligned with the standard basis set at *all* frequencies. Indeed, they are inclined to them at all frequencies at an angle of only 5.7° since

$$\theta_i = \cos^{-1} \frac{|(w_i, e_i)|}{\| w_i \|}$$

$$= \cos^{-1} 0.9950 \quad \text{for } i = 1, 2$$

Having outlined the basic relationships underlying generalized frequency-response approaches to the feedback design problem, we will now consider a range of proposed approaches to the design problem.

7. The Inverse Nyquist Array Method

Several methods have been proposed which aim at reducing a multivariable feedback system design problem to a set of classical single-loop design problems. The first such proposal, due to Boksenbom and Hood,[49] is usually referred to as the Non-interactive Control Method. This consisted simply of first choosing a $K(s)$ so that the compensated system $G(s)K(s)$ shown in Figure 16 is diagonal, thus making the resulting overall system completely non-interactive. Subsequent to such a choice of $K(s)$, it was proposed that a set of single-loop controllers $k_1(s), k_2(s), \ldots$ etc. be designed using standard single-loop theory. The required compensating matrix $K(s)$ in such a procedure will necessarily be complicated, and the most succinct objection to this approach is that it is unnecessary to go to such lengths simply to reduce interaction.

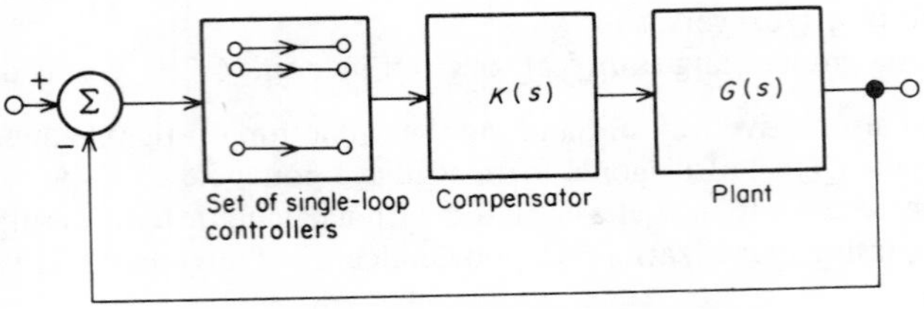

Figure 16. I.N.A. system configuration.

The Inverse Nyquist Array Method, proposed by Rosenbrock,[5] takes a much more sophisticated viewpoint. It essentially chooses a $K(s)$ of simple form (preferably constant) to *reduce* interaction to an amount which will then enable the design process to be completed, as in Figure 16, by a set of single-loop controllers. Unlike the naive non-interactive procedure however, the Rosenbrock approach is based upon a careful and extremely interesting use of a specific criterion of partial interaction – the diagonal-dominance concept.[5, 9]

Rosenbrock's Inverse Nyquist Array method is related to the properties of the corresponding system's set of characteristic loci via a useful and interesting theorem called Gerhgorin's theorem.[6] Since the relationships in this theorem are also important for the method itself, we will deal with this result in Section 7.2 before going on to the details of the method.

7.1. Outline of Inverse Nyquist Array approach

Since the Inverse Nyquist Array (subsequently abbreviated to I.N.A. where appropriate) method involves a number of specific results and definitions, it will be useful to briefly sketch out the overall approach before becoming involved in the details.

The method uses inverse representations for a variety of reasons. One of these is that the relatively complicated relationship for the standard feedback configuration between closed-loop and open-loop transfer-function matrices

$$R(s) = [I_m + Q(s)H(s)]^{-1} Q(s) \tag{7.1}$$

becomes the much simpler relationship

$$R^{-1}(s) = Q^{-1}(s) + H(s) \tag{7.2}$$

between their inverses. In the I.N.A. method, this gives a quick and neat way of converting between open-loop and closed-loop quantities.

The main concept exploited is that of diagonal-dominant matrices (and thus, by a mild abuse of language, of diagonal-dominant systems). A matrix (or the system it represents via a transfer-function matrix) is said to be diagonal-dominant at some specific frequency (or over a specified frequency range) when the moduli of its diagonal elements are greater than the sum of the moduli of the corresponding off-diagonal elements, taken by row or by column. If the open-loop inverse transfer-function matrix Q^{-1} is dominant everywhere on the Nyquist contour, then the stability of the closed-loop system can be inferred from an extended inverse-Nyquist-type set of criteria applied to bands of circles of known radius (Gershgorin bands) swept out by the diagonal elements, and hence stability is inferred from the frequency-response behaviour of these diagonal elements. Since in this method one is faced with the notational difficulty of distinguishing between the elements of an inverse matrix and the inverses of the elements of the original matrix (which are, of course, usually different) the inverses Q^{-1} and R^{-1} are denoted by $\hat{Q}$ and $\hat{R}$. Thus the inverse of the ith diagonal elements of Q and $Q^{-1} = \hat{Q}$ are respectively denoted by q_{ii}^{-1} and $\hat{q}_{ii}$ and

$$q_{ii}^{-1} \neq \hat{q}_{ii} \quad \text{in general.}$$

Diagonal-dominance is achieved by means of a precompensator, usually chosen to be real, and the design process is then finished off via a set of single-loop controllers. In this second stage of the method, a further use of bands of circles swept out by diagonal elements of an inverse matrix (Gershgorin bands or, a new set, the Ostrowski bands) are used to locate the inverse transmittances seen when all loops except the ith are connected. This enables the partially uncoupled loops to be accurately handled one at a time on a single-loop basis.

7.2. Gershgorin's Theorem

Gershgorin's theorem states that all the eigenvalues of a matrix A over the complex field are located in the union of circular discs defined by

$$|\lambda - a_{ii}| \leqslant r_i \quad i = 1, 2, \ldots, m \tag{7.3}$$

where the radii r_i are given by

$$r_i = \sum_{\substack{j=1 \\ j \neq i}}^{n} |a_{ij}| \tag{7.4}$$

Since the eigenvalues of A^t are the same as those of A, a similar result is immediately obtained with different radii given by

$$\rho_i = \sum_{\substack{i=1 \\ i \neq j}}^{n} |a_{ij}| \tag{7.5}$$

7.3. Diagonal dominance

An $m \times m$ matrix $Z(s)$ is said to be row-diagonal-dominant on a stipulated contour Γ in the s-plane if

$$|z_{ii}(s)| > \sum_{\substack{j=1 \\ j \neq i}}^{m} |z_{ij}(s)| \tag{7.6}$$

everywhere on Γ. It is said to be column-diagonal dominant on Γ if

$$|z_{ii}(s)| > \sum_{\substack{j=1 \\ j \neq i}}^{m} |z_{ji}(s)| \tag{7.7}$$

If *either* of the conditions (7.5) or (7.6) is satisfied at all points of Γ, then $Z(s)$ is said to be diagonal-dominant on Γ.

7.4. Rosenbrock's stability theorems

For the usual standard multivariable feedback configuration of Figure 6.4 we have

$$\frac{\det R(s)}{\det Q(s)} = \frac{1}{\det\,[I + Q(s)H(s)]}$$
$$= \frac{\text{open-loop characteristic polynomial}}{\text{closed-loop characteristic polynomial}} \tag{7.8}$$

Let D be the usual Nyquist contour, and let $\det Q(s)$ map D into a locus Γ_Q in the complex plane while $\det R(s)$ maps D into a locus Γ_R. As the complex-variable point s is traced once around D in a clockwise direction, let Γ_Q encircle the origin in the complex plane N_Q times clockwise, and let Γ_R encircle the origin N_R times clockwise.

Now suppose that the open-loop system characteristic polynomial has p_0 zeros in the closed right-half complex plane, and that the closed-loop characteristic polynomial has p_c zeros in the closed right-half plane. Then it follows from eqn. (7.8) that

$$N_R - N_Q = p_0 - p_c \tag{7.9}$$

Thus since $p_c = 0$ for asymptotic stability of the closed-loop system, we have that a necessary and sufficient condition for closed-loop system stability is that

$$N_R - N_Q = p_0 \tag{7.10}$$

For reasons which will become apparent (and which are inferred in the name itself) the Inverse Nyquist Array Method uses inverse matrices $\hat{Q} = Q^{-1}$ and $\hat{R} = R^{-1}$ as the main representations for the feedback problem. From elementary determinantal relationships we then have that

$$\frac{\det R}{\det Q} = \frac{\det \hat{Q}}{\det \hat{R}} = \frac{OLCP(s)}{CLCP(s)} \tag{7.11}$$

Thus if the map of D under det $\hat{Q}$ is $\Gamma_{\hat{Q}}$ and encircles the origin $N_{\hat{Q}}$ times clockwise while that of det $\hat{R}$ is $\Gamma_{\hat{R}}$ and encircles the origin $N_{\hat{R}}$ times we will have that

$$N_{\hat{R}} - N_{\hat{Q}} = -p_0 + p_c \tag{7.12}$$

since we are now using inverse polar plots.

Suppose $\hat{Q}(s)$ is row (or column) dominant on the Nyquist contour D, having no zero of det $\hat{Q}(s)$ on D and no pole of $\hat{q}_{ii}(s)$ for $i = 1, 2, \ldots, m$ on D. Let $\{\hat{q}_{ii}(s)\}$ map D into the set of loci $\{\Gamma_{\hat{q}i}\}$ and det $\hat{Q}(s)$ map D into $\Gamma_{\hat{Q}}$. Then, if $\Gamma_{\hat{q}i}$ encircles the origin of the complex plane $N_{\hat{q}i}$ times and $\Gamma_{\hat{Q}}$ encircles the origin $N_{\hat{Q}}$ times (all encirclements being counted positive when clockwise), it can be shown that

$$N_{\hat{Q}} = \sum_{i=1}^{m} N_{\hat{q}i} \tag{7.13}$$

Now suppose that $\hat{R}(s)$ is also dominant on D and that $\hat{r}_{ii}(s)$ maps D into $\Gamma_{\hat{r}i}$ times clockwise. Then, with p_0 defined as above, the closed-loop system will be stable if and only if

$$\sum_{i=1}^{m} N_{\hat{q}i} - \sum_{i=1}^{m} N_{\hat{r}i} = p_0 \tag{7.14}$$

7.5. Graphical determination of dominance and stability

As in Section 7.1 we have that

$$\hat{R}(s) = \hat{Q}(s) + H(s) \tag{7.15}$$

Let $H(s)$ be a diagonal matrix of frequency-independent gains h_i. These equations written out in full give

$$\hat{r}_{ii}(s) = \hat{q}_{ii}(s) + h_i \qquad i = 1, 2, \ldots, m \tag{7.16a}$$

$$\hat{r}_{ij}(s) = \hat{q}_{ij}(s) \qquad \begin{matrix} i, j = 1, 2, \ldots, m \\ i \neq j \end{matrix} \tag{7.16b}$$

Equation (7.16b) shows that the Gershgorin circles have the same radii for both the matrices $\hat{R}$ and $\hat{Q}$; and (7.16a) shows that the diagonal elements of $\hat{R}$ are simply those of $\hat{Q}$ horizontally shifted by the gain h_i.

Thus we have the following simple graphical interpretations of dominance.

(i) If the Gershgorin bands swept out by the diagonal elements of $\hat{Q}(s)$ excludes the origin, $\hat{Q}(s)$ is dominant on the contour involved.

(ii) If the Gershgorin bands swept out by the diagonal elements of $\hat{R}(s)$ exclude the points $(-h_i, 0)$ then $\hat{R}(s)$ is dominant on the contour involved.

We also obtain the following simple graphical interpretation of stability: Let the Gershgorin bands swept out by $\{\hat{q}_{ii}(j\omega)\}$ exclude the origin (so that $\hat{Q}$ is a diagonal-dominant) and encircle the origin $\{N_{\hat{q}i}\}$ times and also exclude the critical points $(-h_i, 0)$ (so that $\hat{R}$ is a diagonal-dominant) and encircle these points $\{N_{\hat{r}i}\}$ times for

$i = 1, 2, \ldots, m$. Then closed-loop stability is ensured if and only if

$$\sum_{i=1}^{m} N_{\hat{q}i} - \sum_{i=1}^{m} N_{\hat{r}i} = p_0 \qquad (7.17)$$

7.6. Relationship between I.N.A. bands and characteristic loci

It follows immediately from Gershgorin's theorem that the Gershgorin bands trap the characteristic loci for the matrix involved.

7.7. Approach to multivariable feedback system design via a succession of single-loop designs

The essence of the I.N.A. approach is that, by means of a suitably-chosen compensation matrix, the multivariable feedback problem is turned into a succession of classical single-loop problems. A crucial relationship is therefore one relating the transmittances between a single reference input #i and controlled output #i, when all the feedback paths are closed and when all except the ith feedback path is closed. The situation is illustrated in Figure 17. As usual, denote the closed-loop transfer function matrix of the standard feedback configuration by $R(s)$ so that

$r_{ii}(s)$ = transmittance between ith reference input and ith controlled output when all feedback paths are closed, i.e. $h_i \neq 0 \quad i = 1, 2, \ldots, m$

and define a quantity $l_i(s)$ by

$l_i(s)$ = transmittance between ith reference input and ith controlled output when the feedback loops $1, 2, \ldots, i-1, i+1, \ldots, m$ are closed and the ith feedback loop is open. That is $h_j \neq 0, j \neq i; h_i = 0$.

Then it is an immediate consequence of these definitions and the standard relationship between open and closed-loop responses for single-input single-output systems that

$$r_{ii}(s) = \frac{l_i(s)}{1 + l_i(s)h_i} \qquad (7.18)$$

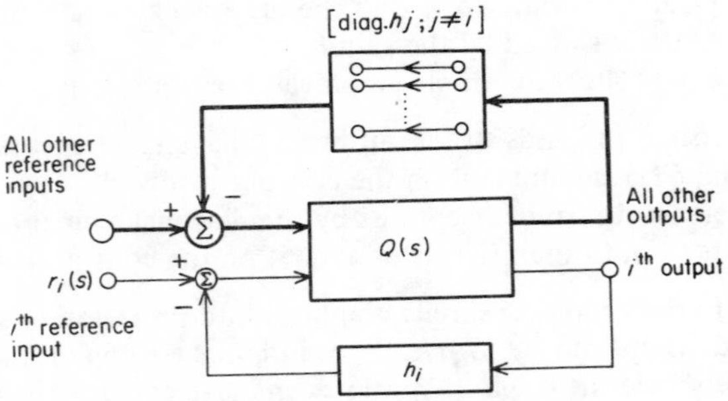

Figure 17. One-loop-at-a-time situation.

from which we get the corresponding relationship between inverse quantities as

$$r_{ii}^{-1}(s) = l_i^{-1}(s) + h_i \tag{7.19}$$

Now if we wanted to carry out a succession of single-loop designs, opening one feedback path at a time and keeping all the other loops closed, it is this quantity $l_i(s)$ with which we would have to deal. The importance of the relationship, as exploited by Rosenbrock, is that it can be used to show how inverse loci $l_i^{-1}(j\omega)$ can be located within firstly an appropriate set of Gershgorin bands and secondly within a narrower set of bands, called Ostrowski bands. These results depend on a theorem of Ostrowski's, which we now quote.

7.8. Ostrowski's theorem [6, 50]

Let a rational $m \times m$ matrix $Z(s)$ be row dominant on any closed elementary contour C having on it no pole of $\{z_{ii}(s): i = 1, 2, \ldots, m\}$. Then if s_0 is a point on C, $Z(s_0)$ has an inverse which we will denote by $\hat{Z}(s_0)$ such that for $i = 1, 2, \ldots, m$

$$|\hat{z}_{ii}(s_0) - z_{ii}^{-1}(s_0)| < \Phi_i d_i(s_0) < d_i(s_0) \tag{7.20}$$

where

$$d_i(s_0) = \sum_{\substack{j=1 \\ j \neq i}}^{m} |z_{ij}(s_0)| \tag{7.21}$$

are the radii of a set of Gershgorin circles centred on $z_{ii}(s_0)$ and Φ_i are a set of "shrinking factors" defined by

$$\Phi_i(s_0) = \max_{\substack{j \\ j \neq i}} \frac{d_j(s_0)}{|z_{jj}(s_0)|} \tag{7.22}$$

If $Z(s)$ is column-dominant on C then an equivalent relationship holds with $d_i(s_0)$ replaced by

$$d_i'(s_0) = \sum_{\substack{j=1 \\ j \neq i}}^{m} |z_{ji}(s_0)| \tag{7.23}$$

and $\Phi_i(s_0)$ replaced by

$$\Phi_i'(s_0) = \max_{\substack{j \\ j \neq i}} \frac{d_j'(s_0)}{|z_{jj}(s_0)|} \tag{7.24}$$

An immediate graphical interpretation of the Ostrowski theorem is that it firstly locates the diagonal elements of an inverse matrix within a Gershgorin band of circles swept out by the diagonal elements of the original matrix. Secondly it locates them within a narrower band of circles, which are naturally referred to as the Ostrowski band; these smaller circles are obtained by applying the shrinking factors Φ_i to the radii of the Gershgorin circles.

To see how this original Ostrowski theorem is adapted to the situation considered in the I.N.A. approach, we take

$$Z(s) = \hat{R}(s) = \hat{Q}(s) + H \qquad (7.25)$$

so that Ostrowski's theorem then gives us that, for each s on the Nyquist contour D, the diagonal elements of the closed-loop transfer function matrix $R(s)$ will satisfy the relationships

$$|r_{ii}^{-1}(s) - [h_i + \hat{q}_{ii}(s)]| < \Phi_i(s) d_i(s) < d_i(s) \qquad (7.26)$$

for row-dominance or

$$|r_{ii}^{-1}(s) - [h_i + \hat{q}_{ii}(s)]| < \Phi_i'(s) d_i'(s) < d_i'(s) \qquad (7.27)$$

for column-dominance. In terms of the quantities h_i and $\hat{q}_{ii}(s)$, the shrinking factors are given by

$$\Phi_i(s) = \max_{j \neq i} \frac{d_j(s)}{|f_j + \hat{q}_{jj}(s)|} \qquad (7.28)$$

$$\Phi_i'(s) = \max_{j \neq i} \frac{d_j'(s)}{|f_j + \hat{q}_{jj}(s)|} \qquad (7.29)$$

Now since, from (7.19)

$$l_i^{-1}(s) = r_{ii}^{-1} - h_i \qquad (7.30)$$

we may re-write expressions (7.26) and (7.27)

$$|l_i^{-1}(s) - \hat{q}_{ii}(s)| < \Phi_i(s) d_i(s) < d_i(s) \qquad (7.31)$$

for a row-dominant $\hat{R}(s)$, or

$$|l_i^{-1}(s) - \hat{q}_{ii}(s)| < \Phi_i'(s) d_i'(s) < d_i'(s) \qquad (7.32)$$

for a column-dominant $\hat{R}(s)$.

These have the following obvious graphical interpretation. For each s on the Nyquist contour D, $l_i^{-1}(s)$ lies within a circle centred on $\hat{q}_{ii}(s)$ and having radius $\Phi_i(s)d_i(s) < d_i(s)$ if $\hat{R}$ is row-dominant at s (or having radius $\Phi_i' d_i(s) < d_i'(s)$ if $\hat{R}$ is column-dominant at s). As s traverses the contour D, these circles will sweep out a set of Ostrowski bands which will lie inside the Gershgorin bands for $\hat{Q}(s)$.

In the I.N.A. approach, these Ostrowski bands fulfil two functions.

(i) They locate the inverse transfer functions $l_i^{-1}(s)$. If one wishes to design a single-loop compensator for the ith loop, then the transfer-function for which it must be designed is $l_i(s)$. As the other feedback gains $h_1, h_2, \ldots, h_{i-1}, h_{i+1}, \ldots, h_m$ vary, the observed transmittance $l_i(s)$ will change. However, so long as dominance of R is maintained, $l_i^{-1}(s)$ will lie within the appropriate Ostrowski bands, evaluated for $\{h_i(s): i = 1, 2, \ldots, m\}$. It is important to notice that the shrinking factors $\Phi_i(s)$ and $\Phi_i'(s)$ will depend on the gains in the other loops, and thus the width of the ith Ostrowski band will depend on these gains. The Gershgorin band, however, is independent of the loop gains and so always gives an outside bound for the Ostrowski bands.

(ii) The Ostrowski bands may be used to determine the stability margins of the loops being designed. When only one of the feedback gains h_i is being varied, a single-loop situation essentially exists. If the Ostrowski band is narrow enough, it may in practice be treated as though it were a single-loop inverse Nyquist plot.

8. The Sequential Return Difference Method

The Sequential Return Difference Method, proposed by Mayne,[37] attempts, like the Rosenbrock I.N.A. method, to reduce the multivariable feedback design to a set of m conventional single-loop problems. Its main feature is a simple procedure for calculating the effect on the overall system transfer function matrix of closing a set of loops one at a time. It also uses a precompensator to modify a given plant transmittance matrix to an appropriate form from which the design process may be completed via a set of single loops. The system considered is shown in Figure 18. The

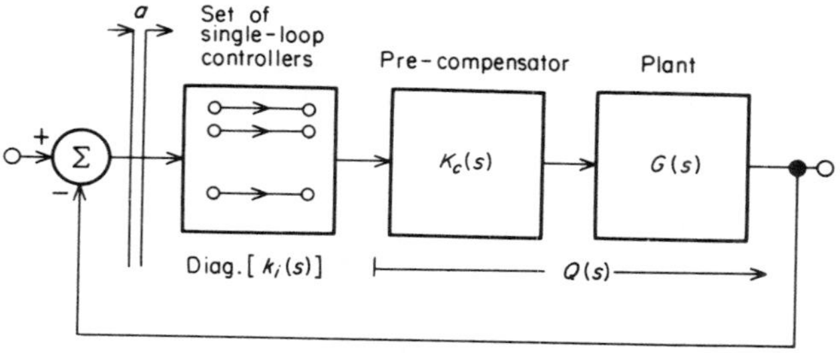

Figure 18. SRD system configuration.

given plant transfer function matrix is $G(s)$, assumed square of order $m \times m$; $K_c(s)$ is a precompensator matrix which will normally be chosen such that det $K_c(s) = 1$; and

$$K(s) = \text{diag}\,[k_1(s), k_2(s), \ldots, k_m(s)] \tag{8.1}$$

is a diagonal matrix of single-loop controllers. The break point "a" is chosen as a convenient point to which to refer the calculation of return-difference matrices. Let

$$K^i(s) = \text{diag}\,[k_1(s), \ldots, k_i(s), 0, \ldots, 0] \tag{8.2}$$

and

$$Q(s) = G(s)K_c(s) \tag{8.3}$$

so that $Q(s)$ represents the compensated plant. Let the sequence of return-difference matrices calculated at the break point "a" which are obtained as the various loops denoted by the diagonal elements of $K(s)$ are switched in one at a time be denoted by

$$F_i = I_m + QK^i \tag{8.4}$$

and let

$$Q^i = F_i^{-1}Q \tag{8.5}$$

Let q_{ij}^k denote the element of the matrix Q^k at the intersection of ith row and jth column. Now suppose the first $(i-1)$ loops of $K(s)$ are closed. Then the scalar return-difference observed at "a" for injection of signals into the ith loop will be given by

$$f_i(s) = 1 + k_i(s)q_{ii}^{i-1}(s) \tag{8.6}$$

and it can be shown that

$$\det F_i(s) = \prod_{j=1}^{i} f_j(s) \tag{8.7}$$

This result naturally leads to a stability theorem.[37]

Mayne's Stability Theorem: Let $\{f_i(s): i = 1, 2, \ldots, m\}$ be the scalar return-difference set defined in (8.6) and let them map the usual Nyquist contour D into a set of loci $\{\gamma_i: i = 1, 2, \ldots, m\}$ in the complex plane. Then if each of the loci satisfy the usual Nyquist stability criterion for return differences (that is to say γ_i does not encircle or pass through the origin in the complex plane), then the set of systems obtained by the successive closing of the various loops as $\{k_i: i = 1, 2, \ldots, m\}$ are inserted into the feedback arrangement are all stable.

In order to implement the Sequential Return Difference Method, formulae are required to recursively compute Q^i and f_i. These are:

$$Q^i = Q^{i-1} - \frac{k_i}{f_i} q_{.i}^{i-1} q_{i.}^{i-1} \tag{8.8}$$

$$f_i = 1 + k_i q_{ii}^{i-1} \tag{8.9}$$

where $q_{.i}^{i-1}$ is the ith column of Q^{i-1}
and $q_{i.}^{i-1}$ is the ith row of Q^{i-1}.

8.1. Outline of Sequential Return Difference Method[37]

The method assumes that a satisfactory sequence of single-loop designs can be carried out one at a time. As each single-loop design is satisfactorily completed, the corresponding loop gain k_j is "wound up tight". What is thus needed to enable the next design to be carried out is a formula which gives the transmittance seen by the ith controller when the gains of the previously designed loops are tightened up to appropriately high values. If $\{\Delta_k(s)\}$ denotes the set of principal minors of $Q(s)$, then Rosenbrock and Mayne[37] have shown that with all previous loops tight,

$$q_{ii}^{i-1}(s) \to \frac{\Delta_i(s)}{\Delta_{i-1}(s)} \tag{8.10}$$

This shows that the transmittances seen when designing the individual single-loop controllers in this method are defined by the ratios of principal minors of $Q(s) = G(s)K_c(s)$. Thus the precompensator $K_c(s)$ is chosen so that Δ_1 (which is simply q_{11}), Δ_2, etc. are of a satisfactory form and the sequence of single loops designed one at a time by classical methods. For example for

$$G(s) = \begin{bmatrix} \dfrac{(1-s)}{(1+s)^2} & \dfrac{(0.333-s)}{(1+s)^2} \\ \dfrac{(2-s)}{(1+s)^2} & \dfrac{(1-s)}{(1+s)^2} \end{bmatrix}$$

a precompensator of the form

$$K_c = \begin{bmatrix} 1 & 0 \\ -2 & 1 \end{bmatrix}$$

gives

$$Q(s) = \begin{bmatrix} \dfrac{(0.333+s)}{(1+s)^2} & \dfrac{(0.333-s)}{(1+s)^2} \\ \dfrac{2}{(1+s)^2} & \dfrac{(1-s)}{(1+s)^2} \end{bmatrix}$$

With no loops closed, the transmittance seen by the first controller is

$$q_{11}^0(s) = \frac{(0.333+s)}{(1+s)^2}$$

which is easily controlled so that a tight loop may be put in. With this gain wound tight

$$q_{22}^1(s) \to \frac{1}{3(1+s)(0.333+s)}$$

which again may be easily controlled.

9. The Dyadic Controller Method

Owens has formulated an interesting and ingenious approach [38, 39] to the design of multivariable feedback systems based on what he terms a dyadic transfer function matrix. Since a variety of dyadic expansions have been used in this survey, the term *real-dyadic* transfer function matrix will be used instead to avoid confusion.

Real-dyadic transfer function matrix: An $m \times m$ transfer function matrix of the form

$$G(s) = \sum_{j=1}^{m} \gamma_j(s) w_j v_j^t \tag{9.1}$$

such that $G^{-1}(0)$ exists and the vectors $\{w_j : j = 1, 2, \ldots, m\}$ and $\{v_j : j = 1, 2, \ldots, m\}$ *are real* will be called a real-dyadic transfer function matrix. In the general case of an arbitrary real-dyadic transfer-function matrix we will have that:

(i) $v_j^t w_k \neq 0$ so that $\{v_j^t\}$ is *not* a reciprocal basis for the set $\{w_j\}$;
(ii) $\{w_j: j = 1, 2, \ldots, m\}$ is *not* an eigenvector set of $G(s)$; and
(iii) $\{\gamma_j(s): j = 1, 2, \ldots, m\}$ are *not* a set of characteristic transfer functions for $G(s)$.

Owens' ingenious approach is based on the observation that for the matrix

$$G(s)G^{-1}(0)$$

we have that:

(i) $\{w_i\}$ and the set $\{v_j^t G^{-1}(0)\}$ are a reciprocal pair of basis vector sets;
(ii) $\{w_i\}$ is an eigenvector set for $G(s)G^{-1}(0)$;
(iii) $\{\gamma_j(s): j = 1, 2, \ldots, m\}$ are a set of characteristic transfer functions for $G(s)G^{-1}(0)$.

We thus have that

$$G(s)G^{-1}(0) = \sum_{j=1}^{m} \gamma_j(s) w_j z_j^t \tag{9.2}$$

where $z_j^t = v_j^t G^{-1}(0)$, gives a characteristic dyadic decomposition of $G(s)G^{-1}(0)$. If therefore a controller for $G(s)$ is chosen which has the form

$$K(s) = G^{-1}(0) \sum_{j=1}^{m} k_j(s) w_j z_j^t \tag{9.3}$$

one gets that

$$\begin{aligned} Q(s) &= G(s)K(s) \\ &= \sum_{i=1}^{m} \gamma_i(s) w_i z_i^t \sum_{j=1}^{m} k_j(s) w_j z_j^t \\ &= \sum_{i=1}^{m} \gamma_i(s) k_i(s) w_i z_i^t \end{aligned} \tag{9.4}$$

and the corresponding closed-loop response is given by

$$\begin{aligned} R(s) &= [I_m + G(s)K(s)]^{-1} G(s)K(s) \\ &= \sum_{i=1}^{m} \left[\frac{\gamma_i(s)k_i(s)}{1 + \gamma_i(s)k_i(s)}\right] w_i z_i^t \end{aligned} \tag{9.5}$$

This shows how the design of the controller may be reduced to a set of m non-interacting single-loop designs.

As an example consider the plant

$$G(s) = \begin{bmatrix} \dfrac{(1-s)}{(1+s)^2} & \dfrac{(2-s)}{(1+s)^2} \\ \dfrac{(0.333-s)}{(1+s)^2} & \dfrac{(1-s)}{(1+s)^2} \end{bmatrix}$$

Its characteristic transfer functions as a matter of interest are

$$g_1(s), g_2(s) = \frac{1}{(1+s)^2}\,[(1-s) \pm \sqrt{(2-s)(0.333-s)}\,]$$

It can be expressed in real-dyadic form as

$$G(s) = \frac{1}{(1+s)^2}\begin{bmatrix} 3 \\ 2 \end{bmatrix}[0.6667 \quad 1] + \frac{1}{(1+s)}\begin{bmatrix} 1 \\ 1 \end{bmatrix}[-1 \quad -1]$$

and one has that:

$$G(s)G^{-1}(0) = \frac{1}{(1+s)^2}\begin{bmatrix} 1-2s & 3s \\ -2s & 1+3s \end{bmatrix}$$

giving

$$z_1 = \begin{bmatrix} 1 \\ -1 \end{bmatrix} \quad z_2 = \begin{bmatrix} -2 \\ 3 \end{bmatrix}$$

A controller is chosen of the form

$$K(s) = G^{-1}(0)\left\{ k_1(s)\begin{bmatrix} 3 \\ 2 \end{bmatrix}[1 \quad -1] + k_2(s)\begin{bmatrix} 1 \\ 1 \end{bmatrix}[-2 \quad 3] \right\}$$

and the design completed by choosing $k_1(s)$ for $\dfrac{1}{(1+s)^2}$ and $k_2(s)$ for $\dfrac{1}{(1+s)}$.

Since the design of a controller is such a straightforward process when the plant is of real-dyadic form, Owens has naturally been led to consider the approximation of arbitrary transfer function matrices by real-dyadic ones. A particular feature of this approach [38] is the comprehensive way in which stability under failure conditions may be studied.

10. The Characteristic Locus Method [33]

The analysis of multivariable feedback systems in terms of characteristic transfer functions and characteristic directions given in Section 6 has been used to develop a design technique called the Characteristic Locus Method. [33] The fullest currently available description has been given by Kouvaritakis. [28] Since all the required analytical background has been given in Section 6, this approach will be illustrated here by an example based on industrial plant data. [28]

The plant has two inputs and two outputs with a transfer function matrix given by:

$$G(s) = \frac{1}{\Delta_0(s)} \begin{bmatrix} \Gamma_{11}(s) & \Gamma_{12}(s) \\ \Gamma_{21}(s) & \Gamma_{22}(s) \end{bmatrix}$$

where

$$\Gamma_{11}(s) = 29.2s + 263.3$$

$$\Gamma_{12}(s) = -3.146s^3 - 32.62s^2 - 89.83s - 31.81$$

$$\Gamma_{21}(s) = 5.679s^3 + 42.67s^2 - 68.84s - 106.8$$

$$\Gamma_{22}(s) = 9.42s + 15.15$$

$$\Delta_0(s) = s^4 + 11.67s^3 + 15.75s^2 - 88.31s + 55.15$$

The poles are at 0.826, 1.445, −5.43 and −8.511, and the zeros are at −1.192 and −5.039. Since there are two right-half plane poles the system is open-loop unstable; the zeros are both in the left-half plane so there should be no intrinsic difficulty in applying feedback control. Since there are no right-half plane branch points, there will be two closed characteristic loci obtained by mapping the Nyquist contour D. The generalized Nyquist stability criterion requires that the characteristic loci must have a sum of encirclements equal to 2, taken in an anti-clockwise direction.

The characteristic loci of the uncompensated plant are shown in Figures 19(a) and (b). An inspection of these plots shows that neither locus encircles the critical point, so that the plant would be closed-loop unstable with direct negative feedback of outputs to correspondingly-numbered inputs. Further inspection shows that equal negative feedback gains of between 1.5 and 6 would result in two anti-clockwise encirclements by one of the loci as illustrated in Figure 20. Such a scheme would however have fairly poor stability margins. It is therefore obvious that some degree of compensation is required. The plant characteristic direction misalignments from the standard basis set in unitary space are shown in Figures 21(a) and (b). These show an unacceptably high degree of misalignment in the high frequency range above 1 rad/sec; hence an adjustment of high-frequency alignment angles is also required.

One of the basic algorithms used in the characteristic locus design technique is for aligning a suitably-constrained frame of vectors with a given vector frame in unitary space. (A frame is any vector set which spans a given space.) The first step in the design process is to find a real frame matrix K_h (that is one having the frame vectors as its columns) which approximates the frame matrix $G^{-1}(j\omega)$ at a high frequency where interaction difficulties are significant. Use of an alignment algorithm gives a high-frequency compensator (designed at $\omega = 30$ r/s) of the form

$$K_h = \begin{bmatrix} 0 & 1 \\ -1 & 0 \end{bmatrix}$$

With this high-frequency controller inserted in series with the plant, the new characteristic direction misalignments are as shown in Figures 22(a) and (b). Both misalignment angles tend to zero with increasing frequency, and fall to acceptably low

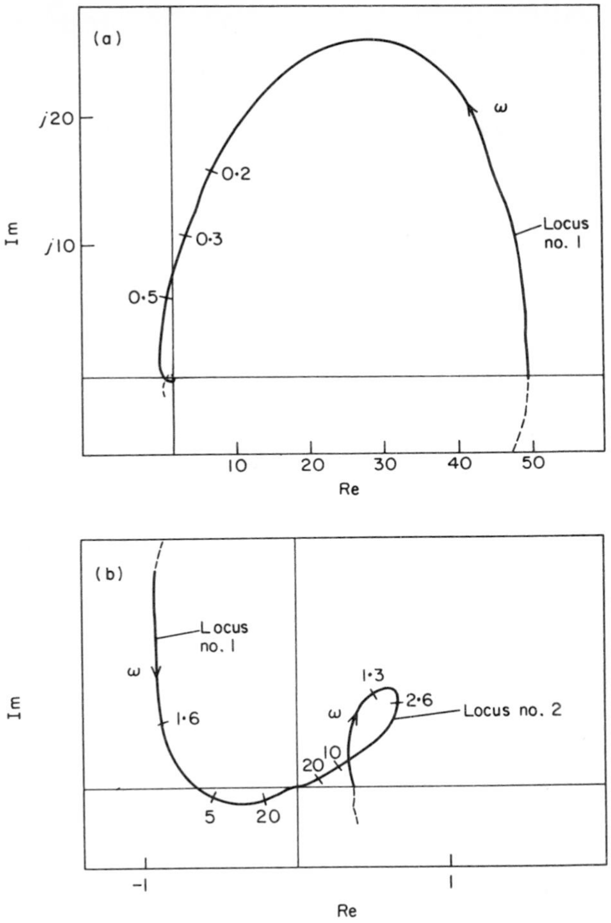

Figure 19. Uncompensated characteristic loci.

values for frequencies greater than about 5 r/s. The characteristic loci for $G(s)K_h$ are given in Figure 23; they show that the generalized Nyquist criterion is now satisfied if a unit feedback matrix is applied. Furthermore, both loci have infinite gain margins, so that a controller matrix of the form kI_2, with an arbitrarily large value of k, could be imposed on the system while still maintaining the two anti-clockwise encirclements of the critical point required for stability, as can be seen by inspection of Figure 24. Thus the phase characteristics of the system are now satisfactory, and no further form of phase compensation is required at intermediate and high frequencies. The design is concluded by balancing up the intermediate-frequency-range gains of the two characteristic loci and incorporating integral action into the controller to give satisfactory off-set levels in response to constant input demands. This

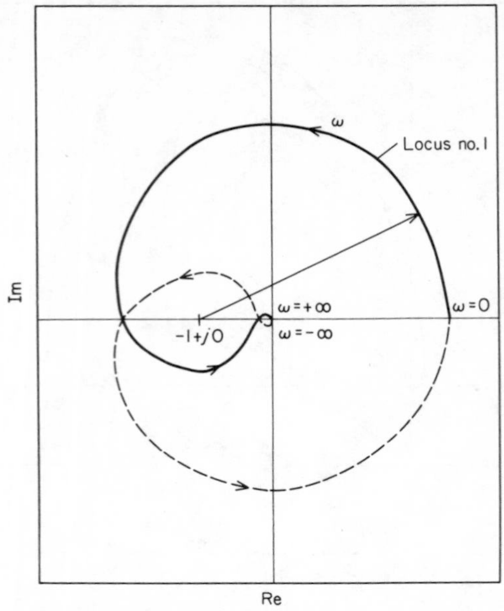

Figure 20. Stable encirclement criterion.

leads to a final overall controller of the form

$$K(s) = k \begin{bmatrix} 0 & \dfrac{s + 0.9}{s} \\ \dfrac{-(s + 2.1)}{s} & \dfrac{-0.8}{s} \end{bmatrix}$$

The misalignment diagrams and characteristic loci obtained with this controller are shown in Figures 25 and 26. The corresponding closed-loop time responses to unit step input in each reference variable are shown for $k = 5$ in Figures 27(a) and (b), and for $k = 10$ in Figures 28(a) and (b).

11. Role of Matrix-Valued Functions of a Complex Variable in Feedback System Design

All of the basic concepts used in classical feedback theory – transfer functions, poles, zeros and frequency response functions – can be generalized and used in the analysis and design of multivariable feedback systems. Furthermore the poles and zeros of the transfer function matrix for a system can be shown to be intimately related to the basic structure of the underlying state space model. In particular, the zeros of a transfer function matrix represent the coupling between the system's characteristic modes of dynamical behaviour and its environment. This inter-relationship between the system's input and output couplings and its zero locations gives a

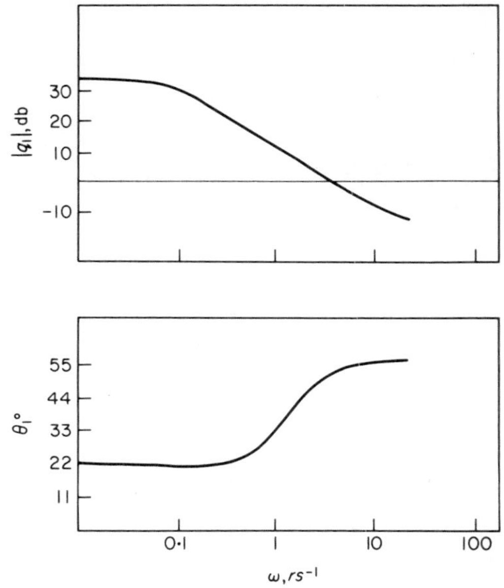

Figure 21(a). Uncompensated misalignment.

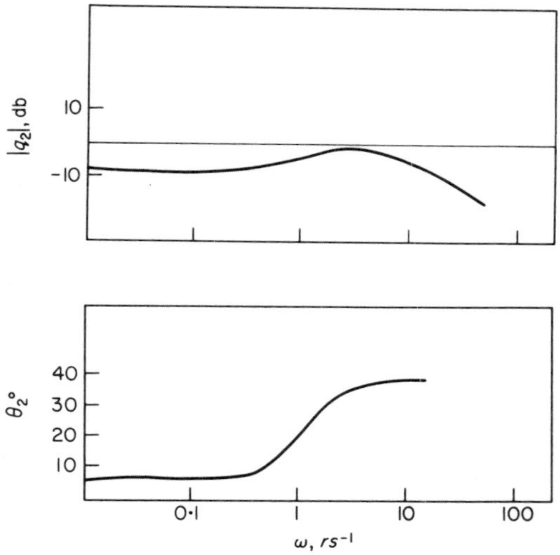

Figure 21(b). Uncompensated misalignment.

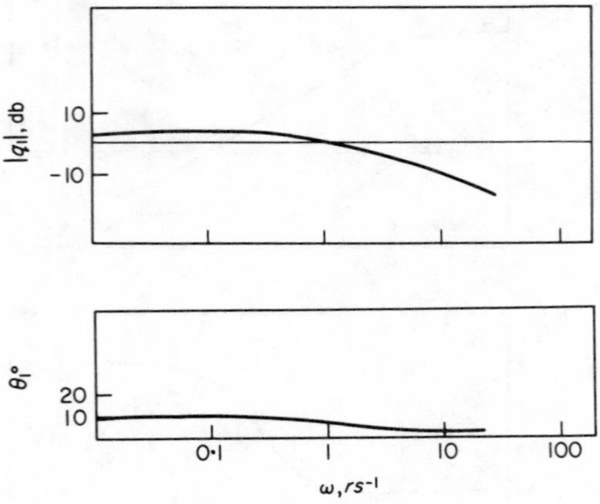

Figure 22(a). Compensated misalignment.

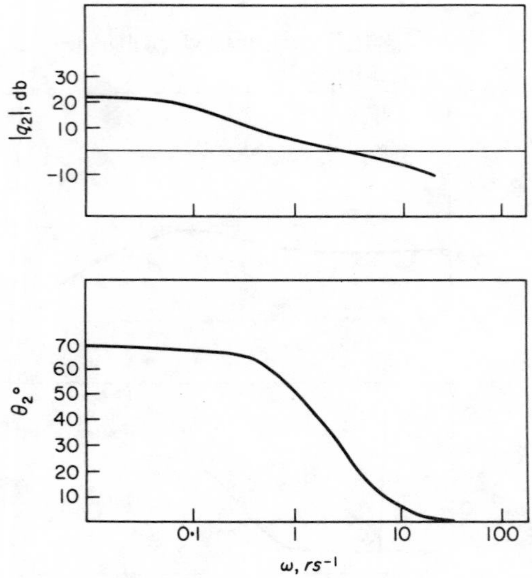

Figure 22(b). Compensated misalignment.

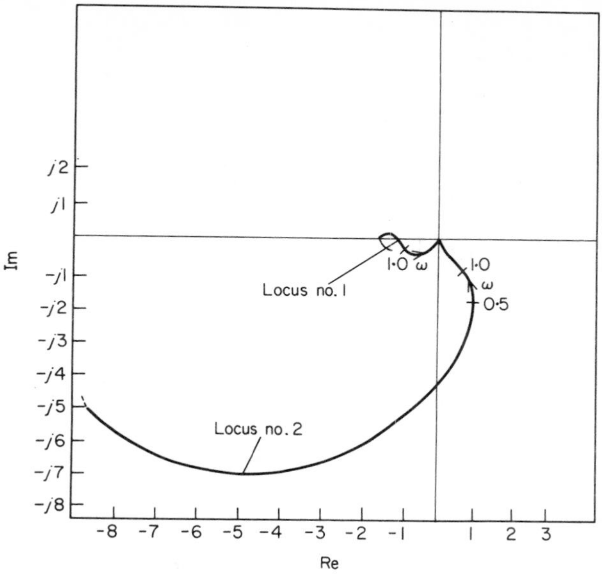

Figure 23. Compensated characteristic loci.

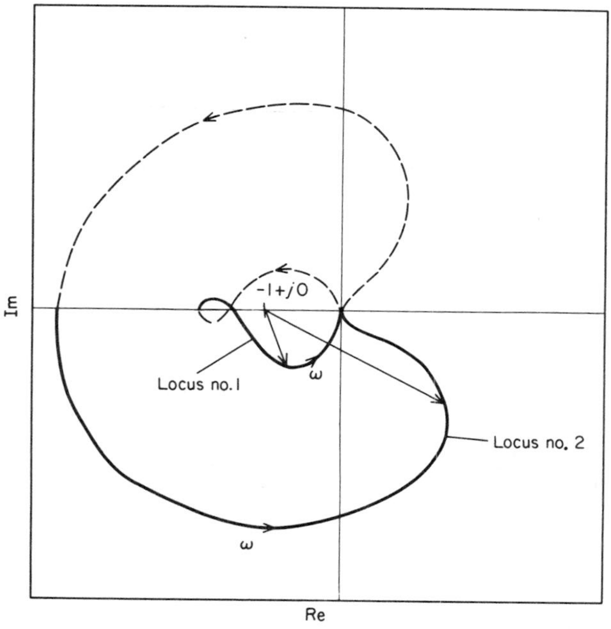

Figure 24. Stable encirclement criterion.

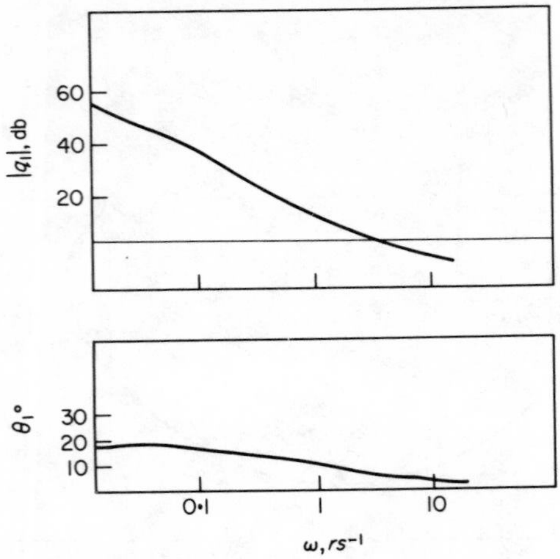

Figure 25(a). Final misalignment.

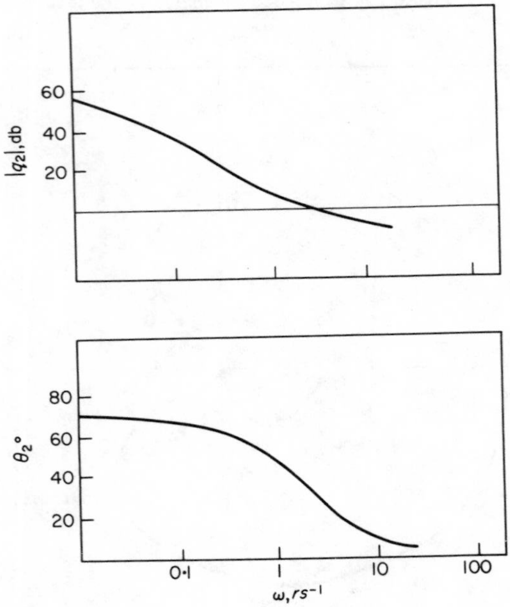

Figure 25(b). Final misalignment.

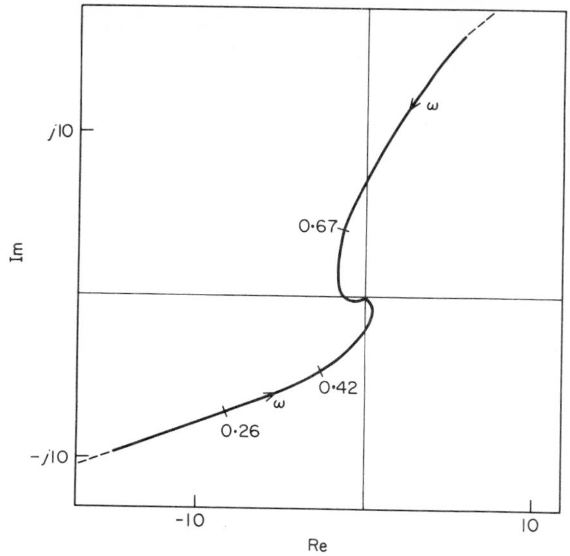

Figure 26. Final loci.

clear picture of the way in which the system state space model parameters are related to its externally-perceived frequency-response behaviour. Suppose an $m \times m$ loop transmittance matrix $L(s)$ has characteristic transfer function branches $\{l_i(s)\colon i = 1, 2, \ldots, m\}$, a set of zeros $\{z_1, z_2, \ldots, z_r\}$ and a set of poles $\{p_1, p_2, \ldots, p_n\}$. Then it can be shown that:

$$\det L(s) = \prod_{i=1}^{m} l_i(s) = \frac{\prod_{j=1}^{r} (s - z_j)}{\prod_{k=1}^{n} (s - p_k)} \times \text{constant} \tag{11.1}$$

which indicates how the phase properties of the characteristic loci are related to the pole–zero pattern of $L(s)$, and thus to the state–space structure generating $L(s)$. This linking role between state–space and frequency-response methods places the concept of multivariable zeros in a central position in the analysis and design of multivariable feedback systems. Work on the problem of choosing output maps to synthesize desired zero locations should enable the ideas underlying classical root-locus design methods to be extended to the multivariable feedback problem. Experience accumulated on a variety of frequency-response approaches to the design problem [5, 15, 28, 33, 38, 39] already shows that the spirit of classical frequency-response design methods can be extended to the general multivariable case. Some promising work has already been done on the frequency-response approach to nonlinear feedback systems. [40, 41, 42, 43]

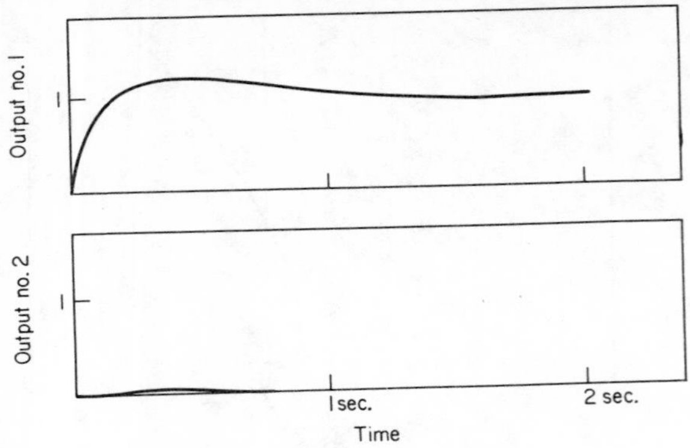

Figure 27(a). Step response, $k = 5$.

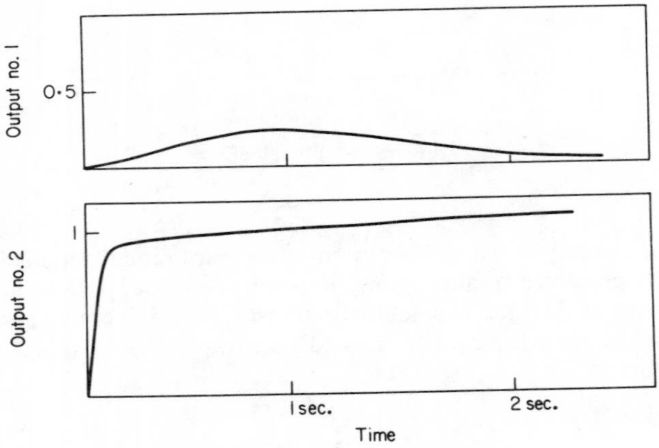

Figure 27(b). Step response, $k = 5$.

Complex-variable methods seem to occupy a centrally important role in feedback system studies; it is hoped that the survey given here will help in promoting interest in their further development and use.

12. Acknowledgements

This paper was originally presented as a survey paper to the Second IFAC Symposium in Multivariable Technological Systems held at the University of Manchester, September 1974. It is reproduced by kind permission of the International Federation of Automatic Control.

The illustrative example in Section 10 was worked out by B. Kouvaritakis.[28] In preparing Section 4, I have made considerable use of Bengtsson's report.[14]

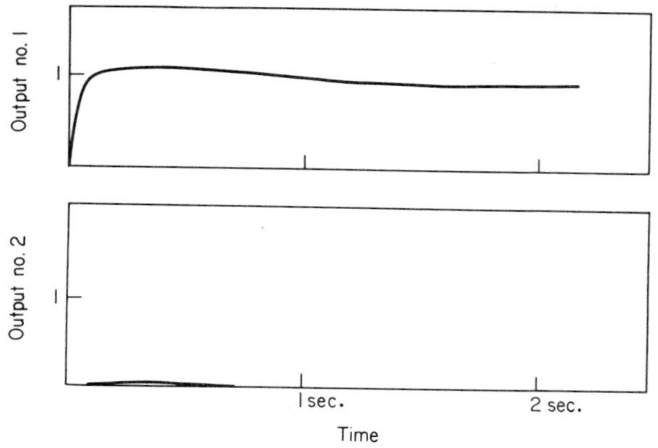

Figure 28(a). Step response, $k = 10$.

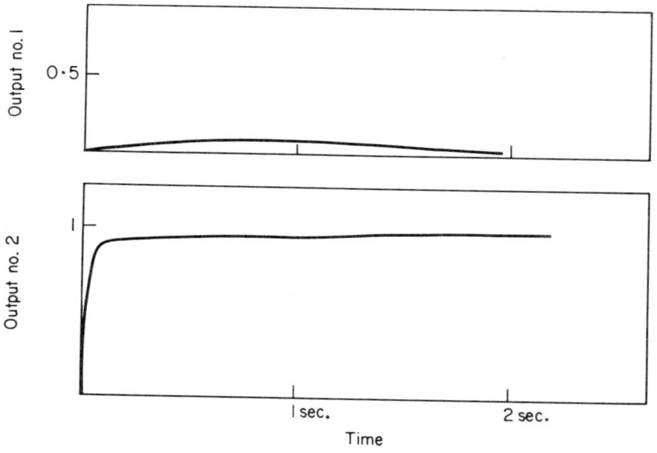

Figure 28(b). Step response, $k = 10$.

13. References

[1] Horowitz, I. M., 1963, Synthesis of Feedback Systems. Academic Press, New York.

[2] Nyquist, H., 1932, Regeneration theory. *Bell Syst. Tech. J.*, **11**, 126–147.

[3] Bode, H. W., 1945, Network Analysis and Feedback Amplifier Design. Van Nostrand, New York.

[4] Evans, W. R., 1954, Control System Dynamics. McGraw-Hill, New York.

[5] Rosenbrock, H. H., 1969, Design of multivariable control systems using the inverse Nyquist array. *Proc. I.E.E.*, **116**, 1929–1936.

[6] Rosenbrock, H. H., 1970, State-space and Multivariable Theory. Nelson, London.

[7] Rosenbrock, H. H. and Rowe, A., 1970, Allocation of poles and zeros. *Proc. I.E.E.*, **117**, 1879–1886.

[8] Rosenbrock, H. H., and McMorran, P. D., 1971, Good, bad or optimal? *I.E.E.E. Trans. Aut. Control*, **AC-16**, 552–554.

[9] Rosenbrock. H. H., 1973, Multivariable Circle Theorems in D. J. Bell (Ed.): Recent Mathematical Developments in Control, Academic Press, London.

[10] Wonham, W. M. and Morse, A. S., 1970, Decoupling and pole assignment in linear multivariable systems: a geometric approach. *SIAM J. Control*, **8**, 1–18.

[11] Wonham, W. M., 1973, Tracking and regulation in linear multivariable systems. *SIAM J. Control*, **11**, 424–437.

[12] Desoer, C. A. and Schulman, J. D., 1973, Cancellations in multivariable continuous-time and discrete-time feedback systems treated by greatest common divisor. *I.E.E.E. Trans. Aut. Control*, **AC-18**, 401–402.

[13] Desoer, C. A. and Schulman, J. D., 1974, Zeros and poles of matrix transfer functions and their dynamical interpretation. *I.E.E.E. Trans. on Circuits and Systems*, **CAS-21**, 3–8.

[14] Bengtsson, G., 1973, A theory for control of linear multivariable systems. Report 7341, Division of Automatic Control, Lund Institute of Technology, Lund.

[15] Bengtsson, G. and Lindahl, S., 1974, A design scheme for incomplete state on output feedback with applications to boiler and power system control, *Automatica*, **10**, 15–30.

[16] Zadeh, L. A. and Desoer, C. A., 1963, Linear System Theory: The State Space Approach. McGraw-Hill, New York.

[17] Halmos, P. R., 1958, Finite-dimensional vector spaces. Van Nostrand, New York.

[18] Fano, G., 1971, Mathematical Methods of Quantum Mechanics. McGraw-Hill, New York.

[19] Volterra, V., 1931, Lecons sur la theorie mathematique de la lutte pour la vie, Paris.

[20] Gilbert, E. G., 1963, Controllability and observability in multivariable control systems. *SIAM J. Control*, **1**, 128–151.

[21] Bracewell, R., 1965, The Fourier Transform and its Applications. McGraw-Hill, New York.

[22] MacFarlane, A. G. J., 1970, The return-difference and return-ratio matrices and their use in the analysis and design of multivariable feedback control systems. *Proc. I.E.E.*, **117**, 2037–2059.

[23] MacFarlane, A. G. J., 1972, A survey of some recent results in linear multivariable feedback theory, *Automatica*, **8**, 455–492.

[24] Barnett, S., 1971, Matrices in Control Theory. Van Nostrand-Reinhold, London.

[25] Kontakos, T., 1973, Algebraic and geometric aspects of multivariable feedback control systems, Ph.D. Thesis, University of Manchester.

[26] Rosenbrock, H. H., 1973, The zeros of a system. *Int. J. Control*, **18**, 297–299.

[27] Rosenbrock, H. H., Correction to "The zeros of a system", *Int. J. Control,* **20**, 525.

[28] Kouvaritakis, B., 1974, Ph.D. Thesis, University of Manchester.

[29] MacFarlane, A. G. J., 1969, Use of power and energy concepts in the analysis of multivariable feedback controllers. *Proc. I.E.E.*, **116**, 1449–1452.

[30] Luenberger, D. G., 1966, Observers for multivariable systems. *I.E.E.E. Trans. Aut. Control*, **AC-11**, 190–197.

[31] Luenberger, D. G., 1971, An introduction to observers. *I.E.E.E. Trans. Aut. Control*, **AC-16**, 596–602.

[32] Bucy, R. S. and Joseph, P. D., 1968, Filtering for stochastic processes with applications to guidance. *Interscience* – Wiley, New York.

[33] MacFarlane, A. G. J. and Belletrutti, J. J., The characteristic locus design method. *Automatica*, **9**, 575–588.

[34] Barman, J. F. and Katzenelson, J., 1973, A generalized Nyquist-type stability criterion for multivariable feedback systems. Memorandum ERL-383, Electronics Research Laboratory, College of Engineering, University of California, Berkeley. (Also published in *Int. J. Control*, **20**, 593.)

[35] Bliss, G. A., 1966, Algebraic functions. Dover, New York.

[36] Springer, G., 1957, Introduction to Riemann Surfaces. Addison-Wesley, Reading, Mass.

[37] Mayne, D. Q., 1973, The design of linear multivariable systems. *Automatica*, **9**, 201–207.

[38] Owens, D. H., 1973, Multivariable-control-system design concepts in failure analysis of a class of nuclear-reactor spatial-control systems. *Proc. I.E.E.*, **120**, 119–125.

[39] Owens, D. H., 1973, Dyadic approximation method for multivariable control-systems analysis with a nuclear-reactor application. *Proc. I.E.E.*, **120**, 801–809.

[40] Freedman, M. I., Falb, P. L. and Zames, G., 1969, A Hilbert space stability theory over locally compact Abelian groups. *SIAM J. Control*, **7**, 479–495.

[41] Mees, A. I., 1973, Describing functions, circle criteria and multiple-loop feedback systems. *Proc. I.E.E.*, **120**, 126–130.

[42] Lighthill, J. and Mees, A. I., 1973, Stability of nonlinear feedback systems in Bell, D. J. (Ed.): Recent Mathematical Developments in Control, pp. 1–19, Academic Press, London.

[43] Freeman, E. A., 1973, Some control system stability and optimality results obtained via functional analysis in Bell, D. J. (Ed.): Recent Mathematical Developments in Control, pp. 45–68, Academic Press, London.

[44] Wonham, W. M., 1967, On pole assignment in multi-input controllable linear systems. *I.E.E.E. Trans. Aut. Control*, **AC-12**, 660–665.

[45] Wolovich, W. A., 1973, On determining the zeros of state-space systems. *I.E.E.E. Trans. Aut. Control*, **AC-18**, 542–544.

[46] Gantmacher, F. R., 1959, Theory of Matrices, Vol. 1, Chelsea, New York.

[47] Kalman, R. E., 1965, Irreducible realizations and the degree of a rational matrix. *SIAM J. Control*, **13**, 520–544.

[48] MacDuffee, C. C., 1956, The Theory of Matrices. Chelsea, New York.

[49] Boksenbom, A. S. and Hood, R., 1949, General algebraic method applied to control analysis of complex engine types. Report NCA-TR-980, National Advisory Committee for Aeronautics, Washington D.C.

[50] Ostrowski, A. M., 1952, Note on bounds for determinants with dominant principal diagonal. *Proc. Am. Math. Soc.*, **3**, 26–30.

Further Results on Pole-Shifting Using Output Feedback

N. MUNRO
Control Systems Centre, University of Manchester Institute of Science and Technology, Sackville Street, Manchester, England

Summary. Some previous results concerning eigenvalue assignment using constant output feedback are extended. Necessary and sufficient conditions for an output feedback solution to exist are shown to be equivalent to conditions imposed by the controllability and observability indices of the given system. An example is provided to illustrate the procedures described.

1. Introduction

Given a linear time-invariant dynamical system described by the state space equations

$$\dot{\mathbf{x}} = A\mathbf{x} + B\mathbf{u} \tag{1}$$

$$\mathbf{y} = C\mathbf{x} \tag{2}$$

where $\mathbf{x}$ is an $n \times 1$ state vector, $\mathbf{u}$ is an $m \times 1$ input vector, and $\mathbf{y}$ is an $l \times 1$ output vector, then it is well known (see Wonham 1967, Anderson and Luenberger 1967, and Simon and Mitter 1968) that, using constant state feedback of the form

$$\mathbf{u} = \mathbf{v} - K_x\mathbf{x} \tag{3}$$

where $\mathbf{v}$ is an $m \times 1$ vector of reference inputs, if the pair $[A, B]$ is completely controllable all of the eigenvalues of the closed-loop system

$$\dot{\mathbf{x}} = (A - BK_x)\mathbf{x} + B\mathbf{v} \tag{4}$$

can be arbitrarily assigned in the s-plane (subject to complex pairing). In fact, for every controllable pair $[A, B]$ and a specified closed-loop eigenvalue pattern, there exists an infinite set of matrices K_x which satisfies this requirement.

The problem of pole assignment using constant output feedback is that of finding a real constant matrix K_y such that the closed-loop system

$$\dot{\mathbf{x}} = (A - BK_yC)\mathbf{x} + B\mathbf{v} \tag{5}$$

has a desired set of eigenvalues.

In a recent paper by Munro and Vardulakis (1973), a simple test in analytic (matrix) terms was given which provided both necessary and sufficient conditions for the assignment of all of the closed-loop system poles using output feedback, and a formula to determine the required output feedback matrix K_y was also given. In this latter paper the output feedback problem was viewed as that of determining an $m \times l$ matrix K_y such that

$$BK_yC = BK_x \tag{6}$$

where the matrices B and C are given, and the $m \times n$ matrix K_x is any one member of the set of state-feedback matrices which achieves the desired pole placement.

These results have now been extended and a set of necessary and sufficient conditions for the existence of an output feedback solution K_y are stated in terms of the given plant A, B and C matrices and the desired closed-loop system matrix A_c. The existence of an appropriate state-feedback solution is implicit in these conditions. However, an explicit solution for the required state-feedback matrix is given.

In the remainder of this paper it is shown that the desired closed-loop system matrix A_c must not only be chosen to have the desired closed-loop eigenvalues but must also be chosen such that the pair $[A_c, B]$ has the same controllability indices as the pair $[A, B]$. This latter constraint is due to a fundamental structure theorem given by Rosenbrock (1970). It is also shown that for an output feedback solution to exist, A_c must in addition be chosen such that the pair $[A_c, C]$ has the same observability indices as the pair $[A, C]$.

Before proceeding to these new results it is useful to first briefly review the previous results obtained using the state-feedback matrix solution K_x.

2. An Analytic Solution

Necessary and sufficient conditions for the matrix equation

$$K_yC = K_x \tag{7}$$

to have a solution for the $m \times l$ matrix K_y can be established in terms of the g_1-inverse (Pringle and Rayner 1971) of the $l \times n$ matrix C. The matrix equation $K_yC = K_x$ is consistent if and only if

$$K_xC^{g_1}C = K_x \tag{8}$$

where

$$CC^{g_1}C = C \tag{9}$$

If the condition given by eqn. (8) is satisfied, then the general solution for K_y is given by

$$K_y = K_xC^{g_1} + Z(I_l - CC^{g_1}) \tag{10}$$

where Z is an arbitrary $m \times l$ matrix. Since Z is arbitrary, it can be set equal to the null matrix, giving K_y simply as

$$K_y = K_xC^{g_1} \tag{11}$$

3. An Explicit Solution for K_x

Luenberger (1967) has shown that given any controllable system $[A, B, C]$ a non-singular transformation T exists such that under this change of basis

$$\tilde{A} = T^{-1}AT \tag{12}$$

has the form

$$\tilde{A} = \begin{bmatrix} \tilde{A}_{11} & \cdots & \tilde{A}_{1m} \\ \vdots & & \vdots \\ \tilde{A}_{m1} & & \tilde{A}_{mm} \end{bmatrix} \tag{13}$$

where the diagonal blocks $\tilde{A}_{ii}$ have the particular companion form

$$\tilde{A}_{ii} = \begin{bmatrix} 0 & 1 & 0 & \cdots & 0 \\ 0 & 0 & 1 & \cdots & 0 \\ \cdot & \cdot & \cdot & & \\ 0 & 0 & 0 & \cdots & 1 \\ X & X & X & \cdots & X \end{bmatrix} \tag{14}$$

where the X's are possibly non-zero and where $\tilde{A}_{ii}$ has dimensions $p_i \times p_i$. The p_i are the controllability indices for the pair $[A, B]$ and satisfy the relationship

$$\sum_{i=1}^{m} p_i = n \tag{15}$$

The off-diagonal blocks $\tilde{A}_{ij}$; $i \neq j$, are null except perhaps for the last row. The matrix $\tilde{B}$ defined by

$$\tilde{B} = T^{-1}B \tag{16}$$

has the special form

$$\tilde{B} = \begin{bmatrix} \tilde{B}_1 \\ \cdot \\ \cdot \\ \cdot \\ \tilde{B}_m \end{bmatrix} \tag{17}$$

where

$$\tilde{B}_i = \begin{bmatrix} & & 0 & & \\ 0 \ldots 0 & & 1 & & X \ldots X \end{bmatrix} \tag{18}$$

$$\uparrow$$
column i

where the X's are possibly non-zero. The matrix C defined by

$$\tilde{C} = CT \tag{19}$$

has no special form.

Now, let

$$\tilde{B} = \bar{B}Q \tag{20}$$

where Q consists of the non-zero rows of $\tilde{B}$, and hence is non-singular, then the blocks $\bar{B}_i$ in $\bar{B}$ have the form

$$\bar{B}_i = \begin{bmatrix} & & 0 & & \\ 0 \ldots 0 & & 1 & & 0 \ldots 0 \end{bmatrix} \tag{21}$$

$$\uparrow$$

$$\text{column } i$$

If we now define the closed-loop system A-matrix as $\bar{A}$ in this new basis, such that $\bar{A}$ has the same block structure as A, then Kalman (1971) has shown that the state-feedback matrix $\bar{K}_x$ required to obtain a desired set of closed-loop eigenvalues can be written down by inspection. The rows of $\bar{K}_x$ are chosen such that the appropriate blocks in $\bar{B}\bar{K}_x$ annihilate the blocks $\tilde{A}_{ij}$ for $i > j$ or for $i < j$ or both, and the appropriate blocks in $\bar{B}\bar{K}_x$ modify the diagonal blocks $\tilde{A}_{ii}$ so that $(\tilde{A} - \bar{B}\bar{K}_x)$ has the desired closed-loop eigenvalues. It is at this point that the constraint due to Rosenbrock's structure theorem (1970) is met, and we are forced, using this approach, to choose the desired closed-loop eigenvalues such that the resulting closed-loop system characteristic polynomial can be factored into polynomials (with real coefficients) which have order equal to the diagonal block sizes in $\tilde{A}$. The required state-feedback matrix in the original basis can then be simply evaluated from

$$K_x = Q^{-1}\bar{K}_x T^{-1} \tag{22}$$

Now, since

$$\bar{B}^t\bar{B} = I_m \tag{23}$$

and a $\bar{K}_x$ can always be found, subject to $[A, B]$ being controllable, such that

$$(\tilde{A} - \bar{A}) = \bar{B}\bar{K}_x \tag{24}$$

in this new basis, we can rewrite (22) as

$$K_x = Q^{-1}\bar{B}^t(\bar{B}\bar{K}_x)T^{-1} \tag{25}$$

i.e.

$$K_x = Q^{-1}\bar{B}^t(\tilde{A} - \bar{A})T^{-1} \tag{26}$$

It is interesting to note that eqn. (26) is the same as the result obtained by Vardulakis (1973) when considering the consistency conditions for the equation

$$\tilde{B}\tilde{K}_x = (\tilde{A} - \bar{A}) \tag{27}$$

to have a solution for $\widetilde{K}_x$. The necessary and sufficient conditions for a solution $\widetilde{K}_x$ to exist are that

$$\widetilde{B}\widetilde{B}^{g_1}(\widetilde{A}-\bar{A}) = (\widetilde{A}-\bar{A}) \tag{28}$$

where B^{g_1} is any g_1-inverse of $\widetilde{B}$. As shown by Pringle and Raynor (1971), if this consistency condition is satisfied, then the general solution for $\widetilde{K}_x$ is given by

$$\widetilde{K}_x = \widetilde{B}^{g_1}(\widetilde{A}-\bar{A}) + (I_m - \widetilde{B}^{g_1}\widetilde{B})Z \tag{29}$$

where Z is any arbitrary $m \times n$ matrix. Since Z is arbitrary, it can be set equal to the null matrix, giving $\widetilde{K}_x$ simply as

$$\widetilde{K}_x = \widetilde{B}^{g_1}(\widetilde{A}-\bar{A}) \tag{30}$$

Now, if B^{g_1} is chosen as the left-inverse of $\widetilde{B}$, defined as

$$\widetilde{B}^{g_1} = (\widetilde{B}^t\widetilde{B})^{-1}\widetilde{B}^t \tag{31}$$

then it can readily be shown that if $\bar{A}$ has the same block structure as $\widetilde{A}$, i.e. $[A_c, B]$ has the same controllability indices as $[A, B]$, the consistency condition given by (28) is automatically satisfied. Also, the K_x resulting from this latter approach is the same as that given by (26).

Now, since

$$\widetilde{B}^{g_1} = B^{g_1}T \tag{32}$$

the consistency condition given by (28) can be rewritten as

$$T^{-1}[BB^{g_1}(A-A_c)]\,T = T^{-1}(A-A_c)T \tag{33}$$

i.e.

$$BB^{g_1}(A-A_c) = (A-A_c) \tag{34}$$

If this condition is satisfied then the required state-feedback solution is given by

$$K_x = B^{g_1}(A-A_c) \tag{35}$$

where A_c must satisfy the conditions stated previously. This result is intuitively obvious since a solution K_x is known to exist if the pair $[A, B]$ is controllable. However, using this approach the constraint due to Rosenbrock's structure theorem must be observed.

4. An Implicit Solution for K_x

Pringle and Rayner (1971) have shown that the necessary and sufficient conditions for the equation

$$BK_yC = (A-A_c) \tag{36}$$

to have a solution for K_y are that

$$BB^{g_1}(A-A_c)C^{g_1}C = (A-A_c) \tag{37}$$

Now, if A_c has been chosen to satisfy (34), then a sufficient condition for a solution K_y to exist is that

$$(A - A_c)C^{g_1}C = (A - A_c) \tag{38}$$

and if both (34) and (38) are satisfied, the required output-feedback matrix K_y is given by

$$K_y = B^{g_1}(A - A_c)C^{g_1} \tag{39}$$

A necessary condition for eqn. (38) to be satisfied is that $[A_c, C]$ has the same observability indices as $[A, C]$. This requirement can be readily verified by transforming A, A_c, C, C^{g_1} to a new basis corresponding to the observable canonical form for the pair $[A, C]$ (see Luenberger, 1967).

The sufficient condition given by (38) was also obtained by Vardulakis (1973) by considering the necessary and sufficient condition for a solution K_y to exist for the equation $K_yC = K_x$. If this condition, as stated in eqn. (8), is satisfied, then substituting in (8) for K_x, as given by (35), the consistency conditions for an output feedback solution can be restated as

$$B^{g_1}(A - A_c)C^{g_1}C = B^{g_1}(A - A_c) \tag{40}$$

Now, eqn. (40) is satisfied if (but not only if) eqn. (38) is satisfied. Here again it is important to note that satisfaction of (34) simultaneously with (40) is implied. Satisfaction of (38) alone, as stated by Vardulakis (1973), is not a sufficient condition.

5. Example

The results given in the previous sections will now be illustrated by means of an example. Consider the controllable and observable system $[A, B, C]$ given by

$$\dot{\mathbf{x}} = \begin{bmatrix} 0 & 1 & 0 \\ -2 & 3 & 0 \\ 5 & 1 & 3 \end{bmatrix}\mathbf{x} + \begin{bmatrix} 0 & 0 \\ 1 & 3 \\ 0 & 1 \end{bmatrix}\mathbf{u} \tag{41}$$

$$\mathbf{y} = \begin{bmatrix} -7 & 0 & 7 \\ 7 & 9 & 0 \end{bmatrix}\mathbf{x} \tag{42}$$

Using the Luenberger transformation $\mathbf{x} = T^{-1}\mathbf{z}$ with

$$T^{-1} = \begin{bmatrix} 1 & 0 & 0 \\ 0 & 1 & 0 \\ -1 & 0 & 1 \end{bmatrix} \quad \text{and} \quad T = \begin{bmatrix} 1 & 0 & 0 \\ 0 & 1 & 0 \\ 1 & 0 & 1 \end{bmatrix} \tag{43}$$

we get

$$\tilde{A} = \left[\begin{array}{cc|c} 0 & 1 & 0 \\ -2 & 3 & 0 \\ \hline 8 & 0 & 3 \end{array}\right], \quad \tilde{B} = \left[\begin{array}{cc} 0 & 0 \\ 1 & 3 \\ \hline 0 & 1 \end{array}\right] \tag{44}$$

and

$$\tilde{C} = \begin{bmatrix} 0 & 0 & 7 \\ 7 & 9 & 0 \end{bmatrix} \tag{45}$$

Here, A and $\tilde{A}$ have eigenvalues $\lambda_1 = 1$, $\lambda_2 = 2$, $\lambda_3 = 3$. Thus, if we wish the closed-loop system to have eigenvalues $\gamma_1 = -3$, $\gamma_2 = -3$, $\gamma_3 = -4$, then a possible choice of the closed-loop system A-matrix might be

$$\bar{A} = \left[\begin{array}{cc|c} 0 & 1 & 0 \\ -9 & -6 & 0 \\ \hline 0 & 0 & -4 \end{array}\right] \tag{46}$$

where the block $\bar{A}_{21}$ has been set equal to zero.

Now, if we require a state-feedback compensator K_x to achieve the desired closed-loop eigenvalues, we find that $\bar{A}$ in the original basis is

$$A_c = T\bar{A}T^{-1} \tag{47}$$

$$= \begin{bmatrix} 0 & 1 & 0 \\ -9 & -6 & 0 \\ 4 & 1 & -4 \end{bmatrix} \tag{48}$$

Since B has maximum rank, a g_1-inverse of B is given by

$$B^{g_1} = (B^tB)^{-1} B^t$$

$$= \begin{bmatrix} 0 & 1 & -3 \\ 0 & 0 & 1 \end{bmatrix} \tag{49}$$

and since $[A_c, B]$ has the same controllability indices as $[A, B]$ the required controller K_x is given by (35) as

$$K_x = B^{g_1}(A - A_c)$$

$$= B^{g_1} \begin{bmatrix} 0 & 0 & 0 \\ 7 & 9 & 0 \\ 1 & 0 & 7 \end{bmatrix}$$

$$= \begin{bmatrix} 4 & 9 & -21 \\ 1 & 0 & 7 \end{bmatrix} \tag{50}$$

This is exactly the same result as that obtained using eqn. (22), i.e.

$$K_x = Q^{-1}\overline{K}_x T^{-1} \tag{51}$$

if $\overline{K}_x$ is specified as

$$\overline{K}_x = \begin{bmatrix} 7 & 9 & 0 \\ 8 & 0 & 7 \end{bmatrix} \tag{52}$$

Now, if $\overline{A}$ is specified such that $\overline{A}_{21} = \widetilde{A}_{21}$, then the corresponding closed-loop matrix A_c is

$$A_c = \begin{bmatrix} 0 & 1 & 0 \\ -9 & -6 & 0 \\ 12 & 1 & -4 \end{bmatrix} \tag{53}$$

and $K_x = B^{g_1}(A - A_c)$ yields

$$K_x = B^{g_1} \begin{bmatrix} 0 & 0 & 0 \\ 7 & 9 & 0 \\ -7 & 0 & 7 \end{bmatrix} = \begin{bmatrix} 28 & 9 & -21 \\ -7 & 0 & 7 \end{bmatrix} \tag{54}$$

which again results in A_c having the desired eigenvalues. However, if we require an output feedback solution, then we must see if the sufficient conditions given by (38) are satisfied. A g_1-inverse of C is

$$C^{g_1} = \begin{bmatrix} 0 & 0 \\ 0 & \frac{1}{9} \\ \frac{1}{7} & 0 \end{bmatrix} \tag{55}$$

and with A_c defined by (48) we have that

$$BB^{g_1}(A - A_c) = \begin{bmatrix} 0 & 0 & 0 \\ 0 & 1 & 0 \\ 0 & 0 & 1 \end{bmatrix} (A - A_c) = (A - A_c) \tag{56}$$

i.e. (34) is satisfied. Therefore, if an output feedback solution exists it is now sufficient to satisfy (38). Thus, we obtain for the left-hand side of (38)

$$(A - A_c)C^{g_1}C = \begin{bmatrix} 0 & 0 & 0 \\ 7 & 9 & 0 \\ 1 & 0 & 7 \end{bmatrix} \begin{bmatrix} 0 & 0 & 0 \\ \frac{7}{9} & 1 & 0 \\ -1 & 0 & 1 \end{bmatrix} \neq (A - A_c) \tag{57}$$

We note here that the observability indices for (A_c, C) are $p_1 = 1$ and $p_2 = 2$, but the observability indices for (A, C) are $p_1 = 2$ and $p_2 = 1$. Thus, although A_c as specified by (48) has the desired closed-loop eigenvalues and satisfies (34), it does not satisfy the condition on the observability indices.

Now, using A_c as defined by (53), we have that (34) is satisfied, i.e.

$$BB^{g_1}(A - A_c) = (A - A_c)$$

and the left-hand side of (38) gives

$$(A - A_c)C^{g_1}C = \begin{bmatrix} 0 & 0 & 0 \\ 7 & 9 & 0 \\ -7 & 0 & 7 \end{bmatrix} \begin{bmatrix} 0 & 0 & 0 \\ \frac{7}{9} & 1 & 0 \\ -1 & 0 & 1 \end{bmatrix}$$

$$= (A - A_c) \tag{58}$$

Therefore, both (34) and (38) are satisfied and the required output feedback solution K_y is given for this choice of A_c by

$$K_y = B^{g_1}(A - A_c)C^{g_1}$$

$$= \begin{bmatrix} -3 & 1 \\ 1 & 0 \end{bmatrix} \tag{59}$$

We note here that (A_c, C) and (A, C) have the same observability indices.

The particular choice of $\bar{A}_{21} = \tilde{A}_{21}$ in $\bar{A}$ as defined by (53) is simply fortuitous. In fact, for A_c specified as

$$A_c = T\bar{A}T^{-1}$$

$$= T \left[\begin{array}{cc|c} 0 & 1 & 0 \\ -9 & -6 & 0 \\ \hline \gamma & \pi & -4 \end{array}\right] T^{-1} \tag{60}$$

$$= \begin{bmatrix} 0 & 1 & 0 \\ -9 & -6 & 0 \\ \gamma + 4 & \pi + 1 & -4 \end{bmatrix} \tag{61}$$

we find that

$$(A - A_c)C^{g_1}C = \begin{bmatrix} 0 & 0 & 0 \\ 7 & 9 & 0 \\ 1 - \gamma & -\pi & 7 \end{bmatrix} C^{g_1}C \tag{62}$$

$$= \begin{bmatrix} 0 & 0 & 0 \\ 7 & 9 & 0 \\ -\frac{7\pi}{9} - 7 & -\pi & 7 \end{bmatrix} \tag{63}$$

and for this to satisfy (38), we have that $-7\pi/9 - 7 = 1 - \gamma$, i.e.

$$\gamma = 8 + \frac{7\pi}{9} \tag{64}$$

We also note that for A_c to satisfy the observability index requirement, the observability matrix Φ_0 for (A_c, C) yields

$$\Phi_0 = \left[\begin{array}{cc:cc} -7 & 7 & 7(\gamma+4) & \\ 0 & 9 & 7\pi & \cdots \\ 7 & 0 & -28 & \end{array}\right] \tag{65}$$

$$\sim \left[\begin{array}{cc:cc} 1 & 0 & * & \\ 0 & 1 & * & \cdots \\ 0 & 0 & \gamma - \frac{7}{9}\pi & \end{array}\right] \tag{66}$$

that is

$$\left.\begin{aligned} &\gamma - \tfrac{7}{9}\pi \neq 0 \\ \text{or} \quad & \\ &\gamma \neq \tfrac{7}{9}\pi \end{aligned}\right\} \tag{67}$$

for (A_c, C) and (A, C) to have the same observability indices.

Here, we recall that a necessary condition for (38) to be satisfied is that the observability index requirement must also be satisfied. For example, if $\bar{A}$ is chosen as

$$\bar{A} = \begin{bmatrix} 0 & 1 & 0 \\ -9 & -6 & 0 \\ 15 & 9 & -4 \end{bmatrix} \tag{68}$$

which satisfies (64), and hence satisfies (67), then

$$A_c = \begin{bmatrix} 0 & 1 & 0 \\ -9 & -6 & 0 \\ 19 & 10 & -4 \end{bmatrix} \tag{69}$$

satisfies both (34) and (38) simultaneously and yields

$$K_y = \begin{bmatrix} -3 & 4 \\ 1 & -1 \end{bmatrix} \tag{70}$$

for the closed-loop eigenvalues to be $\gamma_1 = \gamma_2 = -3$, $\gamma_3 = -4$, as before.

6. Attainable Closed-loop Pole Patterns

As can be seen from the example given in the previous section, it is not easy to satisfy the necessary and sufficient conditions required for an output feedback solution to exist in a given pole assignment problem. However, if these conditions are satisfied, then the required output/feedback matrix is readily determined. It must also be stated that had a different closed-loop system eigenvalue pattern been specified in the illustrative example, then it may not have been possible to achieve this pole set using constant output feedback.

It is interesting to note that if we had left the specification of the non-zero parameters in $\bar{A}$ undefined and observed only the block structure required to satisfy (34), then by forcing the relationships given by (38) to be satisfied a set of m(= number of inputs) root-loci can be generated. These loci show the eigenvalue patterns attainable for the given system under constant output feedback.

For example, if we define $\bar{A}$ as

$$\bar{A} = \begin{bmatrix} 0 & 1 & 0 \\ a & b & 0 \\ c & d & e \end{bmatrix} \tag{71}$$

then in the original basis, we have

$$A_c = \begin{bmatrix} 0 & 1 & 0 \\ a & b & 0 \\ c - e & d + 1 & e \end{bmatrix} \tag{72}$$

giving

$$(A - A_c) = \begin{bmatrix} 0 & 0 & 0 \\ -2 - a & 3 - b & 0 \\ 5 - c + e & -d & 3 - e \end{bmatrix} \tag{73}$$

Now, with C^{g_1} as previously defined by (55), we obtain for the left-hand side of (38)

$$(A - A_c)C^{g_1}C = \begin{bmatrix} 0 & 0 & 0 \\ 7(3 - b)/9 & 3 - b & 0 \\ -\dfrac{7d}{9} - 3 + e & -d & 3 - e \end{bmatrix} \tag{74}$$

and forcing this to be equal to the right-hand side of (38), yields the following equations

$$a = -\frac{13}{3} + \frac{7b}{9} \tag{75}$$

$$c = 8 + \frac{7d}{9} \tag{76}$$

We recall that the eigenvalues of the closed-loop system are determined by the two polynomials

$$(s^2 - bs - a) = 0 \tag{77}$$

$$(s - e) = 0 \tag{78}$$

Thus, substituting (75) into (77), we obtain

$$\left(s^2 + \frac{13}{3}\right) = b\left(s + \frac{7}{9}\right) \tag{79}$$

or

$$\frac{-b(s + \frac{7}{9})}{(s + j2.08)(s - j2.08)} = -1 \tag{80}$$

Equation (80) is easily recognized as the root-locus form for the behaviour of (79) with respect to the parameter b. Thus, by varying b and observing the resulting root-locus and by noting that the third eigenvalue (denoted by e) can assume any wholly real value, we can obtain the attainable closed-loop eigenvalue set for this system under constant output feedback. This is shown in the figure, from which it can be seen that the closed-loop pole set chosen for the illustrative example can be achieved. For instance, $b = -6$ results in $k = -9$ which gives eqn. (77) two equal roots at -3, and $e = -4$ gives the third root at -4 from eqn. (78).

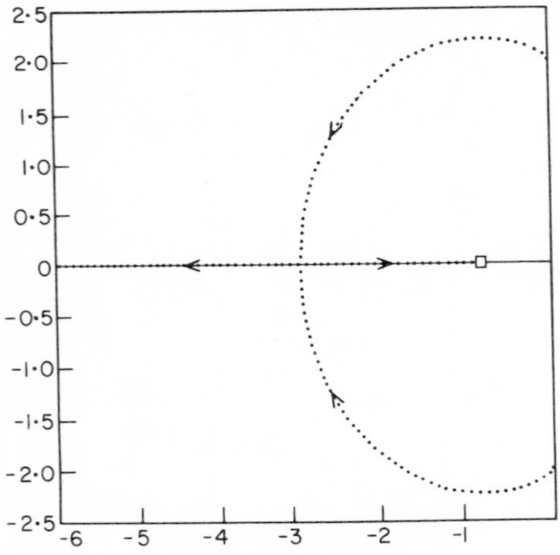

Root-locus of eqn. (80).

7. Conclusions

The results obtained previously by Munro and Vardulakis (1973) have been extended to obtain another set of necessary and sufficient conditions under which a desired closed-loop eigenvalue pattern can be achieved using constant output feedback. A further useful result has been presented in the form of root-locus plots showing the attainable closed-loop eigenvalue patterns. However, it would be useful to explore alternative means of arriving at this latter result which might be more suitable for direct implementation on a digital computer.

Acknowledgments

The author wishes to acknowledge the help obtained in several useful discussions with Professor H. H. Rosenbrock, and also the useful contributions to this work by Mr. A. I. Vardulakis.

References

Anderson, B. D. O., and Luenberger, D. G., 1967, *Proc. Instn elect. Engrs*, **114**, 395.

Kalman, R., 1971, *Ordinary Differential Equations*, edited by L. Weiss (Academic Press), p. 959.

Luenberger, D. G., 1967, *I.E.E.E., Trans. autom. Control*, **12**, 290.

Munro, N., and Vardulakis, A., 1973, *Int. J. Control*, **18**, 1267.

Pringle, R. M., and Rayner, A. A., 1971, *Generalised Inverse Matrices with Applications to Statistics* (Griffin's Statistical Monographs and Courses).

Rosenbrock, H. H., 1970, *State-space and Multivariable Theory* (Nelson).

Simon, D., and Mitter, S. K., 1968, *Inf. Control*, **13**, 316.

Wonham, W. M., 1967, *I.E.E.E., Trans. autom. Control*, **12**, 660.

Vardulakis, A. I., 1973, Ph.D. Thesis, UMIST.

Assignment of Poles and Zeros in a Scalar Transfer Function by State Vector Feedback

P. MURDOCH
Brunel University, Uxbridge, Middlesex, England

Introduction

In some multi-input multi-output linear time-invariant control systems, interest is mainly centred on providing a desired input-output transfer function between one input and one output. The transfer functions between other inputs and outputs are of secondary interest. Such cases lead to consideration of the design of state vector feedback to achieve, as far as possible, a desired scalar input-output transfer function.

The use of unity-rank feedback for this purpose has been considered,[1, 2] but has been shown to be very restrictive, as, with full state vector feedback, a system with r inputs can have at most $(r-1)$ zeros assigned, together with all the poles. This will usually be insufficient to permit the complete specification of a scalar transfer function. The general problem has been considered by Wang and Desoer,[3] who have described a procedure for "exact model matching". This procedure provides conditions for the achievement of specified scalar transfer functions, but gives little guidance as to how to proceed if these conditions are not satisfied.

It is well known that the numerator of a scalar transfer function is unaffected by state vector feedback applied to the input to which the scalar transfer function refers, whereas state vector feedback applied to any other inputs does, in general, affect the numerator of the transfer function. These considerations led to the study of a system with two inputs, as being the most unfavourable case of a multi-input system, in which one input is that to which the desired scalar transfer function refers. The numerator of this transfer function is determined by state vector feedback applied to the other input and, subsequently, the denominator of the transfer function is determined by state vector feedback applied to the original input, without further affecting the numerator.

Two approaches to the problem have been developed. In one, the results of modal control theory for pole assignment are applied to the assignment of zeros as well as poles. In the other approach, the solution is found from a set of linear equations obtained after transformation of the system to a companion form representation.

Since, in most practical cases, the state vector is not available directly for feedback, the problem of providing the two required linear functionals of the state vector by means of a degenerate observer of low order is discussed.

System description

A linear time-invariant system is described by the equations:

$$\dot{x} = Ax + Bu \tag{1}$$

$$y = c^T x \tag{2}$$

where x is a $n \times 1$ state vector, $u = [u_1 u_2]^T$ is a 2×1 input vector, and y is a scalar output. $B = [b_1 \,\vdots\, b_2]$, where the n-vectors b_1 and b_2 are linearly independent. c^T is a constant measurement n-vector. The system is completely controllable through b_2 alone. This latter condition can always be met by the use, if necessary, of suitable feedback initially,[4] if (A, B) is controllable.

Problem statement

The problem is to find the feedback gain vectors k_1^T and k_2^T such that the system:

$$\dot{x} = \left(A + \left[b_1 \,\vdots\, b_2\right]\begin{bmatrix} k_1^T \\ k_2^T \end{bmatrix}\right)x + Bu; y = c^T x \tag{3}$$

has a transfer function between y and u_1 with, as far as possible, specified poles and zeros.

Procedure A

The first procedure,[5] which will now be described, is a generalization of a method [6] developed for the particular case in which $c^T b_1 \neq 0$. This restriction does not apply to the present procedure.

Two sequences of scalars, S_1 and S_2 are formed:

$$S_1 = c^T b_1, c^T A b_1, c^T A^2 b_1, \ldots, c^T A^{p-1} b_1$$

and

$$S_2 = c^T b_2, c^T A b_2, c^T A^2 b_2, \ldots, c^T A^{q-1} b_2.$$

In each case, the sequence terminates at the first non-zero term. The method requires that $q \geqslant p$. If this condition is not satisfied, a proportion h of the input u_1 is added to u_2, so that b_1 becomes $(b_1 + hb_2)$. This will make $q = p$. It will now be assumed that this has been done, if necessary, and that b_1 has been changed accordingly. The procedure is in two stages.

Stage 1

k_2^T is first determined so as to locate the zeros. Let k_1^T be a zero vector at this stage. Using a result obtained by Brockett,[7] the zeros of the transfer function relating y

to u_1 are eigenvalues of the matrix:

$$\left\{I - \frac{b_1 c^T (A + b_2 k_2^T)^{p-1}}{c^T (A + b_2 k_2^T)^{p-1} b_1}\right\} (A + b_2 k_2^T) \tag{4}$$

Since $q \geqslant p$,

$$c^T (A + b_2 k_2^T)^{p-1} = c^T A^{p-1} \tag{5}$$

This is proved in [5]. The matrix (4) may thus be written:

$$A_0 + b_0 k_2^T \tag{6}$$

where:

$$A_0 = \left\{I - \frac{b_1 c^T A^{p-1}}{c^T A^{p-1} b_1}\right\} A$$

$$b_0 = \left\{I - \frac{b_1 c^T A^{p-1}}{c^T A^{p-1} b_1}\right\} b_2 \tag{7}$$

The pair (A_0, b_0) is checked for controllability, using any method that permits the identification of the uncontrollable eigenvalues. Kalman's canonical decomposition method is suitable, as is Gilbert's method, generalized, as necessary, to include multiple eigenvalues. It is proved in [5] that A_0 has the eigenvalue 0 of multiplicity at least p, and that the eigenvalue 0 of multiplicity p is uncontrollable through b_0. The remaining $(n-p)$ eigenvalues of (6) are the zeros of the transfer function. Of these, any that are uncontrollable through b_0 cannot be changed, whilst all the rest may be assigned arbitrarily by using modal control theory [8, 9] to determine k_2^T. The eigenvalue 0 of multiplicity p has no physical significance, and arises only because the degree of the numerator of the transfer function is $(n-p)$.

Stage 2

The system poles will have been changed by the feedback k_2^T, and k_1^T is now determined so as to locate the poles as required. It is first necessary to check for controllability of the pair:

$$((A + b_2 k_2^T), b_1) \tag{8}$$

If this test is satisfied, k_1^T may be found by again using modal control theory, [8, 9] to move the poles to any desired locations. The application of the feedback k_1^T will have no effect on the zeros which were established in Stage 1, because this feedback is applied to the input from which the transfer function is taken.

If the test for controllability of (8) fails, controllability can be achieved by making small adjustments to k_2^T, which means that the zeros in Stage 1 can now be made only arbitrarily close to assigned values, and not necessarily equal to them. This statement is justified by a theorem which is included in [5].

Note

It can be shown, by using the Faddeev-Leverrier algorithm, [10] that, under the conditions stated, the coefficient of the highest power of s, s^{n-p}, in the transfer function numerator polynomial, is $c^TA^{p-1}b_1$, and that this is unaffected by the feedbacks k_1^T and k_2^T. Hence, the numerator and denominator coefficients are completely determined on completion of the procedure described.

Numerical example

The procedure is illustrated by a simple example, in which:

$$A = \begin{bmatrix} 1 & 2 & 0 & 0 \\ 0 & 2 & 0 & 0 \\ 0 & -3 & -1 & 0 \\ 0 & 5 & 0 & -3 \end{bmatrix}; \; b_1 = \begin{bmatrix} 3 \\ 1 \\ 0 \\ 2 \end{bmatrix}; \; b_2 = \begin{bmatrix} 4 \\ 1 \\ 0 \\ 3 \end{bmatrix}$$

$$c^T = [1 \quad -1 \quad 1 \quad -1]$$

The transfer function between y and u_1 is to have zeros at -2 and -4, and poles at $-1.5, -2.5, -3.5$ and -4.5.

Forming the sequences S_1 and S_2 gives:

$$S_1\colon\; c^Tb_1 = 0,\; c^TAb_1 = 1$$

$$S_2\colon\; c^Tb_2 = 0,\; c^TAb_2 = 5$$

Hence $p = q = 2$, so that there will be two zeros and the coefficient of s^2 in the numerator polynomial is 1. Applying (7) to this case gives:

$$A_0 = \begin{bmatrix} -2 & -10 & -3 & 27 \\ -1 & -2 & -1 & 9 \\ 0 & -3 & -1 & 0 \\ -2 & -3 & -2 & 15 \end{bmatrix} : \; b_0 = \begin{bmatrix} -11 \\ -4 \\ 0 \\ -7 \end{bmatrix}$$

A_0 has the eigenvalues 0, 0, 0.101 and 9.899, of which only the last two are controllable through b_0. These are the zeros of the transfer function without feedback. Using modal control theory, the feedback required to move these eigenvalues to -2 and -4 is:

$$k_2^T = [-1.5 \quad 8.125 \quad 0 \quad 0]$$

The matrix $(A + b_2k_2^T)$ then becomes:

$$\begin{bmatrix} -5 & 34.5 & 0 & 0 \\ -1.5 & 10.125 & 0 & 0 \\ 0 & -3 & -1 & 0 \\ -4.5 & 29.375 & 0 & -3 \end{bmatrix}$$

This matrix has the eigenvalues 4.8952, 0.2298, −1 and −3, all of which are controllable through b_1. Again using modal control theory, these eigenvalues are moved to: −1.5, −2.5, −3.5 and −4.5 by the gain vector:

$$k_1^T = [-6.146 \quad 6.433 \quad -2.188 \quad -0.560]$$

This completes the procedure.

Procedure B

This procedure is described in [11], and will be demonstrated by application to the same numerical example as was used in illustrating Procedure A.

The first step is to introduce a new state vector $z = Tx$, such that, with this representation, the system equations (1) and (2) are so transformed that the matrix TAT^{-1} has the companion form shown in (9) for a fourth-order system, and the b_2 vector is transformed into a vector with all elements zero except the last, which is a 1.

$$\begin{bmatrix} 0 & 1 & 0 & 0 \\ 0 & 0 & 1 & 0 \\ 0 & 0 & 0 & 1 \\ -a_0'' & -a_1'' & -a_2'' & -a_3'' \end{bmatrix} \tag{9}$$

The transformation matrix T always exists in this case, because the pair (A, b_2) is controllable. The feedback vector to input u_2, in this representation, becomes $k_2^T T^{-1}$, and the elements of this vector can be written down so as to change the coefficients of the characteristic polynomial of the matrix $(A + b_2 k_2^T)$ to any desired set, $(a_0, \ldots a_{n-1})$.

Let

$$Tb_1 = \begin{bmatrix} b_1 \\ \cdot \\ \cdot \\ b_n \end{bmatrix} \tag{10}$$

and let $c^T T^{-1} = [c_1 \quad \ldots \quad c_n]$.

In this case, the specification of the transfer function relating y to u_1 is given in the form of the coefficients of the numerator and denominator polynomials. Thus, the problem is to find the feedback vectors k_1^T and k_2^T in (3) such that in the transfer function:

$$\frac{\bar{y}}{\bar{u}_1} = \frac{p_{n-1}s^{n-1} + p_{n-2}s^{n-2} + \ldots + p_1 s + p_0}{s^n + a'_{n-1}s^{n-1} + \ldots \quad \ldots + a'_1 s + a'_0} \tag{11}$$

the coefficients $p_0, \ldots, p_{n-2}$ and $a'_0, \ldots, a'_{n-1}$ are, as far as possible, to be given preassigned values. The value of p_{n-1} is $c^T b_1$, and cannot be assigned. In (11), the bar denotes the Laplace transform. The procedure is again in two stages.

Stage 1

In the first stage, k_1^T is set to zero, and k_2^T is determined so as to provide the desired p_j. The required transformation matrix T is:

$$T = \frac{1}{240}\begin{bmatrix} -15 & 69 & 20 & -3 \\ -15 & 33 & -20 & 9 \\ -15 & 141 & 20 & -27 \\ -15 & 57 & -20 & 81 \end{bmatrix} \tag{12}$$

and:

$$T^{-1} = \begin{bmatrix} -18 & -12 & 10 & 4 \\ -3 & -1 & 3 & 1 \\ 9 & -6 & -3 & 0 \\ 1 & -3 & -1 & 3 \end{bmatrix}$$

whence:

$$Tb_1 = \begin{bmatrix} b_1 \\ b_2 \\ b_3 \\ b_4 \end{bmatrix} = \begin{bmatrix} 0.075 \\ 0.025 \\ 0.175 \\ 0.725 \end{bmatrix} \tag{13}$$

and:

$$c^T T^{-1} = [c_1 \quad c_2 \quad c_3 \quad c_4] = [-7 \quad -14 \quad 5 \quad 0] \tag{14}$$

The coefficients $(a_0, \ldots, a_3)$ required are determined from a set of linear equations formed from (13) and (14) by applying the rules given in [11]. These equations are:

$$\begin{bmatrix} (c_1b_1 + c_2b_2 + c_3b_3) & -c_4b_3 & -c_4b_2 & -c_4b_1 \\ (c_1b_2 + c_2b_3) & (c_1b_1 + c_2b_2) & -(c_3b_2 + c_4b_3) & -(c_3b_1 + c_4b_2) \\ c_1b_3 & c_1b_2 & c_1b_1 & -(c_2b_1 + c_3b_2 + c_4b_3) \end{bmatrix} \begin{bmatrix} a_3 \\ a_2 \\ a_1 \\ a_0 \end{bmatrix}$$

$$= \begin{bmatrix} 1 & 0 & 0 \\ 0 & 1 & 0 \\ 0 & 0 & 1 \end{bmatrix} \begin{bmatrix} p_2 \\ p_1 \\ p_0 \end{bmatrix} - \begin{bmatrix} c_1 & c_2 & c_3 \\ 0 & c_1 & c_2 \\ 0 & 0 & c_1 \end{bmatrix} \begin{bmatrix} b_2 \\ b_3 \\ b_4 \end{bmatrix} \tag{15}$$

Inserting the numerical values in equations (15) gives:

$$\begin{bmatrix} 0 & 0 & 0 & 0 \\ -2.625 & -0.875 & -0.125 & -0.375 \\ -1.225 & -0.175 & -0.525 & 0.925 \end{bmatrix} \begin{bmatrix} a_3 \\ a_2 \\ a_1 \\ a_0 \end{bmatrix} = \begin{bmatrix} 1 & 0 & 0 \\ 0 & 1 & 0 \\ 0 & 0 & 1 \end{bmatrix} \begin{bmatrix} p_2 \\ p_1 \\ p_0 \end{bmatrix} - \begin{bmatrix} 1.0 \\ -11.375 \\ -5.075 \end{bmatrix} \tag{16}$$

In the general case, the next step would be a row reduction of equations (16), from which any zero row of the reduced coefficient matrix on the left hand side would yield a linear constraint on the choice of the p_j. The complete set of such constraints must then be satisfied by the chosen set of transfer function numerator coefficients. In this particular case, the only constraint is that $p_2 = 1$. The specified zeros at -2 and -4 then correspond to the requirement that $p_1 = 6$ and $p_0 = 8$. The solution of eqns (16) is non-unique, so that additional specifications could be accommodated. In this case, to permit a direct comparison with the result of Procedure A, two of the eigenvalues of $(A + b_2k_2^T)$ will be specified as -1 and -3. This gives the following set of equations:

$$\begin{bmatrix} 1 & -1 & 1 & -1 \\ 27 & -9 & 3 & -1 \\ 2.625 & 0.875 & 0.125 & 0.375 \\ 1.225 & 0.175 & 0.525 & -0.925 \end{bmatrix} \begin{bmatrix} a_3 \\ a_2 \\ a_1 \\ a_0 \end{bmatrix} = \begin{bmatrix} 1 \\ 81 \\ -17.375 \\ -13.075 \end{bmatrix} \tag{17}$$

which has the solution:

$$\begin{bmatrix} a_3 \\ a_2 \\ a_1 \\ a_0 \end{bmatrix} \begin{bmatrix} -1.125 \\ -16.375 \\ -10.875 \\ 3.375 \end{bmatrix} \tag{18}$$

The coefficients of the characteristic polynomial of A, corresponding to descending powers of s, are $1, -7, -1$ and 6. Hence:

$$k_2^T T^{-1} = [(-3.375 + 6) \quad (10.875 - 1) \quad (16.375 - 7) \quad (1.125 + 1)]$$

and:

$$k_2^T = [-1.5 \quad 8.125 \quad 0 \quad 0] \tag{19}$$

which agrees with the result obtained in Procedure A.

Stage 2

The determination of k_1^T to provide the desired set of denominator coefficients corresponding to the specified transfer function poles may be approached by again transforming the state vector, so that $(A + b_2k_2^T)$ is transformed to the companion form and now b_1 is transformed to a vector with a 1 in the last position and zeros elsewhere. This procedure yields the same result as was given by Procedure A.

Degenerate observer design

The system state vector often will not be available directly, so that, in order to apply the results presented herein, it is necessary to provide an observer, from which reconstructions of the two required linear functionals, $k_1^T x$ and $k_2^T x$, of the state vector, can be obtained. This may be achieved by designing a state observer,[12] from which reconstructions of any desired linear functionals could be obtained. An observer of order $(q - 1)$, with arbitrary dynamics, to provide a single linear functional of the state vector can always be designed, where q is the observability index of the system.[13] A procedure for the design of such an observer, which reveals the degrees of freedom available in the solution, is described in [14]. Further reduction of observer order can be achieved by accepting constraints on the choice of observer poles, and a procedure for the design of a linear functional observer which reveals the constraints on the choice of observer poles imposed by the use of an observer of any order is described in [15]. The general case of designing a degenerate observer to provide a number of linear functionals of the state vector is considered in [16], where a step-by-step design procedure based on the method of [14], is presented. In [17], it is pointed out that, where constraints on the choice of observer poles can be tolerated, further reduction in the order of a degenerate observer can be sought by applying the procedure of [15] at each stage of the procedure.[16] Provided that the observer is stable, and that its speed of response is acceptable at the initial lining-up stage, the presence of an observer does not affect the transfer function as, from this point of view, the system still behaves as if it were of order n.

Conclusion

Two procedures have been described for the design of state vector feedbacks to two inputs of a time-invariant linear system so as to provide, as far as possible, a specified scalar input-output transfer function. Procedure A provides immediate information on the degree of the numerator polynomial, and permits the results of modal control theory to be used directly. Procedure B has the advantage of involving only real arithmetic, and provides information on any constraints on the choice of the coefficients of the transfer function numerator polynomial in the convenient form of a set of linear equations in the coefficients.

Where the system state vector is not available directly, a degenerate observer may be used to provide reconstructions of the required linear functionals, and procedures for the design of such an observer have been discussed.

Acknowledgements

The author is grateful to the IFAC Secretariat for permission to include extracts from reference [5], and to the American Institute of Aeronautics and Astronautics for permission to present the material of references [11] and [15] at the Working Party on Design by Pole-Zero Assignment.

References

[1] Fallside, F. and Patel, R. V., "Pole and zero assignment for linear multivariable systems using unity-rank feedback", *Electron. Lett.*, Vol. 8, pp. 324–325, 1972.

[2] Fallside, F. and Seraji, H., "Design of multivariable systems using unity-rank feedback", *Int. J. Control*, Vol. 17, pp. 351–364, 1973.

[3] Wang, S. H. and Desoer, C. A., "The exact model matching of linear multivariable systems", *I.E.E.E. Trans. Auto. Control*, Vol. AC-17, pp. 347–349, June, 1972.

[4] Davison, E. J. and Wang, S. H., "Properties of linear time-invariant multivariable systems subject to arbitrary output and state feedback", *I.E.E.E. Trans. Auto. Control*, Vol. AC-18, pp. 24–32, February, 1973.

[5] Murdoch, P., "Pole and zero assignment by state vector feedback", *Automatica*, Vol. 11, pp. 199–201, March, 1975.

[6] Murdoch, P., "Pole and zero assignment by proportional feedback", *I.E.E.E. Trans. Auto. Control*, Vol. AC-18, p. 542, October, 1973.

[7] Brockett, R. W., "Poles, zeros and feedback: state space interpretation", *I.E.E.E. Trans. Auto. Control*, Vol. AC-10, pp. 129–135, April, 1965.

[8] Mayne, D. Q. and Murdoch, P., "Modal control of linear time invariant systems", *Int. J. Control*, Vol. 11, pp. 223–227, 1970.

[9] Retallack, D. G. and MacFarlane, A. G. J., "Pole shifting techniques for multivariable feedback systems", *I.E.E. Proc.*, Vol. 117, pp. 1037–1038, 1970.

[10] Gantmacher, F. R., "The theory of matrices", Chelsea Publishing Co., New York, 1960.

[11] Murdoch, P., "Transfer function synthesis by state vector feedback", *A.I.A.A. J.*, Vol. 12, pp. 1765–1767, December, 1974.

[12] Cumming, S. D. G., "Design of observers of reduced dynamics", *Electron. Lett.*, Vol. 5, pp. 213–214, 1969.

[13] Luenberger, D. G., "Observers for multivariable systems", *I.E.E.E. Trans. Auto. Control*, Vol. AC-11, pp. 190–197, April, 1966.

[14] Murdoch, P., "Observer design for a linear functional of the state vector", *I.E.E.E. Trans. Auto. Control*, Vol. AC-18, pp. 308–310, June, 1973.

[15] Murdoch, P., "Low-order observer for a linear functional of the state vector", *A.I.A.A. J.*, Vol. 12, pp. 1288–1289, September, 1974.

[16] Murdoch, P., "Design of degenerate observers", *I.E.E.E. Trans. Auto. Control*, Vol. AC-19, pp. 441–442, August, 1974.

[17] Murdoch, P., "Further comments on 'Observer design for a linear functional of the state vector' ", *I.E.E.E. Trans. Auto. Control*, Vol. AC-19, pp. 620–621, October, 1974.

Multivariable Zeros and their Properties†

R. V. PATEL
NASA Ames Research Center, Moffett Field, California 94035, U.S.A.

Abstract. In this paper some new results concerning zeros of a class of linear, time-invariant, multivariable systems described by the triple (F, G, H) are presented. The zeros are defined as the poles of a system's minimal order right or left inverse (whichever exists). Using a recent factorization procedure for the transfer function matrix of the system (F, G, H), it is shown that the zeros of (F, G, H) are the same as those of a lower order system described by a 4-tuple (A, B, C, D). Some properties of the zeros of (F, G, H) are derived. A method is presented for computing the zeros of invertible systems described by the 4-tuple (A, B, C, D) and examples are given to illustrate the main results of the paper.

1. Introduction

Consider the nth-order, m-input, l-output, linear, time-invariant system described by the equations

$$\dot{x}(t) = Fx(t) + Gu(t) \tag{1a}$$

$$y(t) = Hx(t) + Ju(t) \tag{1b}$$

The transfer function matrix of this system is given by

$$W(s) = H(sI_n - F)^{-1}G + J \tag{2}$$

where I_n is the $n \times n$ identity matrix. For $J \neq 0$ we denote the system (1a–b) by the 4-tuple (F, G, H, J) and for $J = 0$ by the triple (F, G, H). The zeros of (F, G, H, J) and (F, G, H) have been defined in various, mostly equivalent, ways by different researchers.[1–9] The significance of these zeros has been shown by the important part they play in several aspects of control and information theory, e.g. optimal control,[10] system response,[6, 7] model matching,[11, 12] decoupling theory,[3] convolution coding,[13] disturbance rejection,[14] and regulator synthesis.[15, 16]

† This paper is a modified version of the paper entitled "On zeros of multivariable systems" which was published in the International Journal of Control, Vol. 21, No. 4, pp. 599–608, 1975.

The definitions proposed in references 1–4 are applicable to systems described by the triple (F, G, H). Kwakernaak and Sivan[1] have defined the zeros of (F, G, H) in terms of the determinant of $W(s)$; Bengtsson,[2] Morse[3] and Kouvaritakis[4] use geometric state–space concepts. Bengtsson defines the zeros (termed "invariant zeros") of (F, G, H) as the poles of its minimal order right or left inverse (whichever exists). Morse defines the zeros via the "transmission polynomials" of (F, G, H) which consist of the invariant factors of a matrix derived from the system matrices F, G and H. Kouvaritakis obtains the zeros of (F, G, H) as the eigenvalues of a matrix derived using the fact that some of the closed-loop poles approach the zeros as the elements of an output feedback matrix approach infinity.

The definitions given in references 5–9 are applicable to systems (F, G, H, J). Rosenbrock[5] defines the zeros of (F, G, H, J) in terms of the McMillan form of $W(s)$. Davison and Wang[9] use Rosenbrock's system matrix representation for (F, G, H, J) to define its zeros. Desoer and Schulman[6] and Wolovich[7] define the zeros of (F, G, H, J) using a prime factorization of $W(s)$ into a product of a polynomial matrix and the inverse of another polynomial matrix. Moore and Silverman[8] use a Structure Algorithm[17] on the system (F, G, H, J) to obtain a matrix F^*, the invariant factors of which define the numerator polynomials of (F, G, H, J). They have also shown that for the system (F, G, H) these polynomials are the transmission polynomials defined by Morse and for the system (F, G, H, J) they are the numerator polynomials in the McMillan form of $W(s)$. Equivalances between these and other definitions can also be established under certain conditions, e.g. $J = 0$, invertible (F, G, H), no multiple zeros, etc.

In this paper we are concerned with both system (F, G, H) and system (F, G, H, J). We use the definition given by Bengtsson for the zeros of (F, G, H) and define the zeros of (F, G, H, J) in a similar way as the poles of its minimal order right or left inverse (whichever exists). The layout of the paper is as follows: In Section 2 a recent technique[18] for factorizing the transfer function matrix of (F, G, H) is obtained and some of its properties are presented. In Section 3, the factorization is used to show that the zeros of (F, G, H) are the same as those of a lower order system described by a 4-tuple (A, B, C, D). Some properties of the zeros of (F, G, H) are then derived. In Section 4 algorithms are presented for calculating the zeros of systems described by 4-tuples (A, B, C, D) and finally in Section 5 examples are given to illustrate the main results of the paper.

2. Factorization of the Transfer Function Matrix $W(s)$

Consider the nth-order, m-input, l-output, linear, time-invariant system (F, G, H). Assume that (F, G, H) is a minimal realization of $W(s)$. This implies that the pair (F, G) is controllable and the pair (H, F) is observable. Assume further that the matrix H can be partitioned into $[H_1 \;\vdots\; H_2]$ where H_1 is an $l \times l$ matrix of rank l. Any $l \times n$ matrix H having rank l can be brought into this form by a simple coordinate transformation, the effect of which is to rearrange the elements of the state vector $x(t)$. Applying another coordinate transformation defined by

$$z(t) = Tx(t) \tag{3}$$

where $T = \left[\begin{array}{c:c} H_1 & H_2 \\ \hdashline 0 & I_{nl} \end{array}\right]$, $T^{-1} = \left[\begin{array}{c:c} H_1^{-1} & -H_1^{-1}H_2 \\ \hdashline 0 & I_{nl} \end{array}\right]$ and I_{nl} is the $(n-l) \times (n-l)$ identity matrix, the system (F, G, H) becomes

$$\dot{z}(t) = Az(t) + Bu(t) \tag{4a}$$

$$y(t) = Cz(t) \tag{4b}$$

The matrices A, B and C are given by

$$A = TFT^{-1}, B = TG \text{ and } C = HT^{-1} = [I_l \quad 0]$$

where I_l is the $l \times l$ identity matrix. Note that since T is non-singular the transfer function matrix $W(s)$ is invariant under the coordinate transformation defined in eqn. (3). Partitioning A and B in the form

$$A = \left[\begin{array}{c:c} A_{11} & A_{12} \\ \hdashline A_{21} & A_{22} \end{array}\right]\begin{array}{l} l \\ n-l \end{array} \quad \text{and} \quad B = \left[\begin{array}{c} B_1 \\ \hdashline B_2 \end{array}\right]\begin{array}{l} l \\ n-l \end{array}$$
$$\qquad l \qquad\quad n-l$$

the transfer function matrix $W(s)$ can be written as

$$W(s) = [I_l \;\vdots\; 0]\left[\begin{array}{c:c} sI_l - A_{11} & -A_{12} \\ \hdashline -A_{21} & sI_{nl} - A_{22} \end{array}\right]^{-1}\left[\begin{array}{c} B_1 \\ \hdashline B_2 \end{array}\right]$$

From the relation

$$\left[\begin{array}{c:c} sI_l - A_{11} & -A_{12} \\ \hdashline -A_{21} & sI_{nl} - A_{22} \end{array}\right]\left[\begin{array}{c:c} I_l & \underline{0} \\ \hdashline (sI_{nl} - A_{22})^{-1}A_{21} & I_{nl} \end{array}\right]$$

$$= \left[\begin{array}{c:c} sI_l - A_{11} - A_{12}(sI_{nl} - A_{22})^{-1}A_{21} & -A_{12} \\ \hdashline 0 & sI_{nl} - A_{22} \end{array}\right]$$

we have

$$\left[\begin{array}{c:c} sI_l - A_{11} & -A_{12} \\ \hdashline -A_{21} & sI_{nl} - A_{22} \end{array}\right]^{-1} = \left[\begin{array}{c:c} I_l & 0 \\ \hdashline (sI_{nl} - A_{22})^{-1}A_{21} & I_{nl} \end{array}\right]\left[\begin{array}{c:c} Q(s) & -A_{12} \\ \hdashline 0 & sI_{nl} - A_{22} \end{array}\right]^{-1}$$

$$= \left[\begin{array}{c:c} I_l & 0 \\ \hdashline (sI_{nl} - A_{22})^{-1}A_{21} & I_{nl} \end{array}\right]\left[\begin{array}{c:c} Q^{-1}(s) & Q^{-1}(s)A_{12}(sI_{nl} - A_{22})^{-1} \\ \hdashline 0 & (sI_{nl} - A_{22})^{-1} \end{array}\right]$$

where we have substituted $Q(s)$ for $[sI_l - A_{11} - A_{12}(sI_{nl} - A_{22})^{-1}A_{21}]$ and used the well-known result for the inverse of a partitioned matrix. Hence $W(s)$ can be written as

$$W(s) = [I_l \;\vdots\; 0]\left[\begin{array}{c|c} I_l & 0 \\ \hline (sI_{nl} - A_{22})^{-1}A_{21} & I_{nl} \end{array}\right]\left[\begin{array}{c|c} Q^{-1}(s) & Q^{-1}(s)A_{12}(sI_{nl} - A_{22})^{-1} \\ \hline 0 & (sI_{nl} - A_{22})^{-1} \end{array}\right]\left[\begin{array}{c} B_1 \\ \hline B_2 \end{array}\right]$$

$$= [I_l \;\vdots\; 0]\left[\begin{array}{c} Q^{-1}(s)[B_1 + A_{12}(sI_{nl} - A_{22})^{-1}B_2] \\ \hline (sI_{nl} - A_{22})^{-1}B_2 \end{array}\right]$$

$$= Q^{-1}(s)P(s) \tag{5}$$

where

$$Q(s) = sI_l - A_{11} - A_{12}(sI_{nl} - A_{22})^{-1}A_{21} \tag{6}$$

and

$$P(s) = B_1 + A_{12}(sI_{nl} - A_{22})^{-1}B_2 \tag{7}$$

If the matrix G is partitioned into $\left[\begin{array}{c} G_1 \\ \hline G_2 \end{array}\right]$ where G_1 is an $m \times m$ matrix having rank m, and the coordinate transformation

$$\tilde{z}(t) = \tilde{T}x(t) \tag{8}$$

is applied, where $\tilde{T} = \left[\begin{array}{c|c} G_1^{-1} & 0 \\ \hline -G_2G_1^{-1} & I_{nm} \end{array}\right]$, $\tilde{T}^{-1} = \left[\begin{array}{c|c} G_1 & 0 \\ \hline G_2 & I_{nm} \end{array}\right]$ and I_{nm} is the $(n-m) \times (n-m)$ identity matrix, the system (F, G, H) becomes

$$\dot{\tilde{z}}(t) = \tilde{A}\tilde{z}(t) + \tilde{B}u(t) \tag{9a}$$

$$y(t) = \tilde{C}\tilde{z}(t) \tag{9b}$$

The matrices $\tilde{A}$, $\tilde{B}$ and $\tilde{C}$ are given by

$$\tilde{A} = \tilde{T}F\tilde{T}^{-1}, \tilde{B} = \tilde{T}G = \left[\begin{array}{c} I_m \\ \hline 0 \end{array}\right] \text{ and } \tilde{C} = H\tilde{T}^{-1}$$

where I_m is the $m \times m$ identity matrix. Partitioning $\tilde{A}$ and $\tilde{C}$ as

$$\tilde{A} = \begin{array}{c} \left[\begin{array}{c|c} \tilde{A}_{11} & \tilde{A}_{12} \\ \hline \tilde{A}_{21} & \tilde{A}_{22} \end{array}\right] \begin{array}{l} m \\ n-m \end{array} \\ \begin{array}{c|c} \quad m \quad & \quad n-m \quad \end{array} \end{array}, \quad \tilde{C} = \begin{array}{c} [\begin{array}{c|c} \tilde{C}_1 & \tilde{C}_2 \end{array}] \\ \begin{array}{c|c} m & n-m \end{array} \end{array}$$

and following the procedure described above, we obtain the factorization

$$W(s) = R(s)S^{-1}(s) \tag{10}$$

where

$$R(s) = \tilde{C}_1 + \tilde{C}_2(sI_{nm} - \tilde{A}_{22})^{-1}\tilde{A}_{21} \tag{11}$$

and

$$S(s) = sI_m - \tilde{A}_{11} - \tilde{A}_{12}(sI_{nm} - \tilde{A}_{22})^{-1}\tilde{A}_{21} \tag{12}$$

Remark 1. From eqn. (7) it can be seen that $P(s)$ is the transfer function matrix of the following $(n-l)^{\text{th}}$-order, m-input, l-output system denoted by $(A_{22}, B_2, A_{12}, B_1)$

$$\xi = A_{22}\xi + B_2\mu \tag{13a}$$

$$\nu = A_{12}\xi + B_1\mu \tag{13b}$$

Similarly from eqn. (11), $R(s)$ is the transfer function of the $(n-m)^{\text{th}}$-order, m-m-input, l-output system

$$\dot{\tilde{\xi}} = \tilde{A}_{22}\tilde{\xi} + \tilde{A}_{21}\tilde{\mu} \tag{14a}$$

$$\tilde{\nu} = \tilde{C}_2\tilde{\xi} + \tilde{C}_1\tilde{\mu} \tag{14b}$$

Note that systems (13a–b) and (14a–b) are not necessarily of minimal order.

Remark 2. Using the identity for the determinant of a partitioned matrix, i.e.

$$\det \left[\begin{array}{c|c} W & X \\ \hline Y & Z \end{array}\right] = \{\det(Z)\}\{\det(W - XZ^{-1}Y)\}$$

where W and Z are square matrices and Z is nonsingular, it follows that

$$\det(sI_n - A) = \det \left[\begin{array}{c|c} sI_l - A_{11} & -A_{12} \\ \hline -A_{21} & sI_{nl} - A_{22} \end{array}\right]$$

$$= \{\det(sI_{nl} - A_{22})\}\{\det[sI_l - A_{11} - A_{12}(sI_{nl} - A_{22})^{-1}A_{21}]\}$$

$$= \{\det(sI_{nl} - A_{22})\}\det(Q(s))$$

and since $A = TFT^{-1}$, $\det(sI_n - A) = \det(sI_n - F)$. Hence

$$\det(Q(s)) = \frac{\det(sI_n - F)}{\det(sI_{nl} - A_{22})} \tag{15}$$

Similarly it can be shown that

$$\det(S(s)) = \frac{\det(sI_n - F)}{\det(sI_{nm} - \tilde{A}_{22})} \tag{16}$$

Theorem 1.

(i) The pair (A_{12}, A_{22}) is observable.
(ii) The pair $(\tilde{A}_{22}, \tilde{A}_{21})$ is controllable.

Proof of Theorem 1

(i) If a pair (C, A) is observable, the pair (A^T, C^T) is controllable. Now Rosenbrock [5] has shown that the pair (A^T, C^T) is controllable if and only if $sI_n - A^T$ and C^T are relatively left prime, i.e.

$$\text{rank}\,[sI_n - A^T \;\vdots\; C^T] = n$$

for all (complex) s. For the system (4a–b), the pair (C, A) is observable since the pair (H, F) is observable. Hence

$$\text{rank}\left[\begin{array}{c:c:c} sI_l - A_{11}^T & -A_{21}^T & I_l \\ \hdashline -A_{12}^T & sI_{nl} - A_{22}^T & 0 \end{array}\right] = n$$

for all s, which implies that

$$\text{rank}\,[-A_{12}^T \;\vdots\; sI_{nl} - A_{22}^T] = n - l$$

for all s. Consequently the pair (A_{22}^T, A_{12}^T) is controllable and therefore the pair (A_{12}, A_{22}) is observable.

(ii) This result follows directly from the fact that since $(\tilde{A}, \tilde{B})$ is controllable

$$\text{rank}\left[\begin{array}{c:c:c} sI_m - \tilde{A}_{11} & -\tilde{A}_{12} & I_m \\ \hdashline -\tilde{A}_{21} & sI_{nm} - \tilde{A}_{22} & 0 \end{array}\right] = n$$

for all s.

3. Zeros of the System (F, G, H)

In this section we define the zeros of a class of systems described by the triple (F, G, H) and derive some of their properties. The systems which we shall consider are those for which rank $(W(s)) = \min(l, m)$ where the rank of $W(s)$ is defined as the order of its largest minor which is not identically zero. This class therefore corresponds to the class of systems (F, G, H) which are invertible. A system (F, G, H) with rank $(W(s)) = \min(l, m)$ is right invertible for $l < m$ and left invertible for $l > m$; for $l = m$, right and left inverses are the same as the normal inverse. A right inverse of $W(s)$ satisfies the relationship

$$W(s)W_R(s) = I_l \tag{17}$$

and a left inverse satisfies the relationship

$$W_I(s)W(s) = I_m \tag{18}$$

Remark 3. An obvious choice for $W_R(s)$ is

$$W_R(s) = W^T(s)[W(s)W^T(s)]^{-1} \tag{19}$$

and that for $W_L(s)$ is

$$W_L(s) = [W^T(s)W(s)]^{-1}W^T(s) \tag{20}$$

Note that in general $W_R(s)$ and $W_L(s)$ satisfying eqns (17) and (18) respectively are not unique.

Next we define a minimal order right (left) inverse of $W(s)$ as that $W_R(s)(W_L(s))$ which has a characteristic polynomial of lowest degree. A minimal order inverse is also not necessarily unique. We shall use the superscript m, e.g. $W_R^m(s)(W_L^m(s))$ to denote minimal order inverses. The zeros of $W(s)$ can then be defined as follows [2]:

Definition 1. The zeros of $W(s)$ are the poles of $W_R^m(s)$ for $l \leqslant m$ and of $W_L^m(s)$ for $l \geqslant m$.

Remark 4. It can be shown [2] that the characteristic polynomial of a minimal order right (left) inverse divides the characteristic polynomials of all other right (left) inverses. In other words if a complex number p is a pole of a minimal order right (left) inverse then it is also a pole of any other right (left) inverse.

Remark 5. Taking the transpose of both sides of eqns (18) and (20) it can be seen that a left inverse of $W(s)$ is a right inverse of $W^T(s)$. Therefore in the remainder of this section, unless stated otherwise, we shall assume that $l \leqslant m$ and consider only right and normal inverses of $W(s)$. The case $m < l$ can be treated in a similar way by considering the dual system (F^T, H^T, G^T) having the transfer function matrix $W^T(s)$.

Since $l \leqslant m$, $W(s)$ has full rank l and therefore from the factorizations in (5) and (10), the $l \times m$ rational function matrices $P(s)$ and $R(s)$ also have full rank l. Consequently we can express $W_R(s)$ as

$$W_R(s) = P_R(s)Q(s) \tag{21}$$

or

$$W_R(s) = S(s)R_R(s) \tag{22}$$

where the $m \times l$ rational function matrices $P_R(s)$ and $R_R(s)$ are right inverses of $P(s)$ and $R(s)$ respectively and are defined in a similar manner to $W_R(s)$. Denoting the corresponding minimal order inverses by $P_R^m(s)$ and $R_R^m(s)$ the zeros of $P(s)$ and $R(s)$ can be defined in an analogous way to the zeros of $W(s)$:

Definition 2. The zeros of $P(s)$ are the poles of $P_R^m(s)$.

Definition 3. The zeros of $R(s)$ are the poles of $R_R^m(s)$.

Remark 6. Note that $P_R^m(s)$ and $R_R^m(s)$ are the transfer function matrices of minimal order right inverses of $(A_{22}, B_2, A_{12}, B_1)$ and $(\tilde{A}_{22}, \tilde{A}_{21}, \tilde{C}_2, \tilde{C}_1)$ respectively. Consequently if the systems $(A_{22}, B_2, A_{12}, B_1)$ and $(\tilde{A}_{22}, \tilde{A}_{21}, \tilde{C}_2, \tilde{C}_1)$ are minimal realizations of $P(s)$ and $R(s)$ respectively, then their zeros are the same as those of

$P(s)$ and $R(s)$ defined above. However if these systems are not of minimal order, then they have some cancellable poles and zeros and these zeros will not appear as the poles of the corresponding minimal order inverses. Now since the pair (A_{12}, A_{22}) is observable (Theorem 1), the system $(A_{22}, B_2, A_{12}, B_1)$ not having minimal order implies uncontrollability only for the system $(A_{22}, B_2, A_{12}, B_1)$. Similarly, since the pair $(\tilde{A}_{22}, \tilde{A}_{21})$ is controllable, a non-minimal order $(\tilde{A}_{22}, \tilde{A}_{21}, \tilde{C}_2, \tilde{C}_1)$ has only unobservable modes. Using this information we can construct controllable and observable, and therefore minimal order systems $(\hat{A}_{22}, \hat{B}_2, A_{12}, B_1)$ and $(\bar{A}_{22}, \tilde{A}_{21}, \bar{C}_2, \tilde{C}_1)$ which have the same set of zeros as $(A_{22}, B_2, A_{12}, B_1)$ and $(\tilde{A}_{22}, \tilde{A}_{21}, \tilde{C}_2, \tilde{C}_1)$ respectively.

Theorem 2

(i) If the system $(A_{22}, B_2, A_{12}, B_1)$ is a non-minimal realization of $P(s)$, then a minimal order system $(\hat{A}_{22}, \hat{B}_2, A_{12}, B_1)$ can always be constructed such that it has the same set of zeros as $(A_{22}, B_2, A_{12}, B_1)$.

(ii) If the system $(\tilde{A}_{22}, \tilde{A}_{21}, \tilde{C}_2, \tilde{C}_1)$ is a non-minimal realization of $R(s)$, then a minimal order system $(\bar{A}_{22}, \tilde{A}_{21}, \bar{C}_2, \tilde{C}_1)$ can always be constructed such that it has the same set of zeros as $(\tilde{A}_{22}, \tilde{A}_{21}, \tilde{C}_2, \tilde{C}_1)$.

Proof of Theorem 2

(i) Consider the system

$$\dot{\xi}^* = A_{22}^T \xi^* + A_{12}^T u^* \tag{23a}$$

$$y^* = B_2^T \xi^* + B_1^T u^* \tag{23b}$$

which is the dual of system (13a–b). Since the pair (A_{12}, A_{22}) is observable (Theorem 1), the pair (A_{22}^T, A_{12}^T) is controllable. Therefore we can always find a state feedback matrix L^T such that the pair $(B_2^T - B_1^T L^T, A_{22}^T - A_{12}^T L^T)$ is observable. It is well known that state feedback does not affect the controllability of a system, i.e. the pair $(A_{22}^T - A_{12}^T L^T, A_{12}^T)$ is controllable. Hence the system $(\hat{A}_{22}^T, A_{12}^T, \hat{B}_2^T, B_1^T)$ where $\hat{A}_{22}^T = A_{22}^T - A_{12}^T L^T$ and $\hat{B}_2^T = B_2^T - B_1^T L^T$, has minimal order. In the Appendix it is shown that the zeros of the system $(A_{22}^T, A_{12}^T, B_2^T, B_1^T)$ are invariant under state feedback. Therefore the systems $(A_{22}^T, A_{12}^T, B_2^T, B_1^T)$ and $(\hat{A}_{22}^T, A_{12}^T, \hat{B}_2^T, B_1^T)$ have the same set of zeros. To complete the proof we use the fact that a system and its dual have the same set of zeros. Then it follows that $(A_{22}, B_2, A_{12}, B_1)$ and $(\hat{A}_{22}, \hat{B}_2, A_{12}, B_1)$ have the same zeros.

(ii) The proof follows along similar lines to the proof of part (i) using the property that the zeros of $(\tilde{A}_{22}, \tilde{A}_{21}, \tilde{C}_2, \tilde{C}_1)$ are invariant under state feedback (see the Appendix) and the fact that since the pair (A_{22}, A_{21}) is controllable, we can always find a state feedback matrix $\bar{L}$ such that the resulting closed-loop system $(\bar{A}_{22}, \tilde{A}_{21}, \bar{C}_2, \tilde{C}_1)$ is controllable and observable.

Remark 7. As a consequence of Theorem 2, in the rest of the paper we shall assume without loss of generality that the systems $(A_{22}, B_2, A_{12}, B_1)$ and $(\tilde{A}_{22}, \tilde{A}_{21}, \tilde{C}_2, \tilde{C}_1)$ have minimal order.

Theorem 3. The system (F, G, H) has the same set of zeros as

(i) the system $(A_{22}, B_2, A_{12}, B_1)$,
(ii) the system $(\tilde{A}_{22}, \tilde{A}_{21}, \tilde{C}_2, \tilde{C}_1)$.

Proof of Theorem 3. Since (F, G, H) is a minimal realization of $W(s)$, it has the same set of poles and zeros as $W(s)$. From the factorization of $W(s)$ in eqn. (5), we can write

$$[sI_l - A_{11} - A_{12}(sI_{nl} - A_{22})^{-1}A_{21}]\, W(s) = B_1 + A_{12}(sI_{nl} - A_{22})^{-1}B_2 \tag{24}$$

Now from Remark 2, the matrix $[sI_l - A_{11} - A_{12}(sI_{nl} - A_{22})^{-1}A_{21}]$ has poles at the roots of $\det(sI_{nl} - A_{22}) = 0$ and zeros at the roots of $\det(sI_n - F) = 0$. Consequently after cancelling the common poles and zeros at the roots of $\det(sI_n - F) = 0$, the left-hand side of eqn. (24) has zeros at the zeros of $W(s)$ and poles at the roots of $\det(sI_{nl} - A_{22}) = 0$. The term on the right-hand side of eqn. (24) is the transfer function matrix, $P(s)$, of the system $(A_{22}, B_2, A_{12}, B_1)$ and has poles at the roots of $\det(sI_{nl} - A_{22}) = 0$ and zeros at the zeros of $(A_{22}, B_2, A_{12}, B_1)$. Hence result (i) of the theorem follows. Result (ii) can be obtained by a similar argument using the factorization of $W(s)$ in eqn. (10).

Theorem 4. The system (F, G, H) has at most $n - \max(l, m)$ zeros.

Proof of Theorem 4. For the systems $(A_{22}, B_2, A_{12}, B_1)$ and $(\tilde{A}_{22}, \tilde{A}_{21}, \tilde{C}_2, \tilde{C}_1)$ which are invertible, we can always construct inverses such that the inverse characteristic polynomials have degrees less than or equal to $n - l$ and $n - m$ respectively. Then from Definitions 2 and 3, Remark 4 and Theorem 3, the result of the theorem follows.

Theorem 5. The zeros of the system (F, G, H) are invariant with respect to

(i) coordinate transformations,
(ii) state feedback, and
(iii) non-singular input transformations.

Proof of Theorem 5. Result (i) follows directly from the fact that the zeros of (F, G, H) are the zeros of $W(s)$ and that $W(s)$ is invariant under coordinate transformations.

To prove results (ii) and (iii) implement state feedback and input transformations on the system (9a–b), defined by

$$u(t) = Mv(t) - \tilde{K}\tilde{z}(t)$$

where M is an $m \times m$ non-singular matrix. Then carry out a coordinate transformation defined by

$$\bar{z}(t) = \bar{T}\tilde{z}(t)$$

where $\overline{T} = \left[\begin{array}{c|c} M^{-1} & 0 \\ \hline 0 & I_{nm} \end{array}\right]$. This results in the system

$$\dot{\bar{z}}(t) = \left[\begin{array}{c|c} M^{-1}(\tilde{A}_{11} - \tilde{K}_1)M & M^{-1}(\tilde{A}_{12} - \tilde{K}_2) \\ \hline \tilde{A}_{21}M & \tilde{A}_{22} \end{array}\right] \bar{z}(t) + \left[\begin{array}{c} I_m \\ \hline 0 \end{array}\right] u(t)$$

$$y(t) = [\tilde{C}_1 M \;\vdots\; \tilde{C}_2]\bar{z}(t)$$

where we have partitioned $\tilde{K}$ into $[\tilde{K}_1 \;\vdots\; \tilde{K}_2]$ where $\tilde{K}_1$ is an $m \times m$ matrix. The factorization in eqn. (10) becomes

$$W(s) = [\tilde{C}_1 + \tilde{C}_2(sI_{nm} - \tilde{A}_{22})^{-1}\tilde{A}_{21}]\,[sI_m - (\tilde{A}_{11} - \tilde{K}_1) - - (\tilde{A}_{12} - \tilde{K}_2)(sI_{nm} - \tilde{A}_{22})^{-1}\tilde{A}_{21}]^{-1}M$$

Note that the system $(\tilde{A}_{22}, \tilde{A}_{21}, \tilde{C}_2, \tilde{C}_1)$ remains invariant under the state feedback and input transformations and results (ii) and (iii) therefore follow from Theorem 3(ii).

Theorem 6. The system (F, G, H) with $l = m$ and rank $(HG) = l$ has exactly $n - l$ zeros.

Proof of Theorem 6. From the coordinate transformation in eqn. (3), it is easy to see that $HG = B_1$. Hence rank $(HG) = l$ implies rank $(B_1) = l$. By Theorem 3(i) the zeros of (F, G, H) are the same as those of $(A_{22}, B_2, A_{12}, B_1)$. Since B_1 is an $l \times l$ matrix having rank l, the system $(A_{22}, B_2, A_{12}, B_1)$ has a unique inverse given by

$$\dot{\xi} = (A_{22} - B_2B_1^{-1}A_{12})\xi + B_2B_1^{-1}\nu \tag{25a}$$

$$\mu = -B_1^{-1}A_{12}\xi + B_1^{-1}\nu \tag{25b}$$

Now since (by assumption) $(A_{22}, B_2, A_{12}, B_1)$ is a minimal realization of $P(s)$, the system (25a–b) has minimal order. Then from Definition 2 and Theorem 3 it follows that the zeros of (F, G, H) are the eigenvalues of the $(n - l) \times (n - l)$ matrix $(A_{22} - B_2B_1^{-1}A_{12})$.

Remark 8. Theorem 6 can also be proved using the system $(\tilde{A}_{22}, \tilde{A}_{21}, \tilde{C}_2, \tilde{C}_1)$. In this case, from the coordinate transformation in eqn. (8), it can be seen that $HG = \tilde{C}_1$.

4. Computation of the Zeros of Systems (F, G, H) and (A, B, C, D)

Using Theorem 3, the problem of computing the zeros of (F, G, H) is reduced to that of computing the zeros of $(A_{22}, B_2, A_{12}, B_1)$ or $(\tilde{A}_{22}, \tilde{A}_{21}, \tilde{C}_2, \tilde{C}_1)$. In this section we present algorithms for computing the zeros of pth-order, m-input, l-output, invertible systems described by the equations

$$\dot{x}(t) = Ax(t) + Bu(t) \tag{26a}$$

$$y(t) = Cx(t) + Du(t) \tag{26b}$$

We assume that $l \leqslant m$; the case $l > m$ can be treated in a similar way by considering the dual system (A^T, C^T, B^T, D^T).

4.1. Case 1: rank $D = l$ [20]

The general solution for $u(t)$ in eqn. (26b) is given by

$$u(t) = D^+(y(t) - Cx(t)) + (I_m - D^+D)\beta(t) \tag{27}$$

where $D^+ = D^T(DD^T)^{-1}$ is a right inverse of D and $\beta(t)$ is an arbitrary m-vector. Since we are primarily interested in the eigenvalues of the state matrix of a right inverse of (A, B, C, D) or more precisely in the poles of its minimal order right inverse, we can set $\beta(t) = Mx(t)$ without any loss of generality. Then substituting for $u(t)$ from (27) into (26a) yields a general representation of a right inverse of (A, B, C, D) for the case rank $D = l$:

$$\dot{x}(t) = [A - BD^+C + B(I_m - D^+D)M]\, x(t) + BD^+y(t) \tag{28a}$$

$$u(t) = [(I_m - D^+D)M - D^+C]\, x(t) + D^+y(t) \tag{28b}$$

Since the characteristic polynomial of a minimal order inverse divides the characteristic polynomials of all other inverses (Remark 4), it follows that those eigenvalues of the matrix $[A - BD^+C + B(I_m - D^+D)M]$ which remain invariant when M is varied are the poles of a minimal order inverse. In order to determine the order of a minimal order inverse and the location of its poles we consider the following state equation

$$\dot{\eta}(t) = (A - BD^+C)\eta(t) + B(I_m - D^+D)\omega(t) \tag{29}$$

and we note that the state matrix in (28a) is obtained by implementing state feedback on the system (29), defined by the feedback law

$$\omega(t) = M\eta(t) \tag{30}$$

Hence if ρ_c is the rank of the controllability matrix of the pair $[A - BD^+C, B(I_m - D^+D)]$, then $p - \rho_c$ eigenvalues of the state matrix in (28a) will remain invariant under the feedback law in (30). Thus it follows that the order of a minimal order inverse of (A, B, C, D) is $p - \rho_c$. In order to determine the poles of this minimal order inverse we can determine the eigenvalues of the state matrix in (28a) for several different values of M and those $p - \rho_c$ eigenvalues which remain invariant are the required poles. The calculation of the zeros of (A, B, C, D) is summarized by the following algorithm. The notation $\sigma(A)$ is used for the set of eigenvalues of a matrix A.

Algorithm 1

(i) Determine the rank (ρ_c) of the controllability matrix of the pair $[A - BD^+C, B(I_m - D^+D)]$. Then the system (A, B, C, D) has $p - \rho_c$ zeros. If $p = \rho_c$ then (A, B, C, D) has no finite zeros.

(ii) Determine the eigenvalues of $(A - BD^+C)$, i.e. setting $M = 0$.

(iii) Choose a suitably large value of M and determine the eigenvalues of the matrix $A_I = [A - BD^+C + B(I_m - D^+D)M]$. If the set $\sigma_z = \sigma(A - BD^+C) \cap \sigma(A_I)$ contains exactly $p - \rho_c$ eigenvalues, then these eigenvalues are the zeros of (A, B, C, D). If σ_z contains more than $p - \rho_c$ eigenvalues, then repeat this step with a different value for M until σ_z has exactly $p - \rho_c$ eigenvalues. Note that σ_z cannot have less than $p - \rho_c$ eigenvalues.

Remark 9. The above algorithm is also valid for the case $l = m$ and rank $D = l$. In this case the matrix $D^+ = D^{-1}$ and consequently the matrix $B(I_m - D^+D) = 0$ which implies that $\rho_c = 0$ and that the system (A, B, C, D) has exactly p zeros and from steps (ii) and (iii) these are simply the eigenvalues of the matrix $(A - BD^{-1}C)$. This agrees with the result obtained earlier in the proof of Theorem 6 for the system $(A_{22}, B_2, A_{12}, B_1)$ with $l = m$ and rank $B_1 = l$.

4.2. Case 2: rank $D = r_0$ $(<l)$

Consider the following algorithm[17, 19]:

Algorithm 2

(i) Since rank $D = r_0$ $(<l)$, there exists a non-singular $l \times l$ matrix N_0 such that $D_0 = N_0 D = \begin{bmatrix} D_{01} \\ \hdashline 0 \end{bmatrix}$ where D_{01} is an $r_0 \times m$ matrix having rank r_0.

(ii) Define a system $\mathscr{S}_0$ as

$$\dot{x}(t) = Ax(t) + Bu(t) \tag{31a}$$

$$y_0(t) = C_0 x(t) + D_0 u(t) \tag{31b}$$

where $y_0(t) = N_0 y(t)$ and $C_0 = N_0 C$.

(iii) Partition $y_0(t)$ and C_0 conformably with D_0 to get

$$y_{01}(t) = C_{01}x(t) + D_{01}u(t) \tag{32a}$$

$$y_{02}(t) = C_{02}x(t) \tag{32b}$$

Differentiate (32b) with respect to t and substitute for $\dot{x}(t)$ from (31a) to obtain

$$\dot{y}_{02}(t) = C_{02}Ax(t) + C_{02}Bu(t) \tag{33}$$

(iv) Write eqns (32a) and (33) together as

$$\bar{y}_0(t) = \bar{C}_0 x(t) + \bar{D}_0 u(t) \tag{34}$$

where $\bar{y}_0(t) = \begin{bmatrix} y_{01}(t) \\ \hdashline \dot{y}_{02}(t) \end{bmatrix}$, $\bar{C}_0 = \begin{bmatrix} C_{01} \\ \hdashline C_{02}A \end{bmatrix}$ and $\bar{D}_0 = \begin{bmatrix} D_{01} \\ \hdashline C_{02}B \end{bmatrix}$

(v) Let $\bar{D}_0$ have rank r_1; then there exists an $l \times l$ non-singular matrix N_1 such that $D_1 = N_1 \bar{D}_0 = \begin{bmatrix} D_{11} \\ \hdashline 0 \end{bmatrix}$ where D_{11} is an $r_1 \times m$ matrix of rank r_1.

(vi) Define a system $\mathscr{S}_1$ as

$$\dot{x}(t) = Ax(t) + Bu(t) \tag{35a}$$

$$y_1(t) = C_1x(t) + D_1u(t) \tag{35b}$$

where $y_1(t) = N_1\bar{y}_0(t)$ and $C_1 = N_1\bar{C}_0$.

We can now repeat steps (iii)–(vi) to get a system $\mathscr{S}_2$ with rank $(D_2) = r_2$, a system $\mathscr{S}_3$ with rank $(D_3) = r_3$, etc. It can be shown[17, 19] that for invertible systems there always exists an integer $q \leqslant p$ such that $r_q = l$. In other words, for invertible systems the above algorithm terminates at a system $\mathscr{S}_q$ defined by

$$\dot{x}(t) = Ax(t) + Bu(t) \tag{36a}$$

$$y_q(t) = C_qx(t) + D_qu(t) \tag{36b}$$

where rank $(D_q) = l$. Note that $y_q(t) = N_q\bar{y}_{q-1}(t)$, $C_q = N_q\bar{C}_{q-1}$ and $D_q = N_q\bar{D}_{q-1}$ and since rank $(\bar{D}_{q-1}) = l$, we can simply set $N_q = I_l$ without loss of generality.

Remark 10. It can be shown[19] that at least one element of the vector $y_q(t)$ contains the qth derivative with respect to t of an element of $y(t)$.

We can now use the procedure described in Section 4.1 to obtain a general right inverse of the system (36a–b). This is given by

$$\dot{x}(t) = [A - BD_q^+C_q + B(I_m - D_q^+D_q)M]\,x(t) + BD_q^+y_q(t) \tag{37a}$$

$$u(t) = [(I_m - D_q^+D_q)M - D_q^+C_q]\,x(t) + D_q^+y_q(t) \tag{37b}$$

where M is an arbitrary $m \times p$ matrix. The zeros of the system (A, B, C_q, D_q) can then be calculated using Algorithm 1. Defining operators

$$\Gamma_i(t) = \left[\begin{array}{c|c} I_{r_i} & 0 \\ \hline 0 & I_{l-r_i}\dfrac{d}{dt} \end{array}\right], \quad i = 0, 1, \ldots, q-1$$

it is clear that the effect of Algorithm 2 can be expressed as

$$y_q(t) = \{\Gamma_{q-1}(t)N_{q-1} \ldots \Gamma_0(t)N_0\}y(t) \tag{38}$$

Now let $W(s)$ and $W_q(s)$ be the transfer function matrices of the systems (A, B, C, D) and (A, B, C_q, D_q) respectively. Then from (38) it follows that

$$\{\Gamma_{q-1}(s)N_{q-1} \ldots \Gamma_0(s)N_0\}W(s) = W_q(s) \tag{39}$$

where

$$\Gamma_i(s) = \left[\begin{array}{c|c} I_{r_i} & 0 \\ \hline 0 & sI_{l-r_i} \end{array}\right], \quad i = 0, 1, \ldots, q-1$$

From (39) it is clear that the set of zeros of (A, B, C_q, D_q) contains the set of zeros of (A, B, C, D). Hence, having obtained the zeros of (A, B, C_q, D_q), we need to identify those zeros which are also the zeros of the system (A, B, C, D). In order to do this we need the following result:

Theorem 7. Let the system (A, B, C, D) be invertible and let q be the first integer such that $r_q = l$. Define a matrix ϕ_q as

$$\phi_q = \begin{bmatrix} C_{02} \\ \hdashline C_{12} \\ \hdashline \cdot \\ \cdot \\ \cdot \\ \hdashline C_{q-1,2} \end{bmatrix} \tag{40}$$

and let ϕ_q have α_q rows. Then the following results can be proved:

(i) The $\alpha_q \times n$ matrix ϕ_q has full row rank α_q.
(ii) There exists an inverse system representation of (A, B, C, D) whose dynamic portion is of order $p - \alpha_q$.
(iii) The system (A, B, C_q, D_q) has a zero at $s = 0$ of order at least α_q.
(iv) The zeros of (A, B, C, D) are those zeros of (A, B, C_q, D_q) which remain after the α_q zeros at $s = 0$ have been eliminated.

Remark 11. Note that the outputs $y_{i2}(t), i = 0, 1, \ldots, q-1$, can be expressed as

$$\begin{bmatrix} y_{02}(t) \\ y_{12}(t) \\ \cdot \\ \cdot \\ \cdot \\ y_{q-1,2}(t) \end{bmatrix} = \phi_q x(t) \tag{41}$$

Remark 12. Results (i) and (ii) of Theorem 7 have been proved by Silverman[19] for the case $l = m$. Using similar arguments these results can be shown for the case $l < m$ and, using the dual system, for the case $l > m$. Results (iii) and (iv) can be deduced by constructing the reduced inverse in result (ii). The reduced inverse is constructed by using a coordinate transformation on the state vector of the system (A, B, C, D) such that the matrix ϕ_q in (40) has the form $[I_{\alpha_q} \mid 0]$ and then redefining the inputs of the inverse system in (37a–b) as

$$[y_{02}^T \mid y_{12}^T \mid \ldots \mid y_{q-1,2}^T \mid y_q^T].$$

From this construction it can be deduced that the inverse system representation in (37a–b) has at least α_q poles at $s = 0$ and that these poles are eliminated in the construction of the reduced inverse and therefore do not appear as the poles of the reduced inverse.

Remark 13. The reduced inverse of dynamic order $p - \alpha_q$ mentioned above is not necessarily of minimal order. However from Remark 4 it follows that the poles of a minimal order inverse of (A, B, C, D) are also the poles of the reduced inverse.

We can now outline an algorithm for determining the zeros of the system (A, B, C, D) with rank $D = r_0$ $(<l)$.

Algorithm 3.

(i) Obtain the system (A, B, C_q, D_q) using Algorithm 2.
(ii) Determine the zeros of (A, B, C_q, D_q) using Algorithm 1.
(iii) Form the matrix ϕ_q defined in Theorem 7 and check that it has full row rank α_q.
(iv) Eliminate the α_q zeros at $s = 0$ of (A, B, C_q, D_q). Then the remaining zeros of (A, B, C_q, D_q) are the zeros of (A, B, C, D).

5. Numerical Examples

To illustrate the main results of the paper we consider the following examples:

5.1. Example 1

Consider the system[7] (F, G, H) described by the equations

$$\dot{x}(t) = \begin{bmatrix} 0 & 1 & 0 \\ 1 & -1 & 2 \\ 0 & 1 & -3 \end{bmatrix} x(t) + \begin{bmatrix} 0 & 0 \\ 1 & 2 \\ 0 & 1 \end{bmatrix} u(t)$$

$$y(t) = \begin{bmatrix} 1 & 1 & -2 \\ 1 & 0 & 1 \end{bmatrix} x(t)$$

Using the coordinate transformation in eqn. (3) with

$$T = \begin{bmatrix} 1 & 1 & -2 \\ 1 & 0 & 1 \\ 0 & 0 & 1 \end{bmatrix} \quad \text{and} \quad T^{-1} = \begin{bmatrix} 0 & 1 & -1 \\ 1 & -1 & 3 \\ 0 & 0 & 1 \end{bmatrix}$$

the system (A, B, C) results, where

$$A = \left[\begin{array}{cc|c} -2 & 3 & 1 \\ 2 & -2 & 3 \\ \hline 1 & -1 & 0 \end{array}\right], \quad B = \left[\begin{array}{cc} 1 & 0 \\ 0 & 1 \\ \hline 0 & 1 \end{array}\right] \quad \text{and} \quad C = \left[\begin{array}{cc|c} 1 & 0 & 0 \\ 0 & 1 & 0 \end{array}\right]$$

The matrices A_{22}, B_2, A_{12} and B_1 are obtained by partitioning A and B as shown and the system $(A_{22}, B_2, A_{12}, B_1)$ is given by

$$\dot{\xi} = 0\xi + [0 \quad 1]\,\mu$$

$$\nu = \begin{bmatrix} 1 \\ 3 \end{bmatrix} \xi + \begin{bmatrix} 1 & 0 \\ 0 & 1 \end{bmatrix} \mu$$

Since $l = m = 2$ and the matrix B_1 ($= HG$) has full rank l, by Theorem 6, the system (F, G, H) has $n - l = 1$ zero and this is the eigenvalue of $(A_{22} - B_2 B_1^{-1} A_{12})$.

$$A_{22} - B_2 B_1^{-1} A_{12} = 0 - [0 \quad 1] \begin{bmatrix} 1 & 0 \\ 0 & 1 \end{bmatrix} \begin{bmatrix} 1 \\ 3 \end{bmatrix}$$

$$= -3$$

Hence

$$\sigma(A_{22} - B_2 B_1^{-1} A_{12}) = -3$$

and the system (F, G, H) has one zero at $s = -3$ which agrees with the result in reference 7.

5.2. Example 2

Consider the system (A, B, C) described by the equations

$$\dot{x}(t) = \left[\begin{array}{cc:cc} 1 & -1 & 1 & 0 \\ 4 & -5 & 0 & 0 \\ \hdashline -2 & 3 & -6 & 2 \\ 0 & 0 & 1 & -2 \end{array}\right] x(t) + \left[\begin{array}{cc} 0 & 1 \\ 0 & 4 \\ \hdashline 6 & 0 \\ 0 & 0 \end{array}\right] u(t) \tag{42a}$$

$$y(t) = \left[\begin{array}{cc:cc} 1 & 0 & 0 & 0 \\ 0 & 1 & 0 & 0 \end{array}\right] x(t) \tag{42b}$$

Using Theorem 3, the zeros of (A, B, C) are the same as the zeros of the system $(A_{22}, B_2, A_{12}, B_1)$ given by

$$\dot{\xi}(t) = \begin{bmatrix} -6 & 2 \\ 1 & -2 \end{bmatrix} \xi(t) + \begin{bmatrix} 6 & 0 \\ 0 & 0 \end{bmatrix} \mu(t) \tag{43a}$$

$$\nu(t) = \begin{bmatrix} 1 & 0 \\ 0 & 0 \end{bmatrix} \xi(t) + \begin{bmatrix} 0 & 1 \\ 0 & 4 \end{bmatrix} \mu(t) \tag{43b}$$

Note that rank $B_1 = 1$ ($<l$); hence we have to use Algorithm 3 in order to obtain the zeros of $(A_{22}, B_2, A_{12}, B_1)$.

(i) With $N_0 = \begin{bmatrix} 1 & 0 \\ -4 & 1 \end{bmatrix}$ we transform (43b) to get

$$\begin{bmatrix} \nu_{01}(t) \\ \hdashline \nu_{02}(t) \end{bmatrix} = N_0\nu(t) = \begin{bmatrix} 1 & 0 \\ \hdashline -4 & 0 \end{bmatrix} \xi(t) + \begin{bmatrix} 0 & 1 \\ \hdashline 0 & 0 \end{bmatrix} \mu(t)$$

Differentiating $\nu_{02}(t)$ with respect to t and substituting for $\dot{\xi}(t)$ from (43a) yields

$$\dot{\nu}_{02}(t) = [24 \quad -8]\ \xi(t) + [-24 \quad 0]\ \mu(t)$$

Hence we can write $\bar{\nu}_0(t) = \begin{bmatrix} \nu_{01}(t) \\ \hdashline \dot{\nu}_{02}(t) \end{bmatrix}$ as

$$\bar{\nu}_0(t) = \begin{bmatrix} 1 & 0 \\ 24 & -8 \end{bmatrix} \xi(t) + \begin{bmatrix} 0 & 1 \\ -24 & 0 \end{bmatrix} \mu(t)$$

and setting $N_1 = \begin{bmatrix} 1 & 0 \\ 0 & 1 \end{bmatrix}$ and defining $\nu_1(t) = N_1\bar{\nu}_0(t)$ we obtain the system

$$\dot{\xi}(t) = \begin{bmatrix} -6 & 2 \\ 1 & -2 \end{bmatrix} \xi(t) + \begin{bmatrix} 6 & 0 \\ 0 & 0 \end{bmatrix} \mu(t) \tag{44a}$$

$$\nu_1(t) = \begin{bmatrix} 1 & 0 \\ 24 & -8 \end{bmatrix} \xi(t) + \begin{bmatrix} 0 & 1 \\ -24 & 0 \end{bmatrix} \mu(t) \tag{44b}$$

(ii) Using Algorithm 1 (see Remark 10), the zeros of the system (44a–b) are the eigenvalues of the matrix

$$\left\{ \begin{bmatrix} -6 & 2 \\ 1 & -2 \end{bmatrix} - \begin{bmatrix} 6 & 0 \\ 0 & 0 \end{bmatrix} \begin{bmatrix} 0 & 1 \\ -24 & 0 \end{bmatrix}^{-1} \begin{bmatrix} 1 & 0 \\ 24 & -8 \end{bmatrix} \right\}$$

and these are $s = 0$ and $s = -2$.

(iii) Since $q = 1$, we form the matrix ϕ_1 as

$$\phi_1 = [-4 \quad 0]$$

and note that ϕ_1 has full row rank 1, i.e. $\alpha_1 = 1$.

(iv) Therefore we eliminate the zero of (44a–b) at $s = 0$ and the remaining zero, i.e. $s = -2$, is the zero of (43a–b) and hence of the system (42a–b).

5.3. Example 3

Consider the system (A, B, C) described by the equations

$$\dot{x}(t) = \left[\begin{array}{c|cc} -1 & -1 & -1 \\ \hline 0 & -1 & -2 \\ 0 & 0 & -3 \end{array}\right] x(t) + \left[\begin{array}{c|c} 1 & 0 \\ \hline 1 & 1 \\ 1 & 0 \end{array}\right] u(t) \tag{45a}$$

$$y(t) = \left[\begin{array}{c|cc} 1 & 0 & 0 \end{array}\right] x(t) \tag{45b}$$

We shall determine the zeros of this system in two ways.

(a) Using Theorem 3, the zeros of (A, B, C) are the zeros of the system $(A_{22}, B_2, A_{12}, B_1)$:

$$\dot{\xi}(t) = \begin{bmatrix} -1 & -2 \\ 0 & -3 \end{bmatrix} \xi(t) + \begin{bmatrix} 1 & 1 \\ 1 & 0 \end{bmatrix} \mu(t)$$

$$\nu(t) = [-1 \quad -1]\ \xi(t) + [1 \quad 0]\ \mu(t)$$

Since B_1 has full rank, we can use Algorithm 1.

(i)

$$A_{22} - B_2 B_1^+ A_{12} = \begin{bmatrix} 0 & -1 \\ 1 & -2 \end{bmatrix}, \quad B_2(I_m - B_1^+ B_1) = \begin{bmatrix} 0 & 1 \\ 0 & 0 \end{bmatrix}$$

The controllability matrix of the pair $[A_{22} - B_2 B_1^+ A_{12}, B_2(I_m - B_1^+ B_1)]$ is $\left[\begin{array}{cc|cc} 0 & 1 & 0 & 0 \\ 0 & 0 & 0 & 1 \end{array}\right]$ and hence $\rho_c = 2$, which is also the order of the system $(A_{22}, B_2, A_{12}, B_1)$. Hence $(A_{22}, B_2, A_{12}, B_1)$ has no finite zeros.

(b) The example can also be considered as belonging to the case: rank $D = r_0 = 0$ $(<l)$. Hence we can use Algorithm 3 to determine the zeros of (A, B, C).

(i) Using Algorithm 2, the system (A, B, C_1, D_1) is given by

$$\dot{x}(t) = \begin{bmatrix} -1 & -1 & -1 \\ 0 & -1 & -2 \\ 0 & 0 & -3 \end{bmatrix} x(t) + \begin{bmatrix} 1 & 0 \\ 1 & 1 \\ 1 & 0 \end{bmatrix} u(t)$$

$$y_1(t) = [-1 \quad -1 \quad -1]\ x(t) + [1 \quad 0]\ u(t)$$

(ii) Using Algorithm 1, the system (A, B, C_1, D_1) has one zero at $s = 0$.

(iii) The matrix ϕ_1 is given by

$$\phi_1 = [1 \quad 0 \quad 0]$$

Hence $\alpha_1 = 1$.

(iv) Eliminating one zero of (A, B, C_1, D_1) at $s = 0$, we find that the system $(A, B, C, 0)$ has no finite zeros, which agrees with (a).

6. Conclusions

In this paper the zeros of an invertible linear, time-invariant, multivariable system have been defined as the poles of its minimal order right or left inverse (whichever exists). The main result of the paper has been to establish that the zeros of an nth-order, m-input, l-output system (F, G, H) are the same as the zeros of an $(n-l)$th [or $(n-m)$th]-order, m-input, l-output system described by a 4-tuple (A, B, C, D) where the matrices A, B, C and D are obtained from F, G and H following a simple coordinate transformation on the state vector of (F, G, H). Some useful properties of the zeros of (F, G, H) have been derived and algorithms have been presented for computing the zeros of invertible systems described by 4-tuples (A, B, C, D).

7. Acknowledgements

The author wishes to acknowledge the financial support of the University of Cambridge in the form of a research fellowship.

8. Appendix

It is required to show that the zeros of the systems $(A_{22}^T, A_{12}^T, B_2^T, B_1^T)$ and $(\tilde{A}_{22}, \tilde{A}_{21}, \tilde{C}_2, \tilde{C}_1)$ are invariant under state feedback. For notational convenience we consider a pth-order, m-input, l-output system (A, B, C, D). Implementing state feedback on this system we have the closed-loop system $(A - BL, B, C - DL, D)$ where L is the state feedback matrix. The transfer function of the closed-loop system is given by

$$W_c(s) = D + (C - DL)(sI_p - A + BL)^{-1}B \tag{A.1}$$

where I_p is the $p \times p$ identity matrix. Writing $(sI_p - A + BL)^{-1} = [I_p + (sI_p - A)^{-1}BL]^{-1}$ $(sI_p - A)^{-1}$, eqn. (A.1) becomes

$$W_c(s) = D + (C - DL)\,[I_p + (sI_p - A)^{-1}BL]^{-1}(sI_p - A)^{-1}B$$

Using the relation $[I_p + \alpha\beta]^{-1}\alpha = \alpha[I_m + \beta\alpha]^{-1}$ where α and β are $p \times m$ and $m \times p$ matrices respectively, we get

$$\begin{aligned} W_c(s) &= D + (C - DL)(sI_p - A)^{-1}B[I_m + L(sI_p - A)^{-1}B]^{-1} \\ &= D\{I_m - L(sI_p - A)^{-1}B[I_m + L(sI_p - A)^{-1}B]^{-1}\} \\ &\quad + C(sI_p - A)^{-1}B[I_m + L(sI_p - A)^{-1}B]^{-1} \end{aligned} \tag{A.2}$$

The first term on the right-hand side of the above expression can be simplified to yield $D[I_m + L(sI_p - A)^{-1}B]^{-1}$ and noting that the transfer function of the open-loop system (A, B, C, D) is

$$W_0(s) = D + C(sI_p - A)^{-1}B$$

eqn. (A.2) can be written as

$$W_c(s) = W_0(s)[I_m + L(sI_p - A)^{-1}B]^{-1} \tag{A.3}$$

Post-multiplying (A.3) by $[I_m + L(sI_p - A)^{-1}B]$ we get

$$W_c(s)[I_m + L(sI_p - A)^{-1}B] = W_0(s) \tag{A.4}$$

Now

$$\det[I_m + L(sI_p - A)^{-1}B] = \det[I_p + (sI_p - A)^{-1}BL] = \frac{\det(sI_p - A + BL)}{\det(sI_p - A)}$$

Hence $[I_m + L(sI_p - A)^{-1}B]$ has zeros at the roots of $\det(sI_p - A + BL) = 0$ and poles at the roots of $\det(sI_p - A) = 0$. Now the closed-loop system has poles at the roots of $\det(sI_p - A + BL) = 0$ and the open-loop system has poles at the roots of det $(sI_p - A) = 0$. Assuming that the system $(A - BL, B, C - DL, D)$ is of minimal order we can cancel out the common poles and zeros at the roots of $\det(sI_p - A + BL) = 0$ on the left-hand side of eqn. (A.4). From the remaining poles and zeros it is easy to see that the systems $(A - BL, B, C - DL, D)$ and (A, B, C, D) have the same set of zeros.

9. References

[1] Kwakernaak, H. and Sivan, R., "Linear Optimal Control Systems". New York: Wiley, 1972.

[2] Bengtsson, G., "A theory for control of linear multivariable systems", Report 7341, Division of Automatic Control, Lund Institute of Technology, Lund, 1973.

[3] Morse, A. S., "Structural invariants of linear multivariable systems", *SIAM J. Control*, Vol. 11, pp. 447–465, Aug. 1973.

[4] Kouvaritakis, B., 1974, "Characteristic locus method for multivariable feedback system design", Ph.D. Thesis, University of Manchester Institute of Science and Technology.

[5] Rosenbrock, H. H., "State Space and Multivariable Theory". London: Nelson, 1970.

[6] Desoer, C. A. and Schulman, J. D., "Zeros and poles of matrix transfer functions and their dynamical interpretation", *I.E.E.E. Trans. Circuits and Systems*, Vol. CAS-21, pp. 3–8, Jan. 1974.

[7] Wolovich, W. A., "On determining the zeros of state–space systems", *I.E.E.E. Trans. Automat. Contr.*, Vol. AC-18, pp. 542–544, Oct. 1973.

[8] Moore, B. C. and Silverman, L. M., "A time domain characterization of the invariant factors of a system transfer function", Proc. Joint Automatic Control Conference, University of Texas, pp. 186–193, 1974.

[9] Davison, E. J. and Wang, S-H., "Properties and calculation of transmission zeros of linear multivariable systems", *Automatica*, Vol. 10, pp. 643–658, Dec. 1974.

[10] Kwakernaak, H. and Sivan, R., "The maximally achievable accuracy of linear optimal regulators and linear optimal filters", *I.E.E.E. Trans. Automat. Contr.*, Vol. AC-17, pp. 79–85, Feb. 1972.

[11] Moore, B. C. and Silverman, L. M., "Model matching by state feedback and dynamic compensation", *I.E.E.E. Trans. Automat. Contr.*, Vol. AC-17, pp. 491–497, Aug. 1972.

[12] Morse, A. S., "Structure and design of linear model following systems", *I.E.E.E. Trans. Automat. Contr.*, Vol. AC-18, pp. 346–354, Aug. 1973.

[13] Forney, Jr., G. D., "Convolutional Codes I: Algebraic Structure", *I.E.E.E. Trans. Information Theory*, Vol. IT-16, pp. 720–738, Nov. 1970.

[14] Patel, R. V., Sinswat, V. and Fallside, F., " 'Disturbance zeros' in multivariable systems", to be published in *Int. J. Control.*

[15] Pearson, J. B., Shields, R. W. and Staats, Jr., P. W., "Robust solutions to linear multivariable control problems", *I.E.E.E. Trans. Automat. Contr.*, Vol. AC-19, pp. 508–517, Oct. 1974.

[16] Francis, B. A. and Wonham, W. M.,"The role of transmission zeros in linear multivariable regulators", Control Systems Report 7501, Department of Electrical Engineering, University of Toronto, Feb. 1975.

[17] Silverman, L. M. and Payne, H. J., "Input–output structure of linear systems with application to the decoupling problem", *SIAM J. Control.* Vol. 9, pp. 199–233, May 1971.

[18] Patel, R. V., "On a factorization of the transfer function matrix of a multivariable system", *Int. J. Sys. Sci.,* Vol. 7, pp. 369–376, 1976.

[19] Silverman, L. M., "Inversion of multivariable, linear systems", *I.E.E.E. Trans. Automat. Contr.*, Vol. AC-14, pp. 270–276, June 1969.

[20] Sinswat, V., Patel, R. V. and Fallside, F., "A method for computing invariant zeros and transmission zeros of invertible systems", *Int. J. Control,* Vol. 23, pp. 183–196, 1976.

Eigenvalue Assignment by State Feedback in Multi-Input Linear Systems Using the Generalized Control Canonical Form

B. PORTER
Department of Aeronautical & Mechanical Engineering
University of Salford
Salford M5 4WT
England

Abstract. In this paper, a state-feedback eigenvalue-assignment algorithm is presented which is based upon the use of the generalized control canonical form. This algorithm deals directly with multi-input systems and thus obviates the necessity to consider the various incidental but non-trivial difficulties associated with the majority of eigenvalue-assignment algorithms which proceed by reducing multi-input systems to "equivalent" single-input systems.

1. Introduction

Since the equivalence between controllability and eigenvalue assignability by state feedback was established by Popov[1] and Wonham[2], numerous eigenvalue-assignment algorithms have been devised for controllable multi-input time-invariant line systems. However, most of these algorithms proceed by reducing multi-input systems to "equivalent" single-input systems in the interests of computational tractability but thus unfortunately introduce difficulties (such as the need to consider the cyclicity of plant matrices[3, 4]) *not* associated with the original multi-input systems. It is accordingly the purpose of this paper to present an eigenvalue-assignment algorithm which deals directly with multi-input systems and which also relates eigenvalue-assignment directly to the fundamental structural properties of controllable multi-input time-invariant linear systems embodied in the results of Brunovsky[5, 6]: this algorithm is thus based upon the use of the generalized control canonical form[7] in much the same way as the algorithm of Vardulakis[8] is based upon the use of the Luenberger control canonical form[9].

2. Analysis

In the case of a controllable linear system governed by a state equation of the form

$$\dot{\mathbf{x}} = \mathbf{F}\mathbf{x} + \mathbf{G}\mathbf{u} \tag{1}$$

where $\mathbf{x} \in R^n$ and $\mathbf{u} \in R^m$, there exist non-singular matrices $\mathbf{A} \in R^{n \times n}$, $\mathbf{B} \in R^{m \times n}$ and a matrix $\mathbf{L} \in R^{m \times n}$ such that

$$\mathbf{F}_c = \mathbf{A}(\mathbf{F} - \mathbf{GL})\mathbf{A}^{-1} \tag{2}$$

and

$$\mathbf{G}_c = \mathbf{AGB} \tag{3}$$

where the pair $(\mathbf{F}_c, \mathbf{G}_c)$ is the generalized control canonical form[7] of the pair $(\mathbf{F}, \mathbf{G})$. The pair $(\mathbf{F}_c, \mathbf{G}_c)$ is defined by the equations

$$\mathbf{F}_c = \text{diag}\,(\mathbf{F}_{k_1}, \mathbf{F}_{k_2}, \ldots, \mathbf{F}_{k_m}) \tag{4}$$

and

$$\mathbf{G}_c = \text{diag}\,(\mathbf{g}_{k1}, \mathbf{g}_{k2}, \ldots, \mathbf{g}_{k_m}), \tag{5}$$

where $k_1, k_2, \ldots, k_m$ are the control invariants[7] of the pair $(\mathbf{F}, \mathbf{G})$, $\mathbf{F}_{k_j}$ is a $k_j \times k_j$ matrix of the form

$$\mathbf{F}_{k_j} = \begin{bmatrix} 0 & 1 & 0 & \ldots & 0 & 0 \\ 0 & 0 & 1 & \ldots & 0 & 0 \\ \cdots & \cdots & \cdots & \cdots & \cdots & \cdots \\ \cdots & \cdots & \cdots & \cdots & \cdots & \cdots \\ 0 & 0 & 0 & \ldots & 0 & 1 \\ 0 & 0 & 0 & \ldots & 0 & 0 \end{bmatrix}, \tag{6}$$

and $\mathbf{g}_{k_j}$ is an $m \times 1$ vector which is null except for the presence of a unit element in its k_jth row. The integers k_j are uniquely determined by the pair $(\mathbf{F}, \mathbf{G})$ and are identical to Kronecker's minimal column indices[10] for the singular pencil of matrices $(s\mathbf{I} - \mathbf{F}, \mathbf{G})$ when ordered such that $k_1 \geqslant k_2 \geqslant \ldots \geqslant k_m$.

These facts can now be used to determine a state-feedback control law of the form

$$\mathbf{u} = \mathbf{Kx} \tag{7}$$

such that the eigenvalues of the plant matrix $(\mathbf{F} + \mathbf{GK})$ of the closed-loop system governed by eqns (1) and (7) are the n members of the set

$$\Lambda = \Lambda_{k_1} \cup \Lambda_{k_2} \cup \ldots \cup \Lambda_{k_m}, \tag{8}$$

where the k_j members of the set Λ_{k_j} are arbitrary complex numbers (subject only to conjugate complex pairing). In order to determine $\mathbf{K} \in R^{m \times n}$, introduce the block-diagonal matrix

$$\mathbf{F}_d = \text{diag}\,(\mathbf{C}_{k_1}, \mathbf{C}_{k_2}, \ldots, \mathbf{C}_{k_m}) \tag{9}$$

corresponding to $\mathbf{F}_c$ where the eigenvalues of the $k_j \times k_j$ companion-form matrix $\mathbf{C}_{k_j}$ are the members of the set Λ_{k_j}. It is then evident that there exists a matrix $\mathbf{\Gamma} \in R^{m \times n}$ such that

$$\mathbf{F}_c + \mathbf{G}_c\mathbf{\Gamma} = \mathbf{F}_d, \tag{10}$$

where $\mathbf{F}_d$ is the plant matrix of the closed-loop system governed by the state and control-law equations

$$\dot{\boldsymbol{\chi}} = \mathbf{F}_c\boldsymbol{\chi} + \mathbf{G}_c\boldsymbol{\omega} \tag{11}$$

and

$$\boldsymbol{\omega} = \boldsymbol{\Gamma}\boldsymbol{\chi}. \tag{12}$$

Indeed, because eqn. (5) indicates that

$$\mathbf{G}_c{}^T\mathbf{G}_c = \mathbf{I}_m, \tag{13}$$

it follows immediately from eqn. (10) that

$$\boldsymbol{\Gamma} = \mathbf{G}_c{}^T(\mathbf{F}_d - \mathbf{F}_c) \tag{14}$$

Finally, since eqns (11) and (12) are related to eqns (1) and (7) by the transformations

$$\boldsymbol{\chi} = \mathbf{A}\mathbf{x}, \tag{15}$$

$$\mathbf{u} = \mathbf{v} - \mathbf{L}\mathbf{x}, \tag{16}$$

and

$$\mathbf{v} = \mathbf{B}\boldsymbol{\omega}, \tag{17}$$

it is evident from eqns (12), (15), (16) and (17) that the required state-feedback matrix in the control-law eqn. (7) has the form

$$\mathbf{K} = \mathbf{B}\boldsymbol{\Gamma}\mathbf{A} - \mathbf{L} \tag{18}$$

where $\boldsymbol{\Gamma}$ is given by eqn. (14).

The determination of $\mathbf{K}$ such that the eigenvalue spectrum (8) is assigned to the plant matrix of the closed-loop system governed by eqns (1) and (7) is thus seen to be equivalent to the computation of the matrices $\mathbf{A}$, $\mathbf{B}$ and $\mathbf{L}$ which transform the pair $(\mathbf{F}, \mathbf{G})$ to its generalized control canonical form $(\mathbf{F}_c, \mathbf{G}_c)$. This method of eigenvalue assignment is therefore computationally attractive since efficient algorithms [11, 12] exist for this purpose which operate directly on the pair $(\mathbf{F}, \mathbf{G})$ and which accordingly avoid any consideration of the eigenvalues and eigenvectors of the open-loop plant matrix $\mathbf{F}$.

3. Illustrative Example

The eigenvalue-assignment algorithm presented in the previous section can be conveniently illustrated by considering a system governed by a state equation of the form (1) in which

$$\mathbf{F} = \begin{bmatrix} 0 & 0 & 4 & 1 \\ 10 & 13 & 2 & 8 \\ -3 & -3 & 0 & -2 \\ -10 & -14 & -5 & -9 \end{bmatrix} \tag{19}$$

and

$$\mathbf{G} = \begin{bmatrix} -2 & 0 \\ 4 & -3 \\ -1 & 1 \\ -3 & 3 \end{bmatrix} \tag{20}$$

In this case, it is found that when

$$\mathbf{A} = \begin{bmatrix} 1 & 2 & 3 & 1 \\ 1 & 3 & 3 & 2 \\ 2 & 4 & 3 & 3 \\ 1 & 1 & 1 & 1 \end{bmatrix}, \tag{21}$$

$$\mathbf{B} = \begin{bmatrix} 1 & 0 \\ 2 & 1 \end{bmatrix}, \tag{22}$$

and

$$\mathbf{L} = \begin{bmatrix} 1 & 2 & 0 & 1 \\ -1 & 0 & 1 & 0 \end{bmatrix}, \tag{23}$$

eqns (2) and (3) indicate that

$$\mathbf{F}_c = \begin{bmatrix} 0 & 1 & 0 & 0 \\ 0 & 0 & 0 & 0 \\ 0 & 0 & 0 & 1 \\ 0 & 0 & 0 & 0 \end{bmatrix} \tag{24}$$

and

$$\mathbf{G}_c = \begin{bmatrix} 0 & 0 \\ 1 & 0 \\ 0 & 0 \\ 0 & 1 \end{bmatrix} \tag{25}$$

so that $k_1 = k_2 = 2$. Furthermore, if

$$\Lambda_{k_1} = \{-2, -3\} \tag{26a}$$

and

$$\Lambda_{k_2} = \{(-1 + i\sqrt{3})/2, (-1 - i\sqrt{3})/2\} \tag{26b}$$

in the notation of eqn. (8), it is evident that

$$\mathbf{F}_d = \begin{bmatrix} 0 & 1 & 0 & 0 \\ -2 & -3 & 0 & 0 \\ 0 & 0 & 0 & 1 \\ 0 & 0 & -1 & -1 \end{bmatrix} \tag{27}$$

in the notation of eqn. (9). It finally follows immediately from eqns (14), (18), (21), (22), (23), (24), (25), and (27) that the required state-feedback matrix is

$$\mathbf{K} = \begin{bmatrix} -6 & -15 & -15 & -9 \\ -12 & -31 & -35 & -20 \end{bmatrix} \tag{28}$$

4. Conclusion

The state-feedback eigenvalue-assignment algorithm presented in this paper deals directly with multi-input systems and thus obviates the necessity to consider the various incidental but non-trivial difficulties associated with indirect methods of eigenvalue assignment which reduce multi-input systems to "equivalent" single-input systems. It should finally be noted that if some or all of the control invariants k_j are *odd* integers in a situation where it is desired to assign an *even* number of complex eigenvalues, then it is necessary to combine the sets in (8) corresponding to the odd k_j in order to avoid the occurrence of complex numbers in the state-feedback matrix **K**. Such combinations must, of course, be made in accordance with the constraints imposed by the fundamental theorem of state-variable feedback[13].

5. References

[1] Popov, V. M., 1964, "Hyperstability and optimality of automatic systems with several control functions", *Rev. Roum. Sci. Techn.-Electrotechn. Energ.*, **9**, pp. 629–690.

[2] Wonham, W. M., 1967, "On pole-assignment in multi-input controllable linear systems", *I.E.E.E. Trans.*, **AC-12**, pp. 660–665.

[3] Gopinath, B., 1971, "On the control of linear multiple input–output systems", *Bell System Tech. J.*, **50**, pp. 1063–1081.

[4] Seraji, H., 1975, "Cyclicity of linear multivariable systems", *Int. J. Control*, **21**, pp. 497–504.

[5] Brunovsky, P., 1966, "On the stabilization of linear systems under a certain class of persistent perturbations", Differential Equations, 2, pp. 401–405.

[6] Brunovsky, P., 1970, "A classification of linear controllable systems", *Kybernetika*, **3**, pp. 173–187.

[7] Kalman, R. E., 1971, "Kronecker invariants and feedback", Proc. Conf. Ordinary Differential Equations, Washington D.C.

[8] Vardulakis, A. I., 1975, "A sufficient condition for n specified eigenvalues to be assigned under constant output feedback", *I.E.E.E. Trans.*, **AC-20**, pp. 428–429.

[9] Luenberger, D. G., 1967, "Canonical forms for linear multivariable systems", *I.E.E.E. Trans.*, **AC-12**, pp. 290–293.

[10] Rosenbrock, H. H., 1970, "State–space and multivariable theory", (Nelson, London).

[11] Prepelita, V., 1971, "La stabilisation des systèmes linéaires discrets par reaction linéaire", *Rev. Roum. Sci. Techn.-Electrotechn. Energ.*, **16**, pp. 725–737.

[12] Aplevich, J. D., 1974, "Direct computation of canonical forms for linear systems by elementary matrix operations", *I.E.E.E. Trans.*, **AC-19**, pp. 124–126.

[13] Dickinson, B. W., 1974, "On the fundamental theorem of linear state-variable feedback", *I.E.E.E. Trans.*, **AC-19**, pp. 577–579.

Singular Perturbation Methods in the Design of Linear Multivariable Disturbance–Rejection Tracking Systems

B. PORTER
Department of Aeronautical & Mechanical Engineering
University of Salford
Salford M5 4WT
England

Abstract. In this paper, singular perturbation methods are used to provide a basis for the systematic design of disturbance-rejection tracking systems for a class of multivariable linear plants whose time-domain behaviour exhibits both slow and fast modes. These general results are illustrated by designing a simple speed control system for a d.c. motor subjected to a piecewise-constant load torque.

1. Introduction

Singular perturbation methods [1] have been used to develop a computationally attractive method for the design of tracking systems [2] for plants whose time-domain behaviour exhibits both slow and fast modes [3] due to the presence of parasitic elements [4]. It is the purpose of this paper to demonstrate that such tracking systems [2] also function simultaneously as disturbance-rejection systems for plants governed by state and output equations of the respective forms

$$\dot{\mathbf{x}} = \mathbf{A}_{11}\mathbf{x} + \mathbf{A}_{12}\mathbf{z} + \mathbf{B}_1\mathbf{u} + \mathbf{E}_1\mathbf{d}, \tag{1a}$$

$$\epsilon\dot{\mathbf{z}} = \mathbf{A}_{21}\mathbf{x} + \mathbf{A}_{22}\mathbf{z} + \mathbf{B}_2\mathbf{u} + \mathbf{E}_2\mathbf{d}, \tag{1b}$$

and

$$\mathbf{y} = \mathbf{C}_1\mathbf{x} + \mathbf{C}_2\mathbf{z}, \tag{2}$$

where ϵ is a small positive parameter associated with the presence of parasitic elements [4], $\mathbf{x}$ and $\mathbf{z}$ are $n \times 1$ and $m \times 1$ state vectors, respectively, $\mathbf{u}$ is a $p \times 1$ control vector, $\mathbf{y}$ is a $q \times 1$ output vector, $\mathbf{d}$ is an $n \times 1$ constant unmeasurable disturbance vector, $\mathbf{A}_{11}$, $\mathbf{A}_{12}$, $\mathbf{A}_{21}$, and $\mathbf{A}_{22}$ are $n \times n$, $n \times m$, $m \times n$, and $m \times m$ plant matrices, respectively, $\mathbf{B}_1$ and $\mathbf{B}_2$ are $n \times p$ and $m \times p$ input matrices, respectively, $\mathbf{C}_1$ and $\mathbf{C}_2$ are $q \times n$ and $q \times m$ output matrices, respectively, and $\mathbf{E}_1$ and $\mathbf{E}_2$ are $n \times n$ and $m \times n$ disturbance matrices, respectively.

It is shown that, provided the parameter ϵ is sufficiently small, the design of disturbance-rejection tracking systems for $(n + m)$th-order plants with inaccessible states governed by state and output equations of the forms (1) and (2) can frequently be reduced to the design of disturbance-rejection tracking systems for nth-order plants whose state and output equations are derived from eqns (1) and (2) by setting $\epsilon = 0$. Such tracking systems incorporate a controller which is required to cause the $q \times 1$ output vector $\mathbf{y}$ to track a constant $q \times 1$ command input vector $\mathbf{v}$ and simultaneously to reject the constant unmeasurable disturbance vector $\mathbf{d}$ in the sense that, for arbitrary initial conditions,

$$\lim_{t \to \infty} \mathbf{y}(t) = \mathbf{v}. \tag{3}$$

2. Analysis

The first stage in the design of the controller involves the introduction of a vector comparator and a vector integrator in order to generate the $q \times 1$ vector $\mathbf{w}$ defined by the equation

$$\dot{\mathbf{w}} = \mathbf{v} - \mathbf{y}. \tag{4}$$

The second stage in the design of the controller involves the introduction of vector feedback loops in order to generate the $p \times 1$ plant input vector according to the control-law equation

$$\mathbf{u} = \mathbf{K}_1 \hat{\mathbf{x}} + \mathbf{K}_2 \mathbf{w}, \tag{5}$$

where $\mathbf{K}_1$ is a $p \times n$ matrix, and $\mathbf{K}_2$ is a $p \times q$ matrix. The third stage in the design of the controller involves the introduction of a full-order observer in order to generate the $n \times 1$ vector $\hat{\mathbf{x}}$ according to the state equation

$$\dot{\hat{\mathbf{x}}} = \mathbf{A}_0 \hat{\mathbf{x}} + \mathbf{B}_0 \mathbf{u} + \mathbf{L}_0(\mathbf{y} - \mathbf{C}_0 \hat{\mathbf{x}} - \mathbf{D}_0 \mathbf{u}) \tag{6}$$

where [5]

$$\mathbf{A}_0 = \mathbf{A}_{11} - \mathbf{A}_{12}\mathbf{A}_{22}^{-1}\mathbf{A}_{21}, \tag{7a}$$

$$\mathbf{B}_0 = \mathbf{B}_1 - \mathbf{A}_{12}\mathbf{A}_{22}^{-1}\mathbf{B}_2, \tag{7b}$$

$$\mathbf{C}_0 = \mathbf{C}_1 - \mathbf{C}_2\mathbf{A}_{22}^{-1}\mathbf{A}_{21}, \tag{7c}$$

$$\mathbf{D}_0 = -\mathbf{C}_2\mathbf{A}_{22}^{-1}\mathbf{B}_2, \tag{7d}$$

and the $m \times m$ plant matrix $\mathbf{A}_{22}$ is required to be invertible. It is then evident from eqns (1), (2), (4), (5), and (6) that the closed-loop disturbance-rejection tracking system is governed by the state equations

$$\begin{bmatrix} \dot{\mathbf{x}} \\ \dot{\mathbf{w}} \\ \dot{\hat{\mathbf{x}}} \end{bmatrix} = \begin{bmatrix} \mathbf{A}_{11}, & \mathbf{B}_1\mathbf{K}_2, & \mathbf{B}_1\mathbf{K}_1 \\ -\mathbf{C}_1, & \mathbf{O}, & \mathbf{O} \\ \mathbf{L}_0\mathbf{C}_1, & \mathbf{B}_0\mathbf{K}_2 - \mathbf{L}_0\mathbf{D}_0\mathbf{K}_2, & \mathbf{A}_0 + \mathbf{B}_0\mathbf{K}_1 - \mathbf{L}_0\mathbf{C}_0 - \mathbf{L}_0\mathbf{D}_0\mathbf{K}_1 \end{bmatrix} \begin{bmatrix} \mathbf{x} \\ \mathbf{w} \\ \hat{\mathbf{x}} \end{bmatrix}$$

$$+ \begin{bmatrix} \mathbf{A}_{12} \\ -\mathbf{C}_2 \\ \mathbf{L}_0\mathbf{C}_2 \end{bmatrix} \mathbf{z} + \begin{bmatrix} \mathbf{O} \\ \mathbf{I} \\ \mathbf{O} \end{bmatrix} \mathbf{v} + \begin{bmatrix} \mathbf{E}_1 \\ \mathbf{O} \\ \mathbf{O} \end{bmatrix} \mathbf{d}, \tag{8a}$$

$$\epsilon\dot{\mathbf{z}} = [\mathbf{A}_{21}, \quad \mathbf{B}_2\mathbf{K}_2, \quad \mathbf{B}_2\mathbf{K}_1] \begin{bmatrix} \mathbf{x} \\ \mathbf{w} \\ \hat{\mathbf{x}} \end{bmatrix} + \mathbf{A}_{22}\mathbf{z} + \mathbf{E}_2\mathbf{d}, \tag{8b}$$

and therefore that the disturbance-rejection tracking characteristics of the closed-loop system can be determined by invoking the following result:

Lemma [6] In the case of an autonomous system governed by the state equations

$$\dot{\chi} = \Gamma_{11}\chi + \Gamma_{12}\zeta, \tag{9a}$$

$$\epsilon\dot{\zeta} = \Gamma_{21}\chi + \Gamma_{22}\zeta, \tag{9b}$$

let Γ_{22} be a Hurwitz matrix. If

$$\Gamma_0 = \Gamma_{11} - \Gamma_{12}\Gamma_{22}^{-1}\Gamma_{21} \tag{10}$$

is a Hurwitz matrix, then there exists an $\epsilon_0 > 0$ such that, for every $\epsilon \in (0, \epsilon_0]$, the plant matrix

$$\Gamma_\epsilon = \begin{bmatrix} \Gamma_{11}, & \Gamma_{12} \\ \Gamma_{21}/\epsilon, & \Gamma_{22}/\epsilon \end{bmatrix} \tag{11}$$

is Hurwitz.

Indeed, it is now possible to prove the following result:

Theorem. If $\mathbf{A}_{22}$ is a Hurwitz matrix, $(\mathbf{A}_0, \mathbf{B}_0)$ is a controllable pair, $(\mathbf{A}_0, \mathbf{C}_0)$ is an observable pair, and

$$\operatorname{rank} \begin{bmatrix} \mathbf{A}_0, & \mathbf{B}_0 \\ -\mathbf{C}_0, & -\mathbf{D}_0 \end{bmatrix} = n + q, \tag{12}$$

then there exist matrices $\mathbf{K}_1, \mathbf{K}_2$, and $\mathbf{L}_0$ and a positive scalar ϵ_0 such that, for every $\epsilon \in (0, \epsilon_0]$, the steady state of the closed-loop disturbance-rejection tracking system governed by eqns (8) is such that

$$\lim_{t\to\infty} \mathbf{y}(t) = \mathbf{v} \tag{13}$$

for any constant unmeasurable disturbance vector $\mathbf{d}$.

Proof. It may be readily verified that the matrix Γ_0 defined by eqn. (10) is given by

$$\Gamma_0 = \begin{bmatrix} \mathbf{A}_0, & \mathbf{B}_0\mathbf{K}_2, & \mathbf{B}_0\mathbf{K}_1 \\ -\mathbf{C}_0, & \mathbf{C}_2\mathbf{A}_{22}^{-1}\mathbf{B}_2\mathbf{K}_2, & \mathbf{C}_2\mathbf{A}_{22}^{-1}\mathbf{B}_2\mathbf{K}_1 \\ \mathbf{L}_0\mathbf{C}_0, & \mathbf{B}_0\mathbf{K}_2, & \mathbf{A}_0 + \mathbf{B}_0\mathbf{K}_1 - \mathbf{L}_0\mathbf{C}_0 \end{bmatrix} \tag{14}$$

for the system governed by eqns (8). Furthermore, since

$$\begin{bmatrix} I, & O, & O \\ O, & I, & O \\ I, & O, & -I \end{bmatrix} \Gamma_0 \begin{bmatrix} I, & O, & O \\ O, & I, & O \\ I, & O, & -I \end{bmatrix}$$

$$= \begin{bmatrix} A_0 + B_0K_1 & , & B_0K_2 & , & -B_0K_1 \\ -C_0 + C_2A_{22}^{-1}B_2K_1, & & C_2A_{22}^{-1}B_2K_2, & & -C_2A_{22}^{-1}B_2K_1 \\ \cdot\, O & , & O & , & A_0 - L_0C_0 \end{bmatrix}$$

it is evident that the eigenvalues of Γ_0 are the eigenvalues of $(A_0 - L_0C_0)$ together with the eigenvalues of

$$\begin{bmatrix} A_0 + B_0K_1 & , & B_0K_2 \\ -C_0 + C_2A_{22}^{-1}B_2K_1, & & C_2A_{22}^{-1}B_2K_2 \end{bmatrix}$$

$$= \begin{bmatrix} A_0\,, & O \\ -C_0, & O \end{bmatrix} + \begin{bmatrix} B_0 \\ -D_0 \end{bmatrix} [K_1, \quad K_2]. \tag{15}$$

In addition, since (A_0, B_0) is a controllable pair and

$$\text{rank} \begin{bmatrix} A_0\,, & B_0 \\ -C_0, & -D_0 \end{bmatrix} = n + q$$

by hypothesis, it is clear [7] that

$$\left\{ \begin{bmatrix} A_0\,, & O \\ -C_0, & O \end{bmatrix}, \begin{bmatrix} B_0 \\ -D_0 \end{bmatrix} \right\} \tag{16}$$

is a controllable pair. In view of eqn. (15) it therefore follows that matrices K_1, K_2, and L_0 exist such that Γ_0 is Hurwitz, since also (A_0, C_0) is an observable pair by hypothesis. The lemma thus indicates that the plant matrix Γ_ϵ of the autonomous closed-loop tracking system governed by eqns (8) is Hurwitz, since A_{22} is a Hurwitz matrix by hypothesis. It finally follows from eqns (8) that

$$\lim_{t\to\infty} \dot{x}(t) = \lim_{t\to\infty} \dot{w}(t) = \lim_{t\to\infty} \dot{\hat{x}}(t) = \lim_{t\to\infty} \dot{z}(t) = O \tag{17}$$

for any constant vectors v and d, and therefore from eqn. (8a) in particular that

$$O = \lim_{t\to\infty} (-C_1x(t) - C_2z(t)) + v \tag{18}$$

so that

$$\lim_{t\to\infty} y(t) = v, \tag{19}$$

as required.

3. Illustrative Example

These results can be conveniently illustrated by designing a speed control system for a small d.c. motor governed by the respective state and output equations [8]

$$\dot{\mathbf{x}} = -0.08\mathbf{x} + 5.20\mathbf{z} - 4.70\mathbf{d}, \tag{20a}$$

$$\dot{\mathbf{z}} = -205\mathbf{x} - 199\mathbf{z} + 188\mathbf{u}, \tag{20b}$$

and

$$\mathbf{y} = \mathbf{x}, \tag{21}$$

where $\mathbf{x}$ is the motor speed (rad/s), $\mathbf{z}$ is the armature current (A), $\mathbf{u}$ is the armature voltage (V), and $\mathbf{d}$ is the load torque (Nm). It is evident that, by choosing $\epsilon = 0.01$, eqns (20) and (21) can be expressed in the form

$$\dot{\mathbf{x}} = -0.08\mathbf{x} + 5.20\mathbf{z} - 4.70\mathbf{d}, \tag{22a}$$

$$\epsilon\dot{\mathbf{z}} = -2.05\mathbf{x} - 1.99\mathbf{z} + 1.88\mathbf{u}, \tag{22b}$$

and

$$\mathbf{y} = \mathbf{x}, \tag{23}$$

so that

$$\mathbf{A}_{11} = [-0.08], \tag{24a}$$

$$\mathbf{A}_{12} = [5.20], \tag{24b}$$

$$\mathbf{A}_{21} = [-2.05], \tag{24c}$$

$$\mathbf{A}_{22} = [-1.99], \tag{24d}$$

$$\mathbf{B}_1 = [0], \tag{24e}$$

$$\mathbf{B}_2 = [1.88], \tag{24f}$$

$$\mathbf{E}_1 = [-4.70], \tag{24g}$$

$$\mathbf{E}_2 = [0], \tag{24h}$$

$$\mathbf{C}_1 = [1], \tag{24i}$$

and

$$\mathbf{C}_2 = [0], \tag{24j}$$

in the notation of eqns (1) and (2). In view of eqns (24), it clearly follows from eqns (7) that

$$\mathbf{A}_0 = [-5.43678], \tag{25a}$$

$$\mathbf{B}_0 = [4.91256], \tag{25b}$$

$$\mathbf{C}_0 = [1], \tag{25c}$$

and

$$\mathbf{D}_0 = [0], \tag{25d}$$

which obviously satisfy the hypotheses of the theorem.

Indeed, it can readily be verified that the characteristic polynomial of the matrix Γ_0 defined by eqn. (14) assumes the form

$$c(\lambda) = (\lambda + 10)(\lambda^2 + 10\lambda + 30) \tag{26}$$

in case the observer and stabilizing controller are selected such that

$$\mathbf{L}_0 = [4.56322], \tag{27a}$$

$$\mathbf{K}_1 = [-0.92889], \tag{27b}$$

and

$$\mathbf{K}_2 = [6.10679]. \tag{27c}$$

It thus finally follows from eqns (8) that, since $\epsilon = 0.01$, the speed control system for the d.c. motor is governed by the state equation

$$\begin{bmatrix} \dot{\mathbf{x}} \\ \dot{\mathbf{w}} \\ \dot{\hat{\mathbf{x}}} \\ \dot{\mathbf{z}} \end{bmatrix} = \begin{bmatrix} -0.08, & 0, & 0, & 5.20 \\ -1, & 0, & 0, & 0 \\ 4.56322, & 30, & -14.56322, & 0 \\ -205, & 1148.08, & -174.631, & -199 \end{bmatrix} \begin{bmatrix} \mathbf{x} \\ \mathbf{w} \\ \hat{\mathbf{x}} \\ \mathbf{z} \end{bmatrix} + \begin{bmatrix} 0 \\ 1 \\ 0 \\ 0 \end{bmatrix} \mathbf{v} + \begin{bmatrix} -4.70 \\ 0 \\ 0 \\ 0 \end{bmatrix} \mathbf{d} \tag{28}$$

which implies that the eigenvalue spectrum of the plant matrix of the closed-loop system is given by

$$\Sigma = \{-9.04874, -5.40770 \pm 2.19180i, -193.779\}. \tag{29}$$

The excellent disturbance-rejection and tracking characteristics of this system are demonstrated by the computer simulation results shown in Figs 1 and 2. It is evident from Fig. 1 that the set-point speed commands shown in Fig. 3 are followed faithfully in the face of the piecewise-constant load-torque variations shown in Fig. 4, whilst it is clear from Fig. 2 that the consequential changes in armature current exhibit no unacceptably large transients.

4. Conclusions

In this paper, a theorem has been presented which provides a basis for the systematic design of disturbance-rejection tracking systems for a class of multivariable linear plants whose time-domain behaviour exhibits both slow and fast modes due to the presence of parasitic elements. The practical significance of this theorem lies principally in the fact that the control-law eqn. (5) and the observer state eqn. (6) are independent of both $\mathbf{z}$ and ϵ. The computational significance of this theorem

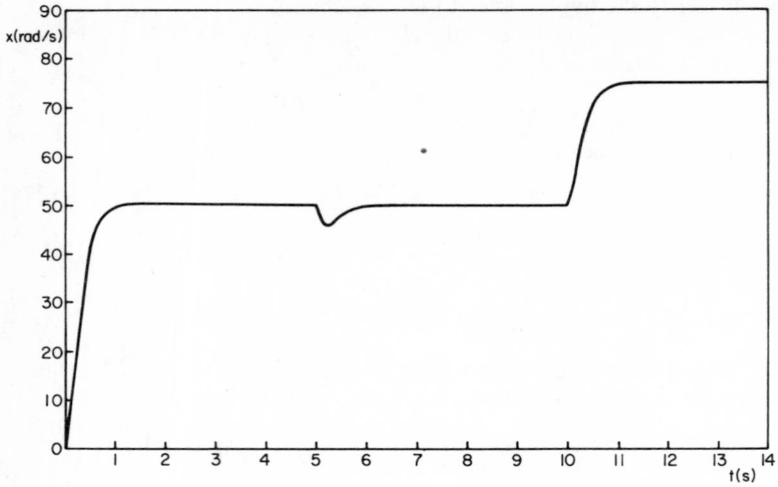

Fig. 1: Motor speed.

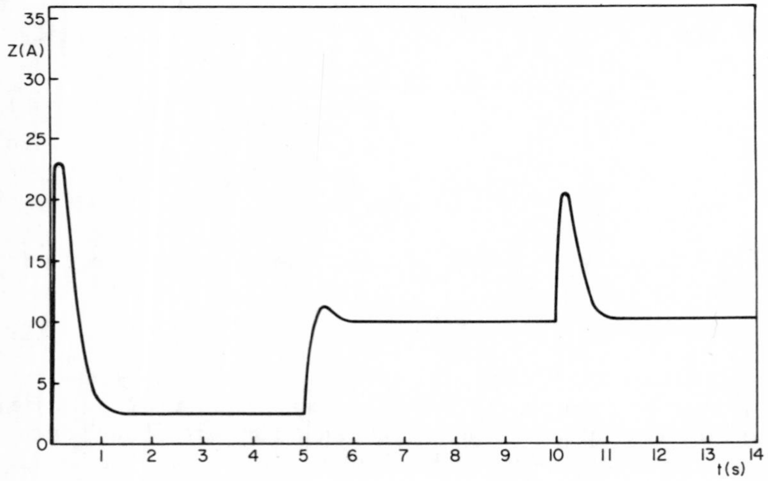

Fig. 2: Motor armature current.

lies principally in the fact that it reduces the design of $(2n + m + q)$th-order closed-loop disturbance-rejection tracking systems for $(n + m)$th-order plants with inaccessible states governed by state and output equations of the forms (1) and (2) (when ϵ is sufficiently small and $\mathbf{A}_{22}$ is Hurwitz) to the separate design by conventional methods of nth-order observers and $(n + q)$th-order stabilizing controllers. These general results have been illustrated by designing a simple speed control system for a d.c. motor subjected to a piecewise-constant load torque.

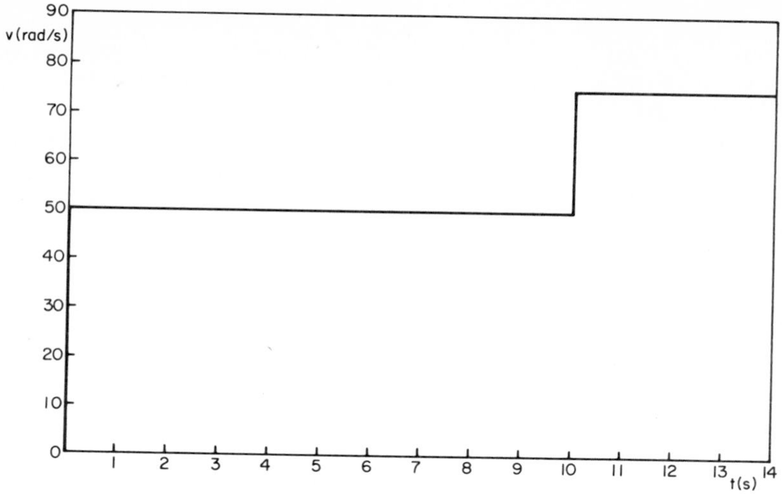

Fig. 3: Motor speed command input.

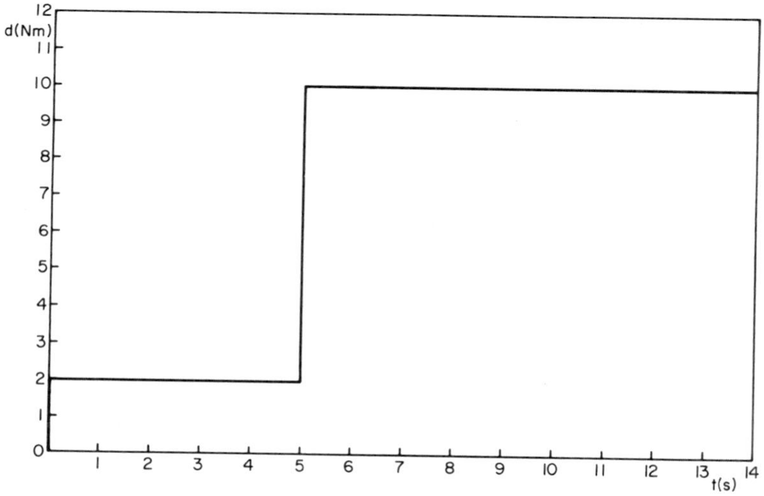

Fig. 4: Motor load torque.

References

[1] Kokotovic, P. V. and Perkins, W. R. (Eds.), 1972, *Singular perturbations: order reduction in control system design*, American Society of Mechanical Engineers, New York.

[2] Porter, B., 1976, "Singular perturbation methods in the design of linear multivariable tracking systems", *Electronics Letters*, **12**, pp. 33–34.

[3] Porter, B., 1975, "Dynamical characteristics of multivariable linear systems with slow and fast modes", *Proc. Fourth World Congress on the Theory of Machines and Mechanisms*, Newcastle-upon-Tyne, England, pp. 987–990.

[4] Shensa, M. J., 1971, "Parasitics and the stability of equilibrium points of non-linear networks", *I.E.E.E. Trans.*, **CT-18**, pp. 481–484.

[5] Porter, B., 1974, "Singular perturbation methods in the design of observers and stabilising feedback controllers for multivariable linear systems", *Electronics Letters*, **10**, pp. 494–495.

[6] Klimushev, A. I. and Krasovskii, N. N., 1961, "Uniform asymptotic stability of systems of differential equations with a small parameter in the derivative terms", *Prikl. Mat. and Mekh*, **25**, pp. 680–690.

[7] Porter, B. and Bradshaw, A., 1974, "Design of linear multivariable continuous-time tracking systems", *Int. J. Systems Sci.*, **5**, pp. 1155–1164.

[8] Smith, H. W. and Davison, E. J., 1972, "Design of industrial regulators: integral feedback and feedforward control", *Proc. I.E.E.*, **119**, pp. 1210–1216.

New Approaches to Eigenvalue Assignment by Output Feedback and Numerator Control by State Feedback

HENRY M. POWER
Department of Electrical Engineering, University of Salford, Salford M5 4WT, England

Abstract. This chapter explores the eigenvalue assignment problem for the system $\frac{dx}{dt} = Ax + Bu, y = Dx, u = u_0 + q \cdot p^T y$, using a novel formulation in which the feedback matrix appears in the Kronecker product $p \otimes q$. The elements of both p and q are treated simultaneously as variables, in an attempt to arrive at the closest approximation to a desired spectrum of eigenvalues. Using a more general full rank state feedback, $u = u_0 + Kx$, the problem of shaping the numerators of the transfer function matrix is approached by identifying a class of variations which can be made to K without affecting the eigenvalues.

At the meeting on which this book is based, my colleagues had to endure the exposition of two ideas which occurred to me during the preceding few months. The first concerns the extent to which eigenvalues can be assigned by means of dyadic (unity rank) output feedback; the second deals with the control – admittedly to a very limited extent – of the numerators in a transfer function matrix, by exploiting freedom to vary parameters in a state feedback law in such a way as not to disturb the eigenvalues. Since the paper on the first idea has since appeared in print,[1] I wish to avail of this opportunity to expound a few additional ideas and insights obtained in the intervening period. My ideas on numerator control have remained stagnant, however (for which be thankful) and so the sections on that topic are merely condensations of material presented to the working party.

1. Kronecker Products in Eigenvalue Assignment

1.1. Review of some basic results

The system considered is the familiar nth order, m input, l output completely state controllable and observable linear system

$$\frac{dx}{dt} = Ax + Bu$$

$$y = Dx \qquad (1)$$

subject to the dyadic feedback law

$$u = u_0 + q \cdot p^T x \qquad (2)$$

The restrictions $l, m < n$, rank $D = l$, rank $B = m$ are imposed in order to ensure that no inputs or output measurements are redundant.

A celebrated theorem, originally due to Davison[2] and refined by him and several other workers,[3, 4, 5] guarantees that, if A is cyclic, at least max (l, m) eigenvalues can be assigned to locations which are arbitrarily close to (but not necessarily coincident with) locations specified at will, subject of course to complex pairing. In proving that at least l eigenvalues can be prescribed, q is first chosen – and this choice is almost arbitrary[6] – in order that (A, Bq) is a controllable pair and it is found that p can then be selected to place the desired l eigenvalues. In proving that at least m eigenvalues can be prescribed, p^T is chosen so that $(A, p^T D)$ is an observable pair and q can then be chosen to place m eigenvalues. This procedure begs the question "what can be achieved by treating the m elements of q and the l elements of p^T as variables simultaneously?" In fact since, if λ is any scalar, we have $qp^T = \left(\frac{1}{\lambda} q\right)(\lambda p^T)$, any non zero element of q or p^T may be set to a convenient value (e.g. unity), and this means that the feedback law considered is completely determined by the values of $m + l - 1$ parameters. Thus, it is tempting to speculate that, under the most favourable conditions, up to min $(n, m + l - 1)$ eigenvalues could be arbitrarily assignable. Sridhar and Lindorff, indeed, showed by example[7] that the Davison theorem sets only a lower limit, but undertook no detailed analysis.

The key to a systematic study of the extent of eigenvalue assignability is a formulation in which the column vectors p and q enter on an equal footing. Such a formulation was developed in [1]. It was shown there that if

$$P(s) = \det(sI - A) = s^n + a_{n-1}s^{n-1} + \ldots + a_1 s + a_0 \qquad (3)$$

and

$$\hat{P}(s) = \det(sI - A - Bq \,.\, p^T D) = s^n + \hat{a}_{n-1}s^{n-1} + \ldots + \hat{a}_1 s + \hat{a}_0 \qquad (4)$$

the vector of changes in the characteristic polynomial

$$\sigma = \text{column}\,[a_0 - \hat{a}_0, a_1 - \hat{a}_1, \ldots, a_{n-1} - \hat{a}_{n-1}] \qquad (5)$$

could be expressed as

$$\sigma = SG\, p \otimes q \qquad (6)$$

where $p \otimes q$ is the Kronecker product of p with q.[8] In eqn. (6), S is the following nonsingular matrix:

$$S = \left[\begin{array}{ccccc} a_1 & a_2 & \dots & a_{n-1} & 1 \\ a_2 & a_3 & \dots & 1 & 0 \\ \hline a_{n-1} & 1 & \dots & 0 & 0 \\ 1 & 0 & \dots & 0 & 0 \end{array}\right] \tag{7}$$

A rule for forming the $n \times ml$ matrix G was given in [1] which, it has since been discovered, can also be expressed in terms of a Kronecker product:

$$G = P(D^T \otimes B) \tag{8}$$

In the $n \times n^2$ matrix P the $(i + 1)$th row, for $i = 0, 1, \dots, n-1$, consists of the rows of A^i laid alongside each other in sequence.

In [1] it was shown that the rank r of G sets an upper limit to the number of eigenvalues arbitrarily assignable. From the dimensions of G we have the restriction $r \leqslant \min(n, ml)$. However, from eqn. (8) we may write

$$r \leqslant \min(\text{rank } P, \text{rank } D^T \otimes B) \tag{9}$$

Since, by hypothesis, the $n \times l$ matrix D^T and the $n \times m$ matrix B have each full rank, it follows from the fundamental properties of Kronecker products that rank $D^T \otimes B = ml$. From the structure of P it can be inferred that rank $P = g$, where g is the degree of the minimum polynomial of A. The minimum polynomial of A is that unique polynomial of minimal degree g

$$P_{\min}(s) = s^g + d_{g-1}s^{g-1} + \dots + d_1 s + d_0 \tag{10}$$

which has the property that

$$A^g + d_{g-1}A^{g-1} + \dots + d_1 A + d_0 I = 0.$$

If P_i^T denotes the ith row of P, the coefficients d_i are those which relate P_{g+1}^T to the leading group of g linearly independent rows:

$$P_{g+1}^T = -(d_0 P_1^T + d_1 P_2^T + \dots + d_{g-1} P_g^T) \tag{11}$$

The coefficient d_i may be found from eqn. (11) once the number g has been determined, and it is very straightforward to establish that g is the dimension of the largest nonvanishing leading principal minor of the $n \times n$ matrix $P^T P$.

The foregoing remarks indicate that the number v of eigenvalues arbitrarily assignable by means of dyadic output feedback lies within the range

$$\max(m, l) \leqslant v \leqslant \min(g, ml) \tag{12}$$

A very interesting feature arises if we have $g < n$ i.e. if A is noncyclic (or, as the more picturesque terminology has it, derogatory). In such a case it follows from the theory of canonical matrices [9] that, no matter how q and p^T are chosen, the number of linearly independent vectors in either of the chains

$$(Bq, ABq, A^2Bq, \dots)$$
$$(p^T D, p^T DA, p^T DA^2, \dots)$$

must be less than or equal to g. Furthermore, if, for example, the rank of the first chain above is u ($\leqslant g$) and we have the relation

$$A^u Bq + e_{u-1}A^{u-1}Bq + \ldots + e_1 ABq + e_0 Bq = 0,$$

the polynomial

$$P_q(s) = s^u + e_{u-1}s^{u-1} + \ldots + e_1 s + e_0 \tag{13}$$

is a factor of the minimum polynomial of A. A similar result holds for the second chain. Now, it was shown in [6] that following the choice of q which gives rise to the polynomial $P_q(s)$, the polynomial

$$Q_q(s) = \frac{P(s)}{P_q(s)} \tag{14}$$

remains a factor of the characteristic polynomial no matter what feedback row p^T is selected. We conclude therefore that, irrespective of the choice of p^T or q, the roots of the polynomial

$$Q_{\min}(s) = \frac{P(s)}{P_{\min}(s)} \tag{15}$$

remain as system eigenvalues. The degree of $Q_{\min}(s)$ is, of course, a lower limit to the number of eigenvalues which remain in their original locations. If u is the rank of the chain of column vectors generated from q and w the rank of the chain of column vectors generated from p^T, it follows that $n - \max(u, w)$ eigenvalues are undisturbed by the feedback. The possibility of deliberately choosing q or p^T so that selected satisfactory eigenvalues are included in the roots of the polynomial $Q_q(s)$, or the corresponding polynomial $Q_p(s)$ formed from p^T, does not appear to have been exploited to date. Further remarks bearing on this are made in the section on numerator control.

1.2. Remarks on the solution or approximate solution of eqn. (6)

In order to study the implications of eqn. (6) in some detail, it was convenient in [1] to express it as the pair of equations

$$\sigma = S[G^*, G^*T]\,\omega \tag{16}$$

$$R\omega = p \otimes q \tag{17}$$

where G^* denotes a collection of r linearly independent columns of G, R a permutation matrix which brings these columns to the leading positions, and T a matrix of dimension $r \times (ml - r)$ whose columns are the coefficients by which the columns excluded from G^* are expressed as unique linear combinations of the columns of G^*.

Equation (16) has a solution if and only if the equation

$$\sigma = SG^*\epsilon \tag{18}$$

is consistent i.e. if and only if rank $[\sigma, SG^*] = r$. If this is the case the solution ϵ is unique and may be displayed explicitly (though not advisedly computed thus) in the form

$$\epsilon = [(SG^*)^T SG^*]^{-1}(SG^*)^T\sigma \tag{19}$$

If eqn. (18) is not consistent the vector ϵ given in eqn. (19) is that which minimizes the norm, N, of the "error vector", where

$$N = (\sigma - SG^*\epsilon)^T(\sigma - SG^*\epsilon) \tag{20}$$

If eqn. (18), for the value of σ following on a specified desired set of eigenvalues, is inconsistent, it is often worthwhile to proceed with the vector ϵ which is obtained from eqn. (19), since the resulting eigenvalue spectrum may well be acceptable. (A similar idea has been used by Fallside[10] and his co-workers, and the reader is referred to their contributions in this volume and elsewhere.)

Following the computation of ϵ, the most general form of ω which solves eqn. (18), or gives the nonzero minimum value for N, is

$$\omega = \left[\begin{array}{c} \epsilon - T\mu \\ \hline \mu \end{array}\right] = \left[\begin{array}{c|c} I_r & -T \\ \hline 0 & I_{ml-r} \end{array}\right]\left[\begin{array}{c} \epsilon \\ \mu \end{array}\right] \tag{21}$$

where μ is an undetermined $(ml - r) \times 1$ column vector. The problem which may now be posed is that of choosing μ so that the equation

$$\bar{\delta} = R\left[\begin{array}{c|c} I_r & -T \\ \hline 0 & I_{ml-r} \end{array}\right]\left[\begin{array}{c} \epsilon \\ \mu \end{array}\right] = p \otimes q \tag{22}$$

is consistent or, failing that, so that the norm

$$\bar{N} = (\bar{\delta} - p \otimes q)^T(\bar{\delta} - p \otimes q) \tag{23}$$

is minimized. The norm minimization problem will be tackled below, but it is instructive (and a useful preliminary) to display the consistency condition first. We note that the first m entries of $p \otimes q$ are p_1q, the second m entries p_2q, and so forth. Thus, if we define $\bar{\delta}_i$ as the ith group of m entries from $\bar{\delta}$, the consistency condition is simply that all the $\bar{\delta}_i$ $(i = 1, 2, \ldots, l)$ should be replicas of a single basic $m \times 1$ column. In other words, if we define the $m \times l$ matrix

$$\Delta = [\bar{\delta}_1, \bar{\delta}_2, \ldots, \bar{\delta}_l] \tag{24}$$

the consistency condition for eqn. (22) is that it should be possible to choose μ to make

$$\text{rank } \Delta = 1 \tag{25}$$

A direct attack on eqn. (22) via this condition is not likely to be successful in general since the rank of a matrix is not a continuous function of its elements and so it is not feasible to devise a systematic strategy for varying μ in an attempt to find a solution. It appears to be preferable by far to seek the vector μ which minimizes $\bar{N}$. This quantity *is* a continuous function of the elements of μ and, as will be shown below, it can be expressed in terms of the trace and largest eigenvalue of a certain matrix, both of which can be determined by standard algorithms. If it happens that the minimum value of $\bar{N}$ is zero then, of course, an exact solution of eqn. (22) will have been determined.

If we consider the $ml \times ml$ unit matrix, denoting the ith group of m columns in it by the symbol U_i eqn. (22) may be re-expressed as

$$\bar{\delta} = [U_1 q, U_2 q, \ldots, U_l q] \,.\, p \tag{26}$$

For any chosen value of q, the norm of the error between left and right hand sides of eqn. (26) is obtained by choosing p as any solution of the consistent equation

$$[U_1 q, U_2 q, \ldots, U_l q]^T \bar{\delta} \\ = [U_1 q, U_2 q, \ldots, U_l q]^T [U_1 q, U_2 q, \ldots, U_l q] p \tag{27}$$

(The fact that eqn. (27) is consistent even though eqn. (26) may not be is a basic result from the theory of generalized inverse matrices.) [11, 12] Elementary manipulations convert eqn. (27) to the much more compact form

$$\Delta^T . q = (q^T q) . p \tag{28}$$

where Δ^T is the transpose of the $m \times l$ matrix defined by eqn. (24).

Working in a similar vein, eqn. (22) may be written as

$$\bar{\delta} = Zq \otimes p \tag{29}$$

where Z is an $ml \times ml$ permutation matrix (whose structure is very simple and is left as an exercise for the reader!) and this, after some manipulation yields the "best" value of q for a chosen value of p as any solution of the equation

$$\Delta p = (p^T p) . q \tag{30}$$

Now, if we substitute for q from eqn. (30) in eqn. (28) the result is

$$\Delta^T \Delta_p = (p^T p)(q^T q) . p \tag{31}$$

This means that p is an eigenvector of the symmetric $l \times l$ matrix $\Delta^T \Delta$ belonging to the eigenvalue $(p^T p)(q^T q)$.

In the same way, the equation

$$\Delta \Delta^T q = (p^T p)(q^T q) . q \tag{32}$$

is obtained. Equations (31) and (32) can be satisfied simultaneously, since $\Delta \Delta^T$ and $\Delta^T \Delta$ have min (m, l) eigenvalues in common. In fact $\Delta \Delta^T$ and $\Delta^T \Delta$ are both symmetric and positive semidefinite, with real eigenvalues which are positive or zero. The positive eigenvalues are common to both and their number equals the rank of Δ. If s_i is any positive eigenvalue, and if, as can be done without loss of generality, p is normalized to unit length, eqn. (31) or (32) gives $q^T q = s_i$, and this is consistent with eqn. (30) which yields $q^T q = p^T \Delta^T \Delta p = s_i (p^T p) = s_i$.

If p is calculated as the normalized eigenvector of $\Delta^T \Delta$ belonging to the eigenvalue s_i, and q is then obtained from eqn. (30), substitution of these values into eqn. (23) yields, after some manipulation,

$$\bar{N} = \text{trace } \Delta^T \Delta - s_i \tag{33}$$

Since the trace of a matrix equals the sum of its eigenvalues, eqn. (33) shows that $\bar{N}$ is minimized by choosing s_i as the *largest* positive eigenvalue of $\Delta^T \Delta$.

Retracing the analysis, it is seen that $\Delta^T \Delta$ is a function of the vector μ through eqn. (22). Since the trace and the largest eigenvalue of a matrix are continuous functions of its elements, it would appear feasible to employ some standard procedure for unconstrained minimization of a function of several real variables to compute the optimum value of μ and, from the resulting matrix $\Delta^T\Delta$, the corresponding best values of p and q.

The analysis in this section blossomed under the stress of preparing this chapter. For the equally crazy manipulations to which eqns (16) and (17) gave rise during the months preceding the working party and for examples which (inevitably!) contain numerical errors, the reader is referred to.[1] After that his conviction that unrepentant matrix mechanics should be banned from control theory will no doubt be strengthened! However, editor permitting, there is worse to follow.

2. How to Vary Transfer Function Numerators without Moving Eigenvalues

My first encounter with the problem of numerator control occurred quite without warning one warm Summer afternoon in 1970. As I lay on the lawn pleasantly mesmerized by the thrilling eigenvalue assignment classics of Anderson and Luenberger[13] and Wonham,[14] I was suddenly conscious of the giddiness which precedes an attack of matrix madness. An inner voice whispered "Eigenvalues aren't everything – what about the numerators?" Some hours later I came to again to find myself possessed of a singularly complicated and useless formula for the effect of state feedback on the transfer function numerator matrix. There was nothing positive to be deduced from it, but a negative observation could be made fairly easily. It is stated here in a somewhat more general form than that under which it made its first appearance.[15]

In the system

$$\frac{dx}{dt} = Ax + Bu$$

$$y = Dx,$$

subject to the feedback law

$$u = u_0 + \bar{K}y \tag{34}$$

the numerator

$$\begin{aligned} W_{ij}(s) &= \{D \operatorname{Adj} (sI - A - B\bar{K}D)B\}_{ij} \\ &= d_i^T \operatorname{Adj} (sI - A - B\bar{K}D)b_j \end{aligned} \tag{35}$$

of the transfer function relating the ith output to the jth input is unaffected by the gains of any feedback links which either emanate from the ith output or terminate on the jth input.

This observation did not, in itself, prove very useful for numerator control. However, the idea that certain features of a transfer function matrix can remain invariant under changes in a feedback matrix was appealing, and it seemed that it might have application. In fact it took several months for me to appreciate that the form to which Anderson and Luenberger, and Wonham, converted the system matrix prior to eigenvalue assignment leaves entries in the transformed feedback matrix which can be varied at will without influencing the eigenvalues. My first published thought [16] on exploitation of that feature was that it could be used to minimize some norms of rows of a state feedback matrix – we are now talking of state as opposed to output feedback, i.e.

$$u = u_0 + Kx \tag{36}$$

in an attempt to penalize excessive feedback gains. Another thought, along the same lines, was to use other entries left blank by Anderson and Luenberger to allow sharing of eigenvalues between adjacent Companion blocks in their transformed system matrix.[17] It may be worthwhile to point out, in passing, that both these ideas cannot be well exploited simultaneously, since they interfere with each other.

What follows now is an attempt to introduce into a state feedback law the greatest possible number of parameters which do not influence eigenvalues, and to suggest how these might be used to obtain some degree of numerator control. At the outset it must be admitted that the degree of control to be expected is not great. The matrix of transfer function numerators for an nth order, m input, l output system can contain up to lmn coefficients, whereas the maximum number of free parameters which can be generated here is $\frac{1}{2}m(m-l)$. In addition, since the greatest freedom is realized with *state* feedback, it is necessary to use some type of observer, e.g. a Luenberger observer,[18] to realize the state feedback law in the case that all state variables are not accessible. The Luenberger observer is superficially very attractive since, if it is arranged in the configuration shown on Figure 1, and the

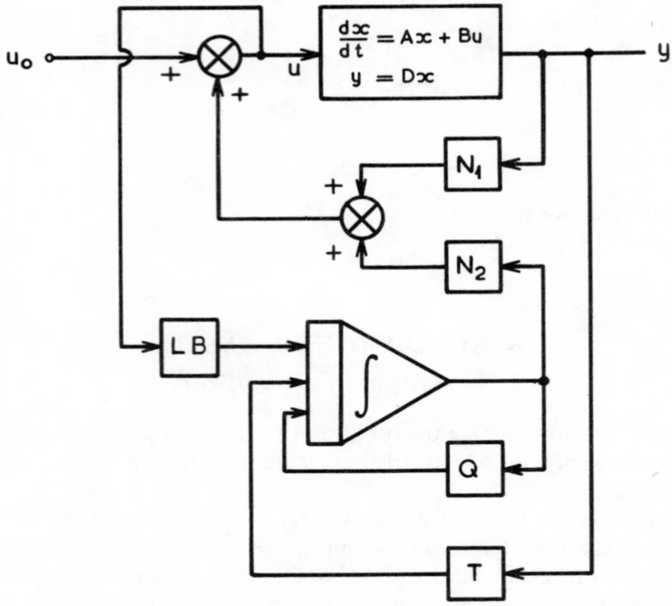

Figure 1

matrices are calculated according to the scheme

$$[N_1, N_2]\begin{bmatrix} D \\ L \end{bmatrix} = K$$

$$[T, Q]\begin{bmatrix} D \\ L \end{bmatrix} = LA \tag{37}$$

the transfer function matrix relating $Y(s)$ to $U_0(s)$ is exactly the same as that of the system $\frac{dx}{dt} = Ax + Bu$, $y = Dx$, $u = u_0 + Kx$. The $n - l$ additional system eigenvalues contributed by the observer under these conditions do not appear explicitly – having been cancelled by numerator terms – but it is well known that L can be chosen to place them in any desired locations, provided that (A, D) is an observable pair.[19, 20] Unfortunately, the dynamic performance of an observer-augmented system is often very sensitive to changes in parameters.

Since the general state feedback matrix has dimension $m \times n$ $(m \leqslant n)$ it may be constructed as a sum of dyads of the form

$$K = \sum_{i=1}^{m} q_i p_i^T \tag{38}$$

where each q_i is an $m \times 1$ column and each p_i a $1 \times n$ row. With this feedback law applied, the system matrix becomes

$$A + BK = A + [Bq_1, Bq_2, \ldots, Bq_m]\begin{bmatrix} p_1^T \\ p_2^T \\ \cdot \\ \cdot \\ \cdot \\ p_m^T \end{bmatrix}$$

$$= A + \hat{B}.\hat{K}$$

Following Anderson and Luenberger[13] we now examine the chain of vectors

$$Bq_1, ABq_1, \ldots, A^{n-1}Bq_1,$$

determine its rank, r_1, and calculate the coefficients of α_{1j} of the relation

$$-A^{r_1-1}Bq_1 = \sum_{j=0}^{r_1-1} \alpha_{1j}A^jBq_1 \tag{40}$$

It will be demonstrated below, using the mode controllability matrix[21] that the column q_1 can be chosen to give

$$r_1 = n - m + 1 \tag{41}$$

and this choice will now be adopted. There is a difficulty that if A has complex eigenvalues the vector q_1 to realize this index could prove to be complex, and that is unacceptable. It is assumed therefore that A has all *real* eigenvalues, this condition having been imposed if necessary by means of a preliminary eigenvalue assignment. The eigenvalues may be restored to desired locations later, as will be shown!

We next try to select q_2 so that the rank of the chain

$$Bq_1, ABq_1, \ldots, A^{r_1-1}Bq_1, Bq_2, ABq_2, \ldots$$

is as short as possible. In fact, if the eigenvalues of A are real, q_2 can be chosen so that only the column Bq_2 is linearly independent of the preceding r_1 columns. With this choice of q_2 we calculate the coefficient α_2 of the relation

$$-ABq_2 = \alpha_2 Bq_2 + \sum_{j=0}^{r_1-1} (\beta_{12})_j A^j Bq_1 \tag{42}$$

Continuing in this vein we now select q_3 so that the rank of the chain

$$Bq_1, ABq_1, \ldots, A^{r_1-1}Bq_1, Bq_2, Bq_3, \ldots$$

is $n - m + 3$, and we compute the coefficient α_3 of the relation

$$-ABq_3 = \alpha_3 Bq_3 + \beta_{23} Bq_2 + \sum_{j=0}^{r_1-1} (\beta_{13})_j A^j Bq_1 \tag{43}$$

Proceeding in this manner, we eventually construct a nonsingular $n \times n$ matrix

$$M = [Bq_1, \ldots, A^{n-m}Bq_1, Bq_2, \ldots, Bq_m]\,\hat{S} \tag{44}$$

with

$$\hat{S} = \left[\begin{array}{ccccc|c} \alpha_{11} & \alpha_{12} & \cdots & \alpha_{1,n-m} & 1 & \\ \alpha_{12} & \alpha_{13} & \cdots & 1 & 0 & \\ \hdashline & & & & & 0 \\ \alpha_{1,n-m} & 1 & \cdots & 0 & 0 & \\ 1 & 0 & & 0 & 0 & \\ \hline & & 0 & & & I_{m-1} \end{array}\right] \tag{45}$$

The following result now follows from well-established analysis: [6, 13]

$$M^{-1}(A + \hat{B}\hat{K})M = \hat{C} + \tilde{B}\,.\,\hat{K}M \tag{46}$$

where

$$\hat{C} = \left[\begin{array}{c|cccc} C_1 & C_{12} & & \cdots & C_{1m} \\ \hline & -\alpha_2 & x & \cdots & x \\ 0 & 0 & -\alpha_3 & \cdots & x \\ \hdashline & 0 & 0 & & -\alpha_m \end{array}\right] \tag{47}$$

with

$$\tilde{B} = \left[\begin{array}{c} 0 \\ \hline I_m \end{array}\right] \tag{48}$$

In eqn. (47) the elements marked "x" are related to the coefficients $(\beta_{ij})_k$ in eqns (42), (43) and their successors; C_1 is the Companion form with characteristic polynomial

$$P_1(s) = s^{n-m+1} + \alpha_{1,n-m}s^{n-m} + \ldots + \alpha_{11}s + \alpha_{10} \tag{49}$$

and each C_{1j} is a column vector of dimension $(n - m + 1) \times 1$.

On account of the structure of B, the successive rows of the matrix

$$\Sigma = \hat{K}M \tag{50}$$

add to the final row of C_1 and the rows below that in $\hat{C}$. Thus, if we constrain Σ to have the structure

$$\Sigma = \left[\begin{array}{c|cccc} (\sigma_{11} \;\ldots\; \sigma_{1,n-m+1}) & \sigma_{1,n-m+2} & & \ldots & \sigma_{1n} \\ \hline 0 & (\sigma_{2,n-m+2}) & & \ldots & \sigma_{2n} \\ & 0 & (\sigma_{3,n-m+3}) & \ldots & \sigma_{3n} \\ \hdashline & 0 & 0 & & (\sigma_{nn}) \end{array}\right] \tag{51}$$

the elements in parentheses may be selected to assign eigenvalues, and the remaining nonzero elements affect only the numerators of the transfer functions. It is convenient to separate the eigenvalue shifting and numerator control portions of Σ as Σ_1 and Σ_2 respectively, thus giving the new system matrix as

$$\hat{A} = A + \hat{B}\hat{K} = A + \hat{B}\Sigma_1 M^{-1} + \hat{B}\Sigma_2 M^{-1} \tag{52}$$

Since the effect of Σ_2 on the transfer function numerator matrix is very complicated, a simple approximation technique may be helpful as an initial step in choosing the free parameters. Let us assume that the desired numerator matrix can be expressed as

$$W_d(s) = D \operatorname{Adj}(sI - \bar{A})B \tag{53}$$

where the matrix $\bar{A}$ does not necessarily have to possess the desired spectrum of eigenvalues. We now examine the equation

$$\bar{A} - A - \hat{B}\Sigma_1 M^{-1} = \hat{B}\Sigma_2 M^{-1} \tag{54}$$

in a search for the matrix Σ_2 of the required structure (i.e. having nonzero elements only in the positions indicated by the elements σ_{ij} not enclosed in parentheses in eqn. 51). If we rearrange eqn. 54 as

$$\Phi = M^{-1}(\bar{A} - A)M - \tilde{B}\Sigma_1 = \tilde{B}\Sigma_2 \tag{55}$$

and form single columns $\overline{\phi}$ and $\overline{\sigma}$ by laying out the columns of $M^{-1}(\overline{A} - A)M - \widetilde{B}\Sigma_1$ and Σ_2 in sequence, one below the other, we convert it to the form

$$\overline{\phi} = [\widetilde{B} \otimes I_n]\,\overline{\sigma} \tag{56}$$

In view of eqn. (48), the matrix $\widetilde{B} \otimes I_n$ is a very simple $n^2 \times nm$ matrix of full rank. The vector $\overline{\sigma}$ contains zeros in defined positions (the first $n - m + 1$ positions, positions $n + 1$ to $2n - m + 2$, positions $2n + 1$ to $3n - m + 3$, etc). If the vector $\overline{\sigma}$ is contracted to a vector $\overline{\sigma}_c$ of dimension $\frac{1}{2}m(m - 1) \times 1$ by removing these zero entries, and if $\widetilde{B} \otimes I_n$ is similarly contracted by removing the corresponding columns, eqn. (56) is converted to the form

$$\overline{\phi} = \Omega \,.\, \overline{\sigma}_c \tag{57}$$

in which Ω is an appropriate selection of $\frac{1}{2}m(m - 1)$ columns from the $n^2 \times n^2$ unit matrix. Since $\Omega^T\Omega$ is a unit matrix, the value of $\overline{\sigma}_c$ which gives the best approximation to a solution of eqn. (57) in the least squares sense is

$$\overline{\sigma}_c = \Omega^T\overline{\phi} \tag{58}$$

which consists simply of an appropriate selection of elements from $\overline{\phi}$. Σ_2 may now be constructed from $\overline{\sigma}_c$, and the complete feedback law (to which must be added any preliminary feedback used to give A all real eigenvalues) is given by

$$\begin{aligned} K &= [q_1, q_2, \ldots q_m]\,\hat{K} \\ &= [q_1, q_2, \ldots q_m]\,(\Sigma_1 + \Sigma_2)M^{-1} \end{aligned} \tag{59}$$

In order to complete the edifice reared here, it remains to discuss how $q_1, q_2, \ldots, q_m$ can be chosen to give $r_1 = n - m + 1$ and to augment the chain of linearly independent columns by one only as each vector Bq_2, Bq_3, etc. is tested. Let us assume that A has *simple* real eigenvalues only. Let V be the (right) modal matrix of A, i.e., the matrix of column eigenvectors. If q_1 can be chosen so that the $n \times 1$ column γ_1 defined by

$$\gamma_1 = V^{-1}Bq_1 \tag{60}$$

contains precisely $m - 1$ zero entries, then Bq_1 is expressible as the linear combination $V\gamma_1$ of precisely $n - m + 1$ eigenvectors of A. If the corresponding eigenvalues are $\lambda_1, \lambda_2, \ldots, \lambda_{n-m+1}$, it follows from mode controllability theory [21] that the coefficients α_{1j} in eqn. (40) are defined by

$$\begin{aligned} &(s - \lambda_1)(s - \lambda_2) \ldots (s - \lambda_{n-m+1}) \\ &\quad = s^{n-m+1} + \alpha_{1,n-m}s^{n-m} + \ldots + \alpha_1 s + \alpha_0 \end{aligned} \tag{61}$$

Since, by hypothesis, the system is completely state controllable, $V^{-1}B$ contains no row consisting entirely of zeros. This feature would allow q_1 to be chosen so that all the entries of γ_1 were nonzero (and this is the basis of dyadic state feedback laws for moving all the eigenvalues). However, any selection of $m - 1$ rows from $V^{-1}B$ must have rank less than m and so, if we denote such a selection by $[V^{-1}B]_{m-1}$, there must exist at least one column q_1 such that

$$[V^{-1}B]_{m-1} \cdot q_1 = 0 \tag{62}$$

Any such q_1 will insert at least $m-1$ zero entries in γ_1: there exists an infinite set of vectors q_1 formed in this way (from various trial selections of $m-1$ rows of $V^{-1}B$ if necessary) which will yield precisely $m-1$ zero entries. In order to permit the subsequent vectors q_2, q_3, etc., to be found readily it is necessary however that the selection of $m-1$ rows have rank $m-1$. This is always possible since, given rank $B=m$, it follows that $V^{-1}B$ contains m linearly independent rows.

Once q_1 has been selected, q_2 may be taken as any solution of the equation

$$[V^{-1}B]_{m-1}\, q_2 = \begin{bmatrix} 1 \\ 0 \\ \cdot \\ \cdot \\ \cdot \\ 0 \end{bmatrix} \tag{63}$$

since this introduces only one nonzero entry in the spaces which were previously filled by zeros in γ_1. If this space brings in the eigenvector belonging to the eigenvalue λ_{n-m+2}, then we have

$$-\alpha_2 = \lambda_{n-m+2} \tag{64}$$

An explicit solution for q_2 (the minimum norm one) may be taken as

$$q_2 = [V^{-1}B]^T_{m-1}\{[V^{-1}B]_{m-1}[V^{-1}B]^T_{m-1}\}^{-1} \cdot \begin{bmatrix} 1 \\ 0 \\ \cdot \\ \cdot \\ 0 \end{bmatrix}$$

$$= N \cdot \begin{bmatrix} 1 \\ 0 \\ \cdot \\ \cdot \\ 0 \end{bmatrix} \tag{65}$$

In a similar manner $q_3, q_4, \ldots, q_m$ may be generated simply by moving the sole nonzero element down by one position for each successive index, which simply extracts the columns of N in succession. If we identify the eigenvalue belonging to the additional eigenvector brought in at each step, the coefficients α_i are recognized by relations like eqn. (64).

In summary, it is seen that, provided A has been processed beforehand, if necessary, to give it simple real eigenvalues, the only step in the process which cannot yet be formulated in simple mechanical terms is the selection of q_1. Once this has been accomplished the feedback matrix K of full rank containing $\frac{1}{2}m(m-1)$ parameters which can be varied at will without affecting eigenvalues can be generated in a straightforward manner and, of course, the eigenvalues can be assigned to desired locations again subject to the restriction (which can be removed simply at the cost of reducing the number of free parameters) that the final system matrix should contain $m-1$ real eigenvalues.

3. References

[1] Power, H. M., "A new result on eigenvalue assignment by means of dyadic output feedback", *Int. J. Control*, Vol. 21, pp. 149–158, Jan. 1975.

[2] Davison, E. J., "On pole assignment in linear systems with incomplete state feedback", *I.E.E.E. Trans. Automat. Contr.*, Vol. AC-15, pp. 348–351, June 1970.

[3] Davison, E. J. and Chatterjee, R., "A note on pole assignment in linear systems with incomplete state feedback", *I.E.E.E. Trans. Automat. Contr.*, Vol. AC-16, pp. 98–99, Feb. 1971.

[4] Sridhar, B. and Lindorff, D. P., "A note on pole assignment", *I.E.E.E. Trans. Automat. Contr.*, Vol. AC-17, pp. 822–823, Dec. 1972.

[5] Davison, E. J. and Chow, S. G., "An algorithm for the assignment of closed-loop poles using output feedback in large linear multivariable systems", *I.E.E.E. Trans. Automat. Contr.*, Vol. AC-18, pp. 74–75, Feb. 1973.

[6] Power, H. M., "Dyadic feedback laws for linear multivariable systems", *Int. J. Syst. Sci.*, Vol. 3, pp. 293–312, Oct. 1972.

[7] Sridhar, B. and Lindorff, D. P., "Pole placement with constant gain output feedback", *Int. J. Control*, Vol. 18, pp. 993–1003, Dec. 1973.

[8] Barnett, S. and Storey, C., *Matrix methods in stability theory* (Nelson, London, 1970).

[9] Turnbull, H. W. and Aitken, A. C., *An introduction to the theory of canonical matrices* (Dover, New York, 1961).

[10] Fallside, F. and Seraji, H., "Pole-shifting procedure for multivariable systems using output feedback", *Proc. I.E.E.*, Vol. 118, pp. 1648–1654, Nov. 1971.

[11] Rao, C. R. and Mitra, S. K., *Generalized inverse of matrices and its applications* (Wiley, New York, 1971).

[12] Pringle, R. M. and Rayner, A. A., *Generalized inverse matrices with applications to statistics* (Griffin, London, 1971).

[13] Anderson, B. D. O. and Luenberger, D. G., "Design of multivariable feedback systems", *Proc. I.E.E.*, Vol. 114, pp. 395–399, March 1967.

[14] Wonham, W. M., "On pole assignment in multi-input controllable linear systems", *I.E.E.E. Trans. Automat. Contr.*, Vol. AC-12, pp. 660–665, Dec. 1967.

[15] Power, H. M., "The effect of state variable feedback on the numerators of transfer functions", *Electron. Lett.*, Vol. 6, pp. 490–491, 23rd July 1970.

[16] Power, H. M., "Design freedom in the method of Anderson and Luenberger for eigenvalue assignment", *Electron. Lett.*, Vol. 7, pp. 71–73, 11th February 1971.

[17] Power, H. M., "Extension to the method of Anderson and Luenberger for eigenvalue assignment", *Electron. Lett.*, Vol. 7, pp. 158–160, 8th April 1971.

[18] Luenberger, D. G., "Observers for multivariable systems", *I.E.E.E. Trans. Automat. Contr.*, Vol. AC-11, pp. 190–197, April 1966.

[19] Power, H. M., "On the solution of a matrix equation in the theory of Luenberger observers", *I.E.E.E. Trans. Automat. Contr.*, Vol. AC-18, pp. 70–71, Feb. 1973.

[20] Power, H. M., "New solution to a problem in Luenberger observer design", *Electron. Lett.*, Vol. 11, pp. 65–67, 6th February 1975.

[21] Porter, B. and Crossley, T. R., *Modal control: theory and applications* (Taylor and Francis, London, 1972).

On Output Feedback Control of Linear Multivariable Systems

H. SERAJI

Department of Electrical Engineering, Arya-Mehr University of Technology, P.O. Box 3406, Tehran, Iran

Abstract. The paper is concerned with the design of three different types of output feedback controllers for pole assignment in a linear multivariable system (i) constant feedback, (ii) dynamic feedback and (iii) proportional-plus-integral feedback. It is shown that the types (ii) and (iii) problems can be formulated as the type (i) problem using an auxiliary system. Numerical methods with guaranteed convergence are then described for solving the general type (i) problem.

1. Introduction

The state–space methods, introduced by modern control theory, have provided a deep insight into the structure of dynamical systems and have greatly helped the analysis of systems. On the other hand, state–space synthesis techniques have faced serious problems in the design of practical control systems. One of the main problems is the requirement of availability or reconstruction of all the state-variables of a system for control purposes. This has hindered the practical applications of modern control theory and has created a gap between the modern theory and industrial practice. As a result, there are relatively few practical design examples using modern control techniques.

In recent years, there has been a move towards bridging the existing gap and bringing the modern theory closer to practice. This is being achieved through the development of practically-oriented techniques for the feedback design of dynamical systems in which emphasis is placed on the available outputs of the system rather than on the system state-variables. This new body of theory where the measurable system outputs play the main role will certainly have more impact on practical applications than the current modern control theory has had.

The result presented in this paper is only a first step in the development of a general output feedback theory. The paper attempts to unify part of the theory by studying the pole assignment problem using three different types of output feedback controllers (i) constant feedback, (ii) dynamic feedback, and (iii) proportional-plus-integral feedback. It is shown that the types (ii) and (iii) problems can be formulated as a general type (i) problem. Numerical methods are then described for solving the general type (i) problem.

2. Type (i) Problem: Constant Output Feedback

The problem of pole assignment in a linear multivariable system by means of constant output feedback can be simply stated as follows:

Given the linear time-invariant multivariable system

$$\dot{x} = \mathrm{A}x + \mathrm{B}u$$

$$y = \mathrm{C}x$$

where x is the $n \times 1$ state vector, u is the $m \times 1$ control input vector and y is the $l \times 1$ output vector, find the $m \times l$ constant output feedback matrix K, $u = u_c - \mathrm{K}y$, such that the resulting closed-loop system (see Figure 1)

$$\dot{x} = (\mathrm{A} - \mathrm{BKC})x + \mathrm{B}u_c$$

has a specified set of poles $\lambda_1, \lambda_2, \ldots, \lambda_n$. In other words, given A, B and C, find K such that

$$|s\mathrm{I} - (\mathrm{A} - \mathrm{BKC})| = (s - \lambda_1)(s - \lambda_2) \ldots (s - \lambda_n)$$

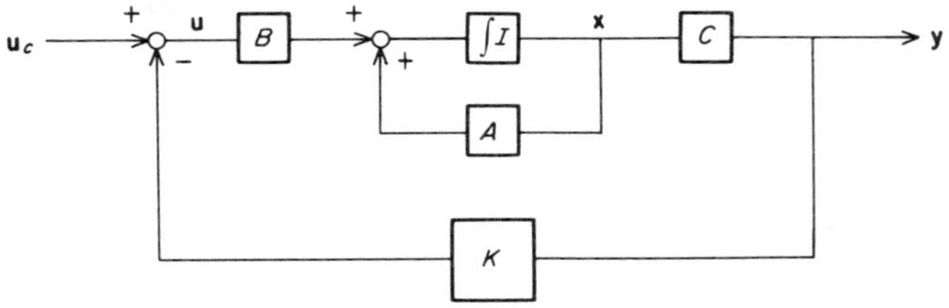

Figure 1. Plant with constant output feedback.

2.1. Example

Given the system

$$\dot{x} = \begin{pmatrix} 0 & 1 & 0 \\ 0 & 0 & 1 \\ 0 & 0 & 0 \end{pmatrix} x + \begin{pmatrix} 1 & 0 \\ 0 & 0 \\ 0 & 1 \end{pmatrix} u$$

$$y = \begin{pmatrix} 1 & 0 & 0 \\ 0 & 0 & 1 \end{pmatrix} x$$

find the output feedback matrix K required to position the poles at −1, −2, −3.

Let us take the general output feedback matrix $\mathrm{K} = \begin{pmatrix} k_{11} & k_{12} \\ k_{21} & k_{22} \end{pmatrix}$ where k_{11}, k_{12},

k_{21} and k_{22} can be specified arbitrarily. Then the closed-loop system matrix A_c becomes

$$A_c = A - BKC = \begin{pmatrix} -k_{11} & 1 & -k_{12} \\ 0 & 0 & 1 \\ -k_{21} & 0 & -k_{22} \end{pmatrix}$$

By direct calculation, the closed-loop characteristic polynomial is found to be

$$H(s) = |sI - A_c| = s^3 + (k_{11} + k_{22})s^2 + (k_{11}k_{22} - k_{12}k_{21})s + k_{21}$$

The desired characteristic polynomial is

$$H(s) = (s+1)(s+2)(s+3) = s^3 + 6s^2 + 11s + 6$$

Equating the two expressions for $H(s)$, we obtain three equations in the four unknown elements of K. Solving in terms of k_{11} we obtain

$$K = \begin{pmatrix} k_{11} & k_{11}(1 - k_{11}/6) - 11/6 \\ 6 & 6 - k_{11} \end{pmatrix} \quad \text{with } k_{11} \text{ arbitrary.}$$

This expression gives an infinite number of output feedback matrices which position the poles at $-1, -2, -3$. In other words, $|sI - A + BKC| = (s+1)(s+2)(s+3)$ for all values of k_{11} and is independent of k_{11}.

3. Type (ii) Problem: Dynamic Output Feedback

The pole assignment problem using a dynamic output feedback compensator can be stated as follows:

Given the linear plant

$$\dot{x} = Ax + Bu$$

$$y = Cx$$

find the pth order dynamic compensator of the form

$$\dot{z} = Dz + Ey$$

$$v = Fz + Gy$$

required to position the poles of the composite closed-loop system with $u = u_c - v$ at specified locations where z is the $p \times 1$ compensator state vector, y is the $l \times 1$ compensator input vector, v is the $m \times 1$ compensator output vector and D, E, F and G are constant compensator matrices with dimensions $p \times p$, $p \times l$, $m \times p$ and $m \times l$ respectively.

We now find the state equation of the composite closed-loop system consisting of the plant and the compensator as shown in Figure 2. Putting $u = u_c - v$ in the plant state equation and using the compensator output equation we obtain

$$\begin{aligned}\dot{x} &= Ax + B(u_c - Fz - GCx) \\ &= (A - BGC)x - BFz + Bu_c\end{aligned}$$

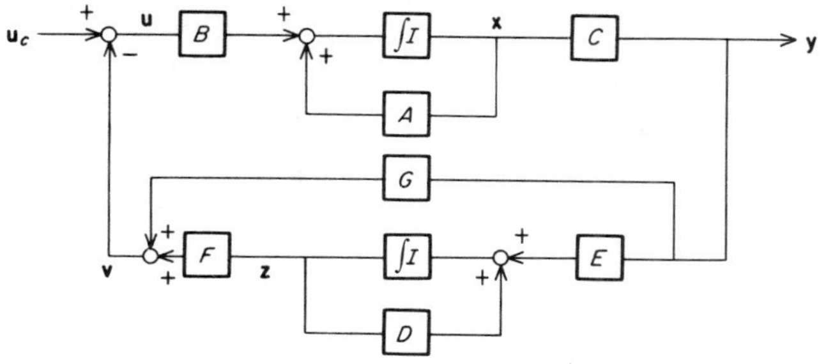

Figure 2. Plant with dynamic output feedback.

and from the compensator state equation we have

$$\dot{z} = \mathrm{EC}x + \mathrm{D}z$$

On combining the $\dot{x}$ and $\dot{z}$ equations we obtain the state equation of the composite closed-loop system as

$$\begin{bmatrix} \dot{x} \\ \dot{z} \end{bmatrix} = \begin{bmatrix} \mathrm{A - BGC} & \mathrm{-BF} \\ \mathrm{EC} & \mathrm{D} \end{bmatrix} \begin{bmatrix} x \\ z \end{bmatrix} + \begin{bmatrix} \mathrm{B} \\ 0 \end{bmatrix} u_c$$

The composite system is of order $n + p$ with the state vector $\begin{bmatrix} x \\ z \end{bmatrix}$ and the $m \times 1$ input vector u_c. The closed-loop system matrix can be expressed as

$$\begin{bmatrix} \mathrm{A - BGC} & \mathrm{-BF} \\ \mathrm{EC} & \mathrm{D} \end{bmatrix} = \begin{bmatrix} \mathrm{A} & 0 \\ 0 & 0 \end{bmatrix} - \begin{bmatrix} \mathrm{B} & 0 \\ 0 & -\mathrm{I} \end{bmatrix} \begin{bmatrix} \mathrm{G} & \mathrm{F} \\ \mathrm{E} & \mathrm{D} \end{bmatrix} \begin{bmatrix} \mathrm{C} & 0 \\ 0 & \mathrm{I} \end{bmatrix}$$

$$= \hat{\mathrm{A}} - \hat{\mathrm{B}} \begin{bmatrix} \mathrm{G} & \mathrm{F} \\ \mathrm{E} & \mathrm{D} \end{bmatrix} \hat{\mathrm{C}}$$

where $\hat{\mathrm{A}} = \begin{bmatrix} \mathrm{A} & 0 \\ 0 & 0 \end{bmatrix}$ is an $(n + p) \times (n + p)$ matrix, $\hat{\mathrm{B}} = \begin{bmatrix} \mathrm{B} & 0 \\ 0 & -\mathrm{I} \end{bmatrix}$ is an $(n + p) \times (m + p)$ matrix and $\hat{\mathrm{C}} = \begin{bmatrix} \mathrm{C} & 0 \\ 0 & \mathrm{I} \end{bmatrix}$ is an $(l + p) \times (n + p)$ matrix. Thus, the closed-loop system matrix of the plant-plus-compensator is equal to the closed-loop matrix of an auxiliary system $(\hat{\mathrm{A}}, \hat{\mathrm{B}}, \hat{\mathrm{C}})$ with the $(m + p) \times (l + p)$ constant output feedback matrix $\hat{\mathrm{K}} = \begin{bmatrix} \mathrm{G} & \mathrm{F} \\ \mathrm{E} & \mathrm{D} \end{bmatrix}$.

The dynamic compensator design problem of type (ii) is thus reduced to an equivalent constant output feedback design problem of type (i) as follows: Given the linear plant (A, B, C), to design the dynamic compensator (D, E, F, G) we first form the auxiliary system $(\hat{\mathrm{A}}, \hat{\mathrm{B}}, \hat{\mathrm{C}})$ and then find the constant output feedback matrix $\hat{\mathrm{K}}$ for this system. The submatrices of $\hat{\mathrm{K}}$ give us the required compensator matrices D, E, F and G.

3.1. Example

Given the plant

$$\dot{x} = \begin{pmatrix} -2 & 1 \\ 0 & -1 \end{pmatrix} x + \begin{pmatrix} 0 \\ 1 \end{pmatrix} u$$

$$y = (1 \quad 0)\, x$$

find the first order dynamic compensator required to position the three poles of the composite system at −3, −3, −3.

Let us take the general first order compensator

$$\dot{z} = dz + ey$$

$$v = fz + gy$$

where d, e, f and g can be specified arbitrarily. We now form the matrices of the auxiliary system ($\hat{\text{A}}$, $\hat{\text{B}}$, $\hat{\text{C}}$) and the constant output feedback matrix $\hat{\text{K}}$ as follows

$$\hat{\text{A}} = \begin{bmatrix} \text{A} & 0 \\ 0 & 0 \end{bmatrix} = \begin{pmatrix} -2 & 1 & 0 \\ 0 & -1 & 0 \\ 0 & 0 & 0 \end{pmatrix}; \quad \hat{\text{B}} = \begin{bmatrix} \text{B} & 0 \\ 0 & -\text{I} \end{bmatrix} = \begin{pmatrix} 0 & 0 \\ 1 & 0 \\ 0 & -1 \end{pmatrix}$$

$$\hat{\text{C}} = \begin{bmatrix} \text{C} & 0 \\ 0 & \text{I} \end{bmatrix} = \begin{pmatrix} 1 & 0 & 0 \\ 0 & 0 & 1 \end{pmatrix}; \quad \hat{\text{K}} = \begin{pmatrix} g & f \\ e & d \end{pmatrix}$$

The closed-loop system matrix A_c then becomes

$$\text{A}_c = \hat{\text{A}} - \hat{\text{B}}\hat{\text{K}}\hat{\text{C}} = \begin{pmatrix} -2 & 1 & 0 \\ -g & -1 & -f \\ e & 0 & d \end{pmatrix}$$

By direct calculation, the closed-loop characteristic polynomial is found to be

$$\text{H}(s) = |s\text{I} - \text{A}_c| = s^3 + (3-d)\,s^2 + (2 - 3d + g)\,s + ef - 2d - gd$$

The desired characteristic polynomial is

$$\text{H}(s) = (s+3)^3 = s^3 + 9s^2 + 9s + 27$$

Equating the two expressions for H(s), we obtain three equations in the four unknown parameters of the compensator. Solving in terms of e we obtain

$$\hat{\text{K}} = \begin{pmatrix} 7 & -27/e \\ e & -6 \end{pmatrix} \quad \text{with } e \text{ arbitrary but non-zero.}$$

The equations of the required compensator are thus

$$\dot{z} = -6z + ey$$

$$v = -\frac{27}{e} z + 7y$$

These equations give an infinite number of first order compensators which position the poles at −3, −3, −3 since $|sI - \hat{A} + \hat{B}\hat{K}\hat{C}| = (s+3)^3$ for all non-zero values of e and is independent of e.

It is interesting to note that the transfer function of the required compensator is $\frac{V(s)}{Y(s)} = \frac{7s+15}{s+6}$ which is independent of the parameter e and is unique. This transfer function agrees entirely with that obtained in Ref. 1 using an entirely different method.

4. Type (iii) Problem: Proportional-plus-integral Output Feedback

The design problem of a proportional-plus-integral controller is stated as follows: Given the linear plant

$$\dot{x} = Ax + Bu$$

$$y = Cx$$

define an additional $l \times 1$ state vector z as

$$z = \int^t (y_r - y)\, dt$$

where y_r is the $l \times 1$ constant reference output vector. The problem is to design a proportional-plus-integral feedback controller $u = -K_1 y - K_2 z$ such that the resulting closed-loop system has a specified set of stable poles. It is noted that because of the introduction of the integral action, in the closed-loop system at the steady-state we have $\dot{z} = 0$ and hence $y_{ss} = y_r$.

We now find the state and output equations of the open-loop plant augmented by the integrator as shown in Figure 3. Since $\dot{z} = y_r - y = -Cx + y_r$ we have

$$\begin{bmatrix} \dot{x} \\ \dot{z} \end{bmatrix} = \begin{bmatrix} A & 0 \\ -C & 0 \end{bmatrix} \begin{bmatrix} x \\ z \end{bmatrix} + \begin{bmatrix} B \\ 0 \end{bmatrix} u + \begin{bmatrix} 0 \\ I \end{bmatrix} y_r$$

$$\begin{bmatrix} y \\ z \end{bmatrix} = \begin{bmatrix} C & 0 \\ 0 & I \end{bmatrix} \begin{bmatrix} x \\ z \end{bmatrix}$$

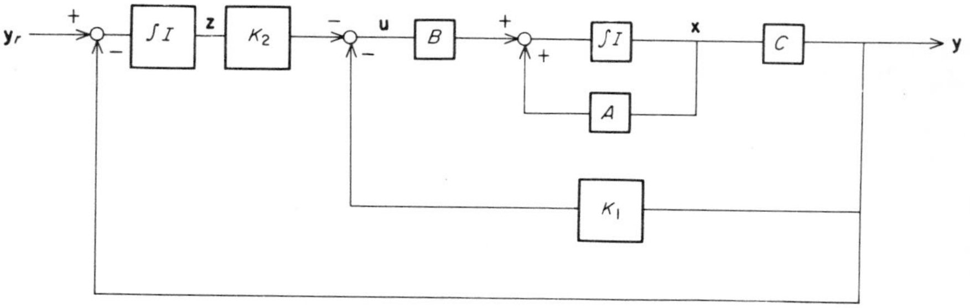

Figure 3. Plant with proportional-plus-integral output feedback.

The augmented system is of order $n + l$ with the state vector $\hat{x} = \begin{bmatrix} x \\ z \end{bmatrix}$ and the $2l \times 1$ output vector $\hat{y} = \begin{bmatrix} y \\ z \end{bmatrix}$. On applying proportional-plus-integral output feedback, we have

$$u = -K_1 y - K_2 z$$

or

$$u = -[K_1 \quad K_2] \begin{bmatrix} y \\ z \end{bmatrix} = -\hat{K}\hat{y}$$

which is proportional output feedback with the $m \times 2l$ feedback matrix $\hat{K} = [K_1 \quad K_2]$ for the augmented system $(\hat{A}, \hat{B}, \hat{C})$ with $\hat{A} = \begin{bmatrix} A & 0 \\ -C & 0 \end{bmatrix}$ an $(n + l) \times (n + l)$ matrix, $\hat{B} = \begin{bmatrix} B \\ 0 \end{bmatrix}$ an $(n + l) \times m$ matrix and $\hat{C} = \begin{bmatrix} C & 0 \\ 0 & I \end{bmatrix}$ a $2l \times (n + l)$ matrix. Thus, the proportional-plus-integral controller design problem of type (iii) is reduced to an equivalent constant output feedback design problem of type (i) as follows: Given the linear plant (A, B, C), to design the proportional-plus-integral controller (K_1, K_2) we first form the augmented system $(\hat{A}, \hat{B}, \hat{C})$ and then find the constant output feedback matrix $\hat{K}$ for this system. The submatrices of $\hat{K}$ give us the proportional and the integral feedback matrices K_1 and K_2.

4.1. Example

Given the plant

$$\dot{x} = \begin{pmatrix} -2 & 1 \\ 0 & -1 \end{pmatrix} x + \begin{pmatrix} 0 & 1 \\ 1 & 0 \end{pmatrix} u$$

$$y = (1 \quad 0)x$$

define $z = \int^t (y_r - y)\, dt$ and find the proportional and integral feedback matrices required to position the three poles of the plant plus integrator at $-1, -2, -3$.

Let us take the general controller

$$u = -K_1 y - K_2 z$$

where K_1 and K_2 are arbitrary feedback matrices. We now form the matrices of the augmented system $(\hat{A}, \hat{B}, \hat{C})$ and the constant output feedback matrix $\hat{K}$ as follows

$$\hat{A} = \begin{bmatrix} A & 0 \\ -C & 0 \end{bmatrix} = \begin{pmatrix} -2 & 1 & 0 \\ 0 & -1 & 0 \\ -1 & 0 & 0 \end{pmatrix}; \quad \hat{B} = \begin{bmatrix} B \\ 0 \end{bmatrix} = \begin{pmatrix} 0 & 1 \\ 1 & 0 \\ 0 & 0 \end{pmatrix}$$

$$\hat{C} = \begin{bmatrix} C & 0 \\ 0 & I \end{bmatrix} = \begin{pmatrix} 1 & 0 & 0 \\ 0 & 0 & 1 \end{pmatrix}; \quad \hat{K} = [K_1 \quad K_2] = \begin{bmatrix} k_1 & k_2 \\ k_3 & k_4 \end{bmatrix}$$

The closed-loop system matrix A_c then becomes

$$A_c = \hat{A} - \hat{B}\hat{K}\hat{C} = \begin{pmatrix} -2 - k_3 & 1 & -k_4 \\ -k_1 & -1 & -k_2 \\ -1 & 0 & 0 \end{pmatrix}$$

By direct calculation, the closed-loop characteristic polynomial is found to be

$$H(s) = |sI - A_c| = s^3 + (k_3 + 3)s^2 + (k_1 + k_3 - k_4 + 2)s - k_2 - k_4$$

The desired characteristic polynomial is

$$H(s) = (s + 1)(s + 2)(s + 3) = s^3 + 6s^2 + 11s + 6$$

Equating the two expressions for $H(s)$, we obtain three equations in the four unknown feedback gains. Solving in terms of k_4 we obtain

$$\hat{K} = \begin{pmatrix} 6 + k_4 & -6 - k_4 \\ 3 & k_4 \end{pmatrix} \quad \text{with } k_4 \text{ arbitrary.}$$

The required controller is thus

$$u = -\begin{bmatrix} 6 + k_4 \\ 3 \end{bmatrix} y - \begin{bmatrix} -6 - k_4 \\ k_4 \end{bmatrix} z$$

This gives an infinite number of proportional-plus-integral controllers which position the poles at $-1, -2, -3$ since $|sI - \hat{A} + \hat{B}\hat{K}\hat{C}| = (s + 1)(s + 2)(s + 3)$ for all values of k_4 and is independent of k_4.

5. Solution of the General Type (i) Problem

In Sections 3 and 4, it was shown that the dynamic compensator design problem of type (ii) and the proportional-plus-integral controller design problem of type (iii) can both be formulated as an equivalent constant output feedback design problem of type (i). In Section 5.2, we describe a numerical method for solving the general type (i) problem. This method requires a technique for solving the special case of unity rank output feedback which is described first in Section 5.1.

5.1. Design of a unity rank output feedback matrix

In this Section, we describe two numerical methods for calculating the unity rank output feedback matrix required for pole assignment in a multivariable system.

Consider a controllable, observable and cyclic multivariable system described by the state and output equations

$$\dot{x}(t) = Ax(t) + Bu(t)$$
$$y(t) = Cx(t)$$

where $x(t)$ is the $n \times 1$ state vector, $u(t)$ is the $m \times 1$ control input vector with $1 < m < n$, $y(t)$ is the $l \times 1$ output vector with $1 < l < n$ and the matrices B and C are of full ranks m and l respectively. The system can be described by the transfer function relationship

$$Y(s) = \mathrm{C}(s\mathrm{I} - \mathrm{A})^{-1}\mathrm{B}U(s) = \frac{\mathrm{W}(s)}{\mathrm{F}(s)} U(s)$$

where $\mathrm{W}(s) = \mathrm{C}\ \mathrm{adj}\ (s\mathrm{I} - \mathrm{A})\mathrm{B}$ is the $l \times m$ numerator polynomial matrix whose elements are polynomials in s of orders $n - 1$ or less, and $\mathrm{F}(s) = |s\mathrm{I} - \mathrm{A}|$ is the nth order open-loop characteristic polynomial. The numerator polynomial matrix $\mathrm{W}(s)$ and the denominator polynomial $\mathrm{F}(s)$ can be expressed in powers of s as

$$\mathrm{W}(s) = \mathrm{W}_n s^{n-1} + \ldots + \mathrm{W}_2 s + \mathrm{W}_1$$

$$\mathrm{F}(s) = s^n + d_n s^{n-1} + \ldots + d_2 s + d_1$$

where W_i's are constant $l \times m$ coefficient matrices and d_i's are constant scalar coefficients.

Let us now apply the constant output feedback control law $u = u_c - \mathrm{K}y$ where u_c is the $m \times 1$ command input vector, and restrict the $m \times l$ constant output feedback matrix K to have the unity rank (dyadic) structure $\mathrm{K} = qk$ where q and k are constant $m \times 1$ and $1 \times l$ vectors respectively. The closed-loop system then becomes

$$\dot{x}(t) = (\mathrm{A} - \mathrm{BKC})x(t) + \mathrm{B}u_c(t)$$

and the characteristic polynomial of the closed-loop system is $\mathrm{H}(s) = |s\mathrm{I} - \mathrm{A} + \mathrm{BKC}|$. In Ref. 2, it is shown that

$$\begin{aligned} \mathrm{H}(s) &= \mathrm{F}(s) + k\mathrm{W}(s)q \\ &= s^n + d_n s^{n-1} + \ldots + d_2 s + d_1 + k[\mathrm{W}_n s^{n-1} + \ldots + \mathrm{W}_2 s + \mathrm{W}_1]q \end{aligned}$$

hence

$$\mathrm{H}(s) = s^n + (k\mathrm{W}_n q + d_n)s^{n-1} + \ldots + (k\mathrm{W}_2 q + d_2)s + k\mathrm{W}_1 q + d_1 \qquad (1)$$

Let us denote the desired closed-loop pole positions by $\lambda_1, \lambda_2, \ldots, \lambda_n$. Then the desired closed-loop characteristic polynomial is

$$\begin{aligned} \mathrm{H}(s) &= (s - \lambda_1)(s - \lambda_2)\ldots(s - \lambda_n) \\ &= s^n + a_n s^{n-1} + \ldots + a_2 s + a_1 \end{aligned} \qquad (2)$$

Equating expressions (1) and (2) and matching coefficients of like powers of s on both sides gives

$$\begin{aligned} k\mathrm{W}_1 q + d_1 &= a_1 \\ k\mathrm{W}_2 q + d_2 &= a_2 \\ &\vdots \\ k\mathrm{W}_n q + d_n &= a_n \end{aligned} \qquad (3)$$

The pole assignment problem thus reduces to finding the $m + l$ unknown elements of the two vectors q and k to satisfy the set of n nonlinear algebraic eqns (3) as closely as possible. Two numerical methods are now described for the calculation of q and k.

5.1.1. *Method one – Recursive pseudoinverse method*

In this method, the two vectors q and k are recursively modified in turn to solve eqn. (3) by minimizing the error function $E(q, k) = \sum_{i=1}^{n} [kW_iq + d_i - a_i]^2$.

Each equation of (3) is a special kind of nonlinear equation called "bilinear" in that for a given q the equation is linear in k and for a given k it is linear in q. We make use of this bilinearity property and solve eqn. (3) as follows: Treating q as constant, eqn. (3) can be written as a set of linear equations in k as

$$Lk^T = f$$

where L is a constant $n \times l$ matrix whose ith row is $q^T W_i^T$ and $f = [a_1 - d_1, \ldots, a_n - d_n]^T$ is a constant $n \times 1$ vector. Alternatively, treating k as constant, eqn. (3) can be written as a set of linear equations in q as

$$Mq = f$$

where M is a constant $n \times m$ matrix whose ith row is kW_i. Consequently, the bilinear eqn. (3) can be expressed as two sets of linear equations

$$Lk^T = f \quad \text{treating } q \text{ as constant} \tag{4}$$

$$Mq = f \quad \text{treating } k \text{ as constant} \tag{5}$$

Equations (4) and (5) are now solved in the least-squares sense by the following recursive algorithm to minimize the error function

$$E(q, k) = \sum_{i=1}^{n} [kW_iq + d_i - a_i]^2 = \|Lk^T - f\|^2 = \|Mq - f\|^2$$

(i) Set $q = q^{(1)}$, the initial value of q, and find the least-squares solution of eqn. (4) as

$$k^{T(1)} = [L(q^{(1)})]^+ f$$

where + denotes pseudoinverse†. The least-squares error of eqn. (4) is then given by

$$E_1 = E(q^{(1)}, k^{(1)}) = \|L(q^{(1)})\, k^{T(1)} - f\|^2$$

(ii) Set $k = k^{(1)}$ and obtain the least-squares solution of eqn. (5) for q as

$$q^{(2)} = [M(k^{(1)})]^+ f$$

The least-squares error of eqn. (5) is then

$$E_2 = E(q^{(2)}, k^{(1)}) = \|M(k^{(1)})\, q^{(2)} - f\|^2$$

(iii) Update q to its refined value $q^{(2)}$ and repeat (i) to obtain $k^{(2)}$, the refined value of k, and evaluate the least-squares error E_3.

† When the $n \times l$ matrix L is of full rank l, its pseudoinverse L^+ is simply calculated from $L^+ = (L^TL)^{-1}L^T$.

(iv) Set $k = k^{(2)}$ and repeat (ii) to obtain $q^{(3)}$ and evaluate the least-squares error E_4.

(v) Set $q = q^{(3)}$ and repeat from (i) until convergence.

In Ref. 3, it is shown that the successive errors are monotonically decreasing for all initial values $q^{(1)}$ until:

(a) The absolute minimum value of E is reached at ith iteration and $E_{min} > 0$. Then the error cannot decrease any further and $E_j = E_i$ for all $j > i$. In this case the pole assignment problem does not have an exact solution and the best approximate solution is given by the last values of q and k in the ith iteration.

or (b) A local minimum of the error function is reached at the ith iteration and E_{i+1} is not outside this local valley. Then again we have $E_j = E_i$ for all $j > i$. In this case different initial values $q^{(1)}$ must be tried in order to avoid the local minimum.

If neither (a) nor (b) occurs, the pole assignment problem has an exact solution and the error decreases monotonically towards zero and the recursive procedure is continued until the value of the error is acceptable.

5.1.2. *Method two – Iteration using Fletcher's method*

In this method, both vectors q and k are iterated simultaneously using Fletcher's method[4] to solve the set of n nonlinear equations

$$e_1(q, k) = kW_1q + d_1 - a_1 = 0$$

$$\vdots \qquad\qquad \vdots$$

$$e_n(q, k) = kW_nq + d_n - a_n = 0$$

The ith residual error function e_i is expressed as

$$\begin{aligned} e_i(q, k) &= kW_iq + d_i - a_i \\ &= [q^T \quad k] \begin{bmatrix} 0 & 0 \\ W_i & 0 \end{bmatrix} \begin{bmatrix} q \\ k^T \end{bmatrix} + d_i - a_i \end{aligned}$$

or

$$e_i(X) = X^T G_i X + f_i \tag{6}$$

where $X = \begin{bmatrix} q \\ k^T \end{bmatrix}$ is an $(m + l) \times 1$ unknown vector, $G_i = \begin{bmatrix} 0 & 0 \\ W_i & 0 \end{bmatrix}$ is an $(m + l) \times (m + l)$ constant matrix and $f_i = d_i - a_i$ is a constant scalar. The solution to the pole assignment problem thus reduces to finding an appropriate value of the vector X

which satisfies the set of n nonlinear equations

$$e_1(X) = X^T G_1 X + f_1 = 0$$
$$\vdots \qquad\qquad \vdots$$
$$e_n(X) = X^T G_n X + f_n = 0$$

as closely as possible. These equations can be written collectively as $e(X) = 0$. Fletcher's method is now used to solve the nonlinear equation $e(X) = 0$, and as a measure of the error we take the scalar function $E(X) = \|e(X)\|^2 = \sum_{i=1}^{n} e_i^2(X)$. In this method the matrix J (Jacobian) of first derivatives of $e(X)$ with respect to X, i.e. $J_{ij} = \frac{\partial e_i}{\partial X_j}$, is used to generate directions of search along which an approximate solution of $e(X) = 0$ is improved, i.e. $E(X)$ is reduced. The expression for $e_i(X)$, eqn. (6), is differentiated with respect to X to give

$$i\text{th row of } J = \frac{de_i}{dX} = X^T(G_i + G_i^T)$$

hence

$$J(X) = \begin{pmatrix} X^T(G_1 + G_1^T) \\ \vdots \\ X^T(G_n + G_n^T) \end{pmatrix}$$

Fletcher's algorithm is then carried out as follows:

(i) Given an initial X, set $i = 1$.
(ii) Compute $e(X^i)$, $J(X^i)$ and $r^i = -[J(X^i)]^+ e(X^i)$ where + denotes pseudo-inverse.
(iii) Set $X^{i+1} = X^i + \alpha_i r^i$, where α_i is a positive scalar multiplier chosen to prevent the iteration process from diverging.
(iv) Set $i = i + 1$ and repeat from (ii) until convergence.

The positive scalar multiplier α_i in (iii) is used to prevent divergence by ensuring that $E(X^i) = \|e(X^i)\|^2$ is a non-increasing function of i. The value of α_i used to determine X^{i+1} can be chosen in various ways, and two of these are now considered[5]. In the first method α_i is chosen to minimize the error $E(X^{i+1}) = \|e(X^{i+1})\|^2$. This is the most obvious choice to make since it gives the greatest immediate reduction of the error and hence the greatest improvement to the approximate solution X^i. However, this requires the vector function $e(X)$ to be evaluated a number of times and this means an increase in the amount of the computation required compared with the alternative method of choosing a value of α_i which merely reduces the error $E(X^{i+1})$. Frequently, the value of unity is sufficient to do this, but even if it is not so, it is considerably easier to reduce the error than to minimize it. Of course, reducing the error does not give as good an immediate improvement to the solution as error minimization but it does mean that less work is involved in calculating X^{i+1}.

Fletcher[4] has shown that in this algorithm the directions of search r^i generated are always downhill, and so the value of the error E(X) is reduced at each iteration, assuming X^i is not already a stationary point in which case $r^i = 0$. It is interesting to note that in the special case where $n = m + l$ and $\alpha_i = 1$, Fletcher's method becomes the well-known Newton's method.

5.2. Design of an unrestricted output feedback matrix

In this Section, we describe a method for calculating an unrestricted rank output feedback matrix required for pole assignment in a multivariable system. In this method, the feedback matrix is constructed as the sum of a number of unity rank feedback matrices. Each unity rank feedback matrix in the summation is calculated using either method of Section 5.1 in order to move the poles "nearer" to their desired locations by reducing the error function E. When E is sufficiently small (assuming a solution exists), exact pole assignment is achieved and the process is discontinued. In this way, by expressing the feedback matrix as the sum of dyads, the simplicity of the dyadic feedback design of Section 5.1 is fully used in the design of an unrestricted feedback matrix.

Let us again consider the controllable, observable and cyclic multivariable system

$$\dot{x} = \mathrm{A}x + \mathrm{B}u$$

$$y = \mathrm{C}x$$

with the output feedback control law $u = u_c - \mathrm{K}y$ where K is the $m \times l$ unrestricted output feedback matrix. The matrix K is constructed in r stages as follows. [6]

Stage one. Take $q = q_1^{(1)}$ (and $k = k_1^{(1)}$) where $q_1^{(1)}$ (and $k_1^{(1)}$) are the initial values of q (and k) for the first stage and use either method of Section 5.1 to calculate the unity rank feedback matrix $\mathrm{K}_1 = q_1 k_1$ after N_1 iterations and find the corresponding error E_1. The closed-loop characteristic polynomial at this stage is $\mathrm{H}_1(s) = \mathrm{F}(s) + k_1 \mathrm{W}_0(s) q_1$ where $\mathrm{W}_0(s) = \mathrm{C}\ \mathrm{adj}\ (s\mathrm{I} - \mathrm{A})\mathrm{B}$ and $\mathrm{F}(s) = |\, s\mathrm{I} - \mathrm{A}\,|$.

This feedback is then implemented on the open-loop system (A, B, C) to obtain the first-stage closed-loop system (A_1, B, C) where $\mathrm{A}_1 = \mathrm{A} - \mathrm{BK}_1\mathrm{C}$.

Stage two. Start with the new system (A_1, B, C) and treat this as an open-loop system†. Take $q = q_2^{(1)}$ (and $k = k_2^{(1)}$) the initial values of q (and k) for the second stage, and calculate the unity rank feedback matrix $\mathrm{K}_2 = q_2 k_2$ after N_2 iterations and the corresponding error E_2.

The closed-loop characteristic polynomial at this stage is $\mathrm{H}_2(s) = \mathrm{H}_1(s) + k_2 \mathrm{W}_1(s) q_2$ where $\mathrm{W}_1(s) = \mathrm{C}\ \mathrm{adj}\ (s\mathrm{I} - \mathrm{A}_1)\mathrm{B}$.

Then implement K_2 on the system (A_1, B, C) to obtain the second-stage closed-loop system (A_2, B, C) where $\mathrm{A}_2 = \mathrm{A}_1 - \mathrm{BK}_2\mathrm{C}$. The total output feedback implemented on the open-loop system at this stage is $\mathrm{K} = \mathrm{K}_1 + \mathrm{K}_2$ and the feedback matrix K is no longer of unity rank.

We continue repeating this procedure r times until the value of the error E_r is

† If A_1 is not cyclic, an arbitrary output feedback is applied to make it cyclic.

sufficiently small (assuming a solution exists). The total output feedback matrix for the open-loop system is then

$$K = \sum_{i=1}^{r} K_i = q_1 k_1 + q_2 k_2 + \ldots + q_r k_r$$

which is not of unity rank and the final closed-loop characteristic polynomial is given by

$$H_r(s) = F(s) + k_1 W_0(s) q_1 + k_2 W_1(s) q_2 + \ldots + k_r W_{r-1}(s) q_r$$

$$= F(s) + \sum_{i=1}^{r} k_i W_{i-1}(s) q_i$$

where $W_i(s) = C \text{ adj } (sI - A + BK_1C + \ldots + BK_iC)B$.

In Ref. 6, it is shown that

$$E_0 > E_1 > E_2 > \ldots E_r \geqslant 0$$

or, in other words, the error function E decreases at each stage in the algorithm and the method has guaranteed uniform convergence. The error function E stops decreasing when:

(i) a solution has been reached in which case $E = 0$.
or (ii) the absolute minimum value of E, E_{min}, is reached and $E_{min} > 0$ in which case a solution does not exist.
or (iii) a local minimum of E is reached at the ith stage and E_{i+1} is not outside this local valley. In this case, it may be possible to avoid the local minimum by altering some of the initial values.

6. Conclusions

The paper studies the problem of pole assignment in a linear multivariable system using three different types of output feedback controllers (i) constant feedback, (ii) dynamic feedback and (iii) proportional-plus-integral feedback. It is shown that the types (ii) and (iii) problems can be formulated as the type (i) problem using an auxiliary system. Numerical methods are then described for solving the general type (i) problem. It must be pointed out that the existence of the required controllers has not been studied in this paper and still remains an open question. However, the methods described here will find a controller if one exists, so long as local minima are avoided or by-passed, and will give the best approximate solution otherwise. The output feedback control of linear multivariable systems poses many challenging problems and it is hoped that this paper will motivate further research in this area.

7. References

[1] Seraji, H., 1975, "An approach to dynamic compensator design for pole assignment", *Int. J. Control*, **21**(6), pp. 955–966.

[2] Fallside, F. and Seraji, H., 1971, "Pole-shifting procedure for multivariable systems using output feedback", *Proc. I.E.E.*, **118**(11), pp. 1648–1654.

[3] Seraji, H., 1975, "Pole assignment techniques for multivariable systems using unity rank output feedback", *Int. J. Control*, **21**(6), pp. 945–954.

[4] Fletcher, R., 1968, "Generalized inverse methods for the best least-squares solution of systems of non-linear equations", *Computer Journal*, **10**, pp. 392–399.

[5] Broyden, C. G., 1965, "A class of methods for solving nonlinear simultaneous equations", *Mathematics of Computation*, **19**, pp. 577–593.

[6] Seraji, H., 1975, "Pole assignment in multivariable systems with unrestricted output feedback". Arya-Mehr University, Control Systems Group, Technical Report TR3.

Investigation of Rank 2 and Higher Output Feedback for Pole Placement

BANAVAR SRIDHAR†
Dynamics Research Corporation, Wilmington, Mass, U.S.A.

Abstract. One common feature of several pole placement techniques is the use of a dyadic (Rank 1) feedback matrix. The limitation of this design is examined and a design involving output feedback matrices of Rank greater than one is developed as a logical extension of the dyadic feedback design. An example is presented to illustrate the design procedure.

1. Introduction

Modal control has been suggested as a design tool in an effort to circumvent some of the problems in the design of multivariable systems using optimal control (Rosenbrock, 1962). In modal control the eigenvalues of the system matrix are changed to achieve the desired control objective. Much of the work which relates to the concept of modal control has been termed "pole placement". The design of linear multivariable control systems, with pole placement as a specification, has attracted the attention of several authors (Davison, 1970; Retallack and McFarlane, 1970; Fallside and Seraji, 1971; Sridhar and Lindorff, 1973). One common feature of these design methods is a dyadic feedback matrix. This paper discusses some of the disadvantages of this approach and extends the design procedure to feedback matrices of rank greater than one.

2. Statement of the Problem

Consider a controllable and observable linear time invariant multivariable system

$$\left.\begin{aligned} \dot{x} &= \hat{A}x + \hat{B}u \\ y &= \hat{C}x \end{aligned}\right\} \tag{1}$$

where x is an n vector of states, u is an m vector of inputs and y is a p vector of outputs. Let $(\lambda_1, \lambda_2, \ldots, \lambda_n)$ and $(\rho_1, \rho_2, \ldots, \rho_n)$ be the poles of the open loop and

† This work was done while the author was at Ames Research Center, Moffett Field, Ca, U.S.A.

closed loop system, respectively. The problem of pole placement is to find the feedback matrix K such that the closed loop system matrix $(\hat{A} - \hat{B}K\hat{C})$ has the eigenvalues $(\rho_1, \rho_2, \ldots, \rho_n)$.

3. Characteristic Polynomials

Let T be the $n \times n$ non-singular matrix of eigenvectors. We have open loop characteristic polynomial $= |sI - \hat{A}|$

$$= (s - \lambda_1)(s - \lambda_2) \ldots (s - \lambda_n) \tag{2}$$

and

$$\text{closed loop characteristic polynomial} = |sI - \hat{A} + \hat{B}K\hat{C}| = (s - \rho_1)(s - \rho_2) \ldots (s - \rho_n) \tag{3}$$

Further,

$$|sI - \hat{A}| = |T^{-1}|\, |sI - \hat{A}|\, |T| = |sI - T^{-1}\hat{A}T| = |sI - \Lambda| \tag{4}$$

where

$$\Lambda = \text{diag}\,(\lambda_1, \lambda_2, \ldots, \lambda_n)$$

Also,

$$|sI - \hat{A} + \hat{B}K\hat{C}| = |T^{-1}|\, |sI - \hat{A} + \hat{B}K\hat{C}|\, |T| = |T^{-1}(sI - \hat{A} + \hat{B}K\hat{C})T| = |sI - \Lambda + BKC| \tag{5}$$

where $C = \hat{C}T$ and $B = T^{-1}\hat{B}$. Define $M \triangleq BKC$. Then, it is shown in the appendix that

$$\begin{aligned} |sI - \Lambda + BKC| &= |M| + \sum_{i=1}^{n} (s - \lambda_i)M_i \\ &+ \sum_{i=1}^{n-1} \sum_{j=i+1}^{n} (s - \lambda_i)(s - \lambda_j)M_{ij} \\ &+ \sum_{i=1}^{n-2} \sum_{j=i+1}^{n-1} \sum_{k=j+1}^{n} (s - \lambda_i)(s - \lambda_j)(s - \lambda_k)M_{ijk} \\ &+ \ldots + \sum_{i=1}^{n-1} \sum_{j=i+1}^{n} \frac{\overline{M}_{ij} \cdot \Delta}{(s - \lambda_i)(s - \lambda_j)} + \sum_{i=1}^{n} \frac{m_{ii} \cdot \Delta}{s - \lambda_i} + \Delta \end{aligned} \tag{6}$$

where $M_i, M_{ij}, M_{ijk} \ldots$ are the determinant of the matrices obtained by deleting the ith row and jth column, i, j rows and columns, i, j, k rows and columns, ..., respectively. In addition, m_{ij} is the ijth element of M,

$$\overline{M}_{ij} = \begin{vmatrix} m_{ii} & m_{ij} \\ m_{ij} & m_{jj} \end{vmatrix} \quad \text{and} \quad \Delta = (s - \lambda_1)(s - \lambda_2) \ldots (s - \lambda_n)$$

For clarity, further development is carried out in terms of a system with distinct open loop eigenvalues. The open loop and closed loop characteristic polynomials are related by the equation

$$\frac{|sI - \hat{A} + \hat{B}K\hat{C}|}{|sI - \hat{A}|} = 1 + \sum_{i=1}^{n} \frac{\alpha_i}{s - \lambda_i} \tag{7}$$

The value of α_i depends on the closed loop eigenvalues $(\rho_1, \ldots, \rho_n)$. From eqns (6) and (7), we have

$$\begin{aligned}\sum_{i=1}^{n} \frac{\alpha_i}{s-\lambda_i} &= \frac{|M|}{\Delta} + \frac{1}{\Delta}\sum_{i=1}^{n} (s-\lambda_i)M_i \\ &+ \frac{1}{\Delta}\sum_{i=1}^{n-1}\sum_{j=i+1}^{n} (s-\lambda_i)(s-\lambda_j)M_{ij} \\ &+ \frac{1}{\Delta}\sum_{i=1}^{n-2}\sum_{j=i+1}^{n-1}\sum_{k=j+1}^{n} (s-\lambda_i)(s-\lambda_j)(s-\lambda_k)M_{ijk} \\ &+ \ldots \sum_{i=1}^{n-1}\sum_{j=i+1}^{n} \frac{\overline{M}_{ij}}{(s-\lambda_i)(s-\lambda_j)} + \sum_{i=1}^{n} \frac{m_{ii}}{s-\lambda_i}\end{aligned} \tag{8}$$

Note that $|M| = 0$ except for $m = p = n$.

4. Dyadic K Matrix

Results for this case can be obtained easily as a special case of eqn. (8). When K has rank one, that is,

$$K = fd^T \tag{9}$$

$$m_{ij} = b_i K C_j = b_i f d^T c_j = d^T c_j b_i f \tag{10}$$

where $f = [f_1, f_2, \ldots, f_m]^T$, $d^T = [d_1, d_2, \ldots, d_p]$, b_i is the ith row of B and c_i is the ith column of C. With this choice of K

$$|M|, M_i, M_{ij}, M_{ijk}, \ldots, \overline{M}_{ij} = 0 \tag{11}$$

Now eqn. (8) reduces to

$$\sum_{i=1}^{n} \frac{\alpha_i}{s-\lambda_i} = \sum_{i=1}^{n} \frac{m_{ii}}{s-\lambda_i} \tag{12}$$

Then,

$$\alpha_i = m_{ii} = d^T c_i b_i f \tag{13}$$

Equation (13) is the same as eqn. (9) in Sridhar and Lindorff (1973) and K can be found following the procedure outlined by them.

It is important to recall that the simplicity of the above pole-shifting algorithm is a consequence of K being a dyadic. However, this results in a loss of design freedom available in multivariable design problems. In other words, $K = fd^T$ maps any output vector y into a vector proportional to f. As y varies the range of possible controls varies along the line f instead of the range of y. This is illustrated for $m = p = 2$ in Figure 1. The effect of this is that the feedback will couple all the modes of the

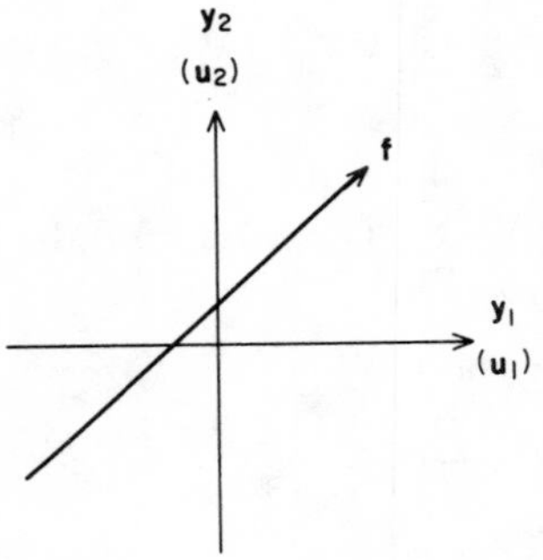

Figure 1. Range of dyadic control ($m = p = 2$).

system although some of the modes of the system may be open loop decoupled and it may be difficult to satisfy performance criteria other than a simple allocation of the closed loop poles. In an effort to overcome some of these difficulties the design is extended to feedback matrices of higher rank in the next section.

5. Feedback Matrix of Rank 2

In this case the determinants of all $l \times l$ matrices formed from M with $l > 2$ are equal to zero and eqn. (8) reduces to

$$\sum_{i=1}^{n} \frac{\alpha_i}{s-\lambda_i} = \frac{|M|}{\Delta} + \sum_{i=1}^{n-1} \sum_{j=i+1}^{n} \frac{\overline{M}_{ij}}{(s-\lambda_i)(s-\lambda_j)} + \sum_{i=1}^{n} \frac{m_{ii}}{s-\lambda_i} \tag{14}$$

Next,

$$\frac{|M|}{\Delta} = \sum_{i=1}^{n} \frac{1}{\prod_{\substack{j=1 \\ j \neq i}}^{n} (\lambda_i - \lambda_j)} \cdot \frac{|M|}{s-\lambda_i} \tag{15}$$

We have

$$\sum_{i=1}^{n-1}\sum_{j=i+1}^{n}\frac{\overline{M}_{ij}}{(s-\lambda_i)(s-\lambda_j)}=\sum_{i=1}^{n-1}\sum_{j=i+1}^{n}\overline{M}_{ij}\left[\frac{1/(\lambda_i-\lambda_j)}{s-\lambda_i}+\frac{1/(\lambda_j-\lambda_i)}{s-\lambda_j}\right]$$

$$=\sum_{i=1}^{n-1}\sum_{j=i+1}^{n}\frac{\overline{M}_{ij}}{\lambda_i-\lambda_j}\left(\frac{1}{s-\lambda_i}-\frac{1}{s-\lambda_j}\right)\tag{16}$$

By expanding the summation on the R.H.S. of (16) and regrouping the terms,

$$\begin{aligned}\sum_{i=1}^{n-1}\sum_{j=i+1}^{n}\frac{\overline{M}_{ij}}{(s-\lambda_i)(s-\lambda_j)}&=\frac{1}{s-\lambda_1}\left[\frac{\overline{M}_{12}}{\lambda_1-\lambda_2}+\frac{\overline{M}_{13}}{\lambda_1-\lambda_3}+\ldots+\frac{\overline{M}_{1,n-1}}{\lambda_1-\lambda_{n-1}}\right]\\
&\quad\frac{1}{s-\lambda_2}\left[-\frac{\overline{M}_{12}}{\lambda_1-\lambda_2}+\frac{\overline{M}_{23}}{\lambda_2-\lambda_3}+\ldots+\frac{\overline{M}_{2,n-1}}{\lambda_2-\lambda_{n-1}}+\frac{\overline{M}_{2n}}{\lambda_2-\lambda_n}\right]\\
&\quad+\frac{1}{s-\lambda_3}\left[-\frac{\overline{M}_{13}}{\lambda_1-\lambda_3}-\frac{\overline{M}_{23}}{\lambda_2-\lambda_3}+\frac{\overline{M}_{34}}{\lambda_3-\lambda_4}+\ldots+\frac{\overline{M}_{3n}}{\lambda_3-\lambda_n}\right]\\
&\quad+\ \vdots\\
&\quad+\frac{1}{s-\lambda_{n-1}}\left[-\frac{\overline{M}_{1,n-1}}{\lambda_1-\lambda_{n-1}}-\frac{\overline{M}_{2,n-1}}{\lambda_2-\lambda_{n-1}}-\ldots-\frac{\overline{M}_{n-2,n-1}}{\lambda_{n-2}-\lambda_{n-1}}+\frac{\overline{M}_{n-1,n}}{\lambda_{n-1}-\lambda_n}\right]\\
&\quad+\frac{1}{s-\lambda_n}\left[-\frac{\overline{M}_{1n}}{\lambda_1-\lambda_n}-\frac{\overline{M}_{2n}}{\lambda_2-\lambda_n}-\ldots-\frac{\overline{M}_{n-2,n-1}}{\lambda_{n-2}-\lambda_n}-\frac{\overline{M}_{n-1,n}}{\lambda_{n-1}-\lambda_n}\right]\end{aligned}\tag{17}$$

observing the fact that

$$\overline{M}_{ij}=\overline{M}_{ji}=\begin{vmatrix}m_{ii} & m_{ij}\\ m_{ji} & m_{jj}\end{vmatrix}$$

eqn. (17) becomes

$$\begin{aligned}\sum_{i=1}^{n-1}\sum_{j=i+1}^{n}\frac{\overline{M}_{ij}}{(s-\lambda_i)(s-\lambda_j)}&=\frac{1}{s-\lambda_1}\sum_{i=2}^{n}\frac{\overline{M}_{1i}}{\lambda_1-\lambda_i}+\frac{1}{s-\lambda_2}\sum_{\substack{i=1\\ i\neq 2}}^{n}\frac{\overline{M}_{2i}}{\lambda_2-\lambda_i}\\
&\quad+\ldots+\frac{1}{s-\lambda_n}\sum_{i=1}^{n-1}\frac{\overline{M}_{ni}}{\lambda_n-\lambda_i}\\
&=\sum_{i=1}^{n}\frac{1}{s-\lambda_i}\sum_{\substack{j=1\\ j\neq i}}^{n}\frac{\overline{M}_{ij}}{\lambda_i-\lambda_j}\end{aligned}\tag{18}$$

Combining eqns (14), (15), and (18) we have

$$\sum_{i=1}^{n} \frac{\alpha_i}{s-\lambda_i} = \sum_{i=1}^{n} \frac{1}{\prod_{\substack{j=1 \\ j \neq i}}^{n} (\lambda_i - \lambda_j)} \cdot \frac{|\mathrm{M}|}{s-\lambda_i} + \sum_{i=1}^{n} \frac{1}{s-\lambda_i} \sum_{\substack{j=1 \\ j \neq i}}^{n} \frac{\overline{\mathrm{M}}_{ij}}{\lambda_i - \lambda_j} + \sum_{i=1}^{n} \frac{m_{ii}}{s-\lambda_i}$$

Equating coefficients of $(s-\lambda_i)^{-1}$,

$$\alpha_i = \frac{|\mathrm{M}|}{\prod_{\substack{j=1 \\ j \neq i}}^{n} (\lambda_i - \lambda_j)} + \sum_{\substack{j=1 \\ j \neq i}}^{n} \frac{\overline{\mathrm{M}}_{ij}}{\lambda_i - \lambda_j} + m_{ii}, \quad i = 1, 2, \ldots, n \tag{19}$$

For $n > 2$, eqn. (19) reduces to

$$\alpha_i = \sum_{\substack{j=1 \\ j \neq i}}^{n} \frac{\overline{\mathrm{M}}_{ij}}{\lambda_i - \lambda_j} + m_{ii}, \quad i = 1, 2, \ldots, n \tag{20}$$

K can be decomposed as the product of two matrices G and H, that is, K = GH where G is a $(m \times 2)$ matrix and H is a $(2 \times p)$ matrix. Further,

$$\mathrm{G} = \begin{bmatrix} g_1 \\ g_2 \\ \cdot \\ \cdot \\ \cdot \\ g_m \end{bmatrix}, \quad \mathrm{H} = [h_1 \quad h_2 \quad \ldots \quad h_p], \quad g_i = [g_{i1} \quad g_{i2}], \quad h_i = \begin{bmatrix} h_{1i} \\ h_{2i} \end{bmatrix}$$

$$\mathrm{K} = \begin{bmatrix} g_1h_1 & g_1h_2 & \ldots & g_1h_p \\ \cdot & & & \\ \cdot & & & \\ \cdot & & & \\ g_mh_1 & g_mh_2 & \ldots & g_mh_p \end{bmatrix}$$

and $m_{ij} = b_i\mathrm{K}c_j = b_i\mathrm{GH}c_j$. Now, we have to solve the n nonlinear equations (20) in $2(m+p)$ variables for pole placement using output feedback matrices of Rank 2.

Example

This simple example illustrates the differences between the dyadic and Rank 2 method of pole placement. Consider the system

$$\dot{x} = \begin{bmatrix} 1 & 0 & 0 \\ 0 & -1 & 0 \\ 0 & 0 & -3 \end{bmatrix} x + \begin{bmatrix} 1 & 0 \\ 0 & 1 \\ 1 & 1 \end{bmatrix} u$$

$$y = \begin{bmatrix} 1 & 0 & 0 \\ 0 & 1 & 1 \end{bmatrix} x$$

The system transfer function is

$$y = \begin{bmatrix} \dfrac{1}{s-1} & 0 \\ \dfrac{1}{s+3} & \dfrac{2s+4}{(s+1)(s+3)} \end{bmatrix} u$$

The system is observable and controllable with $m = 2, p = 2$, and $n = 3$. The output y_1 depends only on the input u_1. The open loop poles are at $1, -1$, and -3. It is desired to stabilize the system while maintaining that y_1 depends only on u_1.

Max $(m, p) = 2$ poles can be placed using the output feedback. Let the closed loop poles be at $-\rho_1 = -0.5, -\rho_2 = -1.5$ while the location of the third pole $-\rho_3$ depends on $(-\rho_1, -\rho_2)$. For this choice of closed loop poles,

$$\alpha_1 = \frac{15}{32}(1 + \rho_3)$$

$$\alpha_2 = \frac{2}{32}(2 + \rho_3)$$

$$\alpha_3 = \frac{15}{32}(-3 + \rho_3)$$

For a dyadic feedback

$$K = \begin{bmatrix} f_1 \\ f_2 \end{bmatrix} [d_1 d_2] = \begin{bmatrix} f_1 d_1 & f_1 d_2 \\ f_2 d_1 & f_2 d_2 \end{bmatrix}$$

Since

$$d^T c_i b_i f = \alpha_i, \quad i = 1, 2, 3$$

We have

$$d_1 f_1 = -3/2(1 + \rho_3)$$

$$d_2 f_2 = 12/5(2 + \rho_3)$$

$$d_2(f_1 + f_2) = 1/10(\rho_3 - 3)$$

Solving these equations with $d_1 = 1$ and $d_2 = -2$, we get

$$f_1 = 0.6104 \quad \text{and} \quad f_2 = 0.0218$$

For this choice of

$$K = \begin{bmatrix} 0.6104 & -1.2208 \\ 0.0218 & -0.0436 \end{bmatrix}$$

two poles can be placed at (−0.5, −1.5) and the third pole is located at −0.3023. However, it is not possible to satisfy the second criterion that y_1 depend only on u_1 as can be seen from the closed loop system matrix

$$A - BKC = \begin{bmatrix} 1 - f_1 d_1 & -f_1 d_2 & -f_1 d_2 \\ -f_2 d_1 & -1 - f_2 d_2 & -f_2 d_2 \\ -(f_1 + f_2) d_1 & -(f_1 + f_2) d_2 & -3 - (f_1 + f_2) d_2 \end{bmatrix}$$

Next consider K with Rank 2 which can be written as

$$K = \begin{bmatrix} f_{11} & f_{12} \\ f_{21} & f_{22} \end{bmatrix} \begin{bmatrix} d_{11} & d_{12} \\ d_{21} & d_{22} \end{bmatrix} = \begin{bmatrix} g_1 \\ g_2 \end{bmatrix} [h_1 \quad h_2]$$

where $g_1 = [f_{11} \quad f_{12}]$, $g_2 = [f_{21} \quad f_{22}]$, $h_1 = [d_{11} \quad d_{21}]^T$ and $h_2 = [d_{12} \quad d_{22}]^T$. The closed loop system matrix with the new feedback is given by

$$A - BKC = \begin{bmatrix} 1 - g_1 h_1 & -g_1 h_2 & -g_1 h_2 \\ -g_2 h_1 & -1 - g_2 h_2 & -g_2 h_2 \\ -(g_1 + g_2) h_1 & -(g_1 + g_2) h_2 & -3 - (g_1 + g_2) h_2 \end{bmatrix}$$

If y_1 should depend only on u_1 then

$$-g_1 h_2 = 0$$

From (20), for pole placement we have to satisfy the equations

$$\sum_{\substack{j=1 \\ j \neq i}}^{3} \frac{\overline{M}_{ij}}{\lambda_i - \lambda_j} + m_{ii} = \alpha_i, \qquad i = 1, 2, 3$$

These equations with the condition $-g_1 h_2 = 0$ reduce to

$$\frac{3}{4} g_1 h_1 \cdot g_2 h_2 + g_1 h_1 = \alpha_1$$

$$-\frac{1}{2} g_1 h_1 \cdot g_2 h_2 + g_2 h_2 = \alpha_2$$

$$-\frac{1}{4} g_1 h_1 \cdot g_2 h_2 + g_2 h_2 = \alpha_3$$

As in the dyadic case, the choice of closed loop poles at (−0.5, −1.5) require that $\alpha_1 = (15/32)(1 + \rho_3)$, $\alpha_2 = (2/32)(2 + \rho_3)$ and $\alpha_3 = (15/32)(-3 + \rho_3)$. Noticing the fact that $g_1h_1 = k_{11}$, $g_2h_2 = k_{22}$ and $g_1h_2 = k_{12}$, the feedback matrix has to be chosen subject to

$$k_{12} = 0$$

$$k_{11} + \frac{3}{4}k_{11} \cdot k_{22} = \frac{15}{32}(\rho_3 + 1)$$

$$k_{22} - \frac{1}{2}k_{11} \cdot k_{22} = \frac{2}{32}(\rho_3 - 1)$$

$$k_{22} - \frac{1}{4}k_{11} \cdot k_{22} = \frac{15}{32}(\rho_3 - 3)$$

Solving these equations

$$\mathrm{K} = \begin{bmatrix} \frac{3}{2} & 0 \\ k_{21} & \frac{3}{4} \end{bmatrix}$$

and the third pole is located at −4. With $k_{21} = -3/2$, the closed loop system transfer function is

$$y = \begin{bmatrix} \dfrac{1}{s + 0.5} & 0 \\ \dfrac{s^2 + 1.55s - 5.5}{(s + 0.5)(s + 1.5)(s + 4)} & \dfrac{2s + 7}{(s + 1.5)(s + 4)} \end{bmatrix} u$$

and the closed loop system meets the design requirements.

6. Other Methods

Feedback matrices of higher rank can be easily computed for the pole placement of multivariable systems using state feedback by Kalman's (1971) method. The given system is transformed to the Luenberger canonical form (Jordan and Sridhar, 1973). Let $\sigma_1, \sigma_2, \ldots, \sigma_m$ be the controllability indices of the system. Then the transformed system is given by

$$\dot{\xi} = \mathrm{A}\xi + \mathrm{B}u$$

where

$$\mathrm{A} = \begin{bmatrix} \mathrm{A}_{11} & \mathrm{A}_{12} & \cdots & \mathrm{A}_{1m} \\ \vdots & & & \vdots \\ \vdots & & & \vdots \\ \mathrm{A}_{m,1} & \mathrm{A}_{m2} & \cdots & \mathrm{A}_{m,m} \end{bmatrix} \quad \text{and} \quad \mathrm{B} = \begin{bmatrix} \mathrm{B}_{11} \\ \mathrm{B}_{12} \\ \vdots \\ \mathrm{B}_{1m} \end{bmatrix}$$

The dimensions of A_{ij} and B_{1i} and $(\sigma_i \times \sigma_j)$ and $(\sigma_m \times m)$, respectively. Further,

$$A_{ii} = \begin{bmatrix} 0 & 1 & 0 & \dots & 0 \\ 0 & 0 & 1 & \dots & 0 \\ & & & \cdot & \\ & & & \cdot & \\ & & & \cdot & \\ 0 & 0 & 0 & \dots & 1 \\ * & * & * & \dots & * \end{bmatrix}, \quad A_{ij} = \begin{bmatrix} 0 & 0 & 0 & \dots & 0 \\ \vdots & \vdots & \vdots & & \vdots \\ * & * & * & \dots & * \end{bmatrix}$$

and

$$B_{1i} = \begin{bmatrix} 0 & 0 & & \dots & & 0 \\ \vdots & & & & & \\ 0 & \dots & 1 & * & & * \end{bmatrix}$$

$\uparrow$ ith column

The * denotes a nonzero element. From a study of the Luenberger's canonical form it is evident that the feedback affects only the $\sigma_1, (\sigma_1 + \sigma_2), \dots, (\sigma_1 + \sigma_2 + \dots, \sigma_m)$ rows of the system matrix. Let A_m, B_m and A_d consist of the $\sigma_1, (\sigma_1 + \sigma_2), \dots, (\sigma_1 + \sigma_2 + \dots, \sigma_m)$ rows of A, B and (A + BK), respectively. Then,

$$A_d = A_m + B_m K \tag{21}$$

and

$$K = B_m^{-1}(A_d - A_m) \tag{22}$$

B_m^{-1} exists since det $B_m = 1$. In particular, if we choose

$$A_d = \begin{bmatrix} 0 & \dots & 1 & & \dots & \dots & 0 \\ 0 & \dots & 0 & \dots & 1 & \dots & 0 \\ \vdots & & & & & & \\ 0 & \dots & 0 & & \dots & 1 & 0 \\ -a_0 & -a_1 & & & \dots & \dots & -a_{n-1} \end{bmatrix}$$

where the last row corresponds to the coefficient of the closed loop characteristic polynomial

$$(s - \rho_1)(s - \rho_2) \dots (s - \rho_n) = s^n + a_{n-1}s^{n-1} + \dots a_1 s + a_0$$

and the 1's appear in the $\sigma_1, (\sigma_1 + \sigma_2), \dots, (\sigma_1 + \sigma_2 + \dots, \sigma_{m-1})$ columns. With this, A_d,

$$A + BK = \begin{bmatrix} 0 & 1 & \dots & 0 \\ \vdots & & \ddots & \vdots \\ 0 & \cdot & \dots & 1 \\ -a_0 & -a_1 & \dots & -a_{n-1} \end{bmatrix}$$

has eigenvalues at $(\rho_1, \rho_2, \ldots, \rho_n)$ and K is given by (22).

The above constructive procedure reduces to

$$KC = B_m^{-1}(A_d - A_m) \tag{23}$$

for pole placement by output feedback. Munro (1973) has given conditions under which eqn. (23) can be solved to obtain arbitrary assignment of all the poles using constant output feedback.

Sankaran (1974) has suggested an iterative procedure for determining the constant gain output feedback matrix that will stabilize a system. If the system matrix A varies to A + δA, then the corresponding variation in the eigenvalue is given by (Rosenbrock, 1965)

$$\delta\lambda_r = \frac{\text{trace}\ [Q \cdot \delta A]}{\text{trace}\ [Q]} \tag{24}$$

where

$$Q = \prod_{\substack{i=1 \\ i \neq r}}^{n} (A - \lambda_i I)$$

Assuming that δA results due to output feedback and denoting the gain matrix by δK, then

$$\delta A = B \cdot \delta K \cdot C$$

and a linear equation can be written for the elements of the gain matrix. Since the equation (24) is valid only for small perturbations, variations in the eigenvalues should be applied in small steps in the desired direction to compute δK.

The relative merits of the Jordan canonical form approach to pole placement outlined in this paper and the Kalman approach to pole placement are discussed in the next few paragraphs. Godbout (1974) has made an extensive comparison of the two methods.

The Kalman method of pole placement uses the Luenberger Canonical Form of a system to shift the modes of that system. However, a system must be completely controllable in order to be transformed to Luenberger form. This restriction implies that the Kalman algorithm cannot be applied to any system that has at least one uncontrollable mode. This is not the case with the Jordan Canonical Form approach to pole placement. This algorithm allows the shifting of any or all of the controllable modes of a system that may also contain uncontrollable modes. This is a significant advantage for the Jordan Canonical Form approach over the Kalman approach.

The control over pole motion is probably the most desirable feature of the Jordan Canonical Form scheme. The method allows the designer to choose the closed-loop value to which a specified open-loop mode will be shifted. The Kalman algorithm does not have this feature. The pole motion cannot be chosen or even determined when using this method.

The Kalman pole placement scheme does have one desirable characteristic in that it is very straightforward. Furthermore, the Kalman method does not require knowledge of the eigenvalues of the system, whereas the Jordan Canonical Form approach needs an accurate estimate of the eigenvalues in order to construct the Jordan form of the system properly. These eigenvalue estimates are generated by Francis' QR method which sometimes has difficulty converging when a system has repeated roots.

7. Conclusions

This paper considers the problem of pole placement in multivariable systems using output feedback matrices of Rank greater than one with particular reference to matrices of Rank 2. The results have been developed for a system with distinct eigenvalues. However, they can be easily extended to systems with multiple eigenvalues. The feedback matrices of higher rank provide considerable design freedom. But, the resulting equations for the feedback matrix are more complex than in the dyadic case.

8. Appendix

Theorem: Let Ω be a diagonal matrix with elements $(\Omega_1, \Omega_2, \ldots, \Omega_n)$ and let M be a $n \times n$ matrix. Then

$$
\begin{aligned}
|\Omega + \mathrm{M}| = |\mathrm{M}| &+ \sum_{i=1}^{n} \Omega_i \mathrm{M}_i + \sum_{i=1}^{n-1} \sum_{j=i+1}^{n} \Omega_i \Omega_j \mathrm{M}_{ij} \\
&+ \sum_{i=1}^{n-2} \sum_{j=i+1}^{n-1} \sum_{k=j+1}^{n} \Omega_i \Omega_j \Omega_k \mathrm{M}_{ijk} + \ldots \\
&+ \sum_{i=1}^{n-1} \sum_{j=i+1}^{n} \frac{\overline{\mathrm{M}}_{ij} \cdot \Delta}{\Omega_i \cdot \Omega_j} + \sum_{i=1}^{n} \frac{m_{ii} \cdot \Delta}{\Omega_i} + \Delta
\end{aligned}
$$

where $\mathrm{M}_i, \mathrm{M}_{ij}, \mathrm{M}_{ijk} \ldots$ are the determinant of the matrices obtained by deleting the ith row and column, i, j rows and columns, i, j, k rows and columns, . . . , respectively. In addition,

$$
\overline{\mathrm{M}}_{ij} = \begin{vmatrix} m_{ii} & m_{ij} \\ m_{ji} & m_{jj} \end{vmatrix}
$$

and $\Delta = \Omega_1 \Omega_2 \ldots \Omega_n$.

Proof: The proof depends on the repeated application of the following Lemma.

Lemma (Stiab, 1969)

Let P, Q and R be three $n \times n$ matrices identical except for their pth rows. Further, let the pth row of R be the vector sum of the pth rows of P and Q. Then,

$$
|\mathrm{R}| = |\mathrm{P}| + |\mathrm{Q}| \tag{A1}
$$

Define

$$M^l \triangleq \begin{bmatrix} \Omega_1 + m_{11} & m_{12} & \cdots & m_{1l} & \cdots & m_{1n} \\ m_{12} & \Omega_2 + m_{22} & \cdots & m_{2l} & \cdots & m_{2n} \\ \vdots & \vdots & \ddots & & & \vdots \\ m_{l1} & m_{l2} & \cdots & \Omega_l + m_{ll} & \cdots & m_{ln} \\ \vdots & \vdots & & \vdots & \ddots & \vdots \\ m_{n1} & m_{n2} & & m_{nl} & & m_{nn} \end{bmatrix}$$

and $M_{12\ldots n} \triangleq 1$. From the lemma,

$$M^1 = \begin{bmatrix} \Omega_1 + m_{11} & m_{12} & \cdots & m_{1n} \\ m_{21} & m_{22} & \cdots & m_{2n} \\ \vdots & & & \vdots \\ m_{n1} & m_{n2} & \cdots & m_{nn} \end{bmatrix} = |M| + \begin{bmatrix} \Omega_1 & 0 & \cdots & 0 \\ m_{21} & m_{22} & \cdots & m_{2n} \\ \vdots & & & \\ m_{n1} & m_{n2} & \cdots & m_{nn} \end{bmatrix}$$

that is,

$$M^1 = |M| + \Omega_1 M_1 \tag{A2}$$

Again from eqns (A1) and (A2)

$$M^2 = \begin{bmatrix} \Omega_1 + m_{11} & m_{12} & \cdots & m_{1n} \\ m_{21} & \Omega_2 + m_{22} & \cdots & m_{2n} \\ \vdots & \vdots & & \\ m_{n1} & m_{n2} & \cdots & m_{nn} \end{bmatrix} = M^1 + \begin{bmatrix} \Omega_1 + m_{11} & m_{12} & \cdots & m_{1n} \\ 0 & \Omega_2 & \cdots & 0 \\ \vdots & \vdots & & \vdots \\ m_{n1} & m_{n2} & \cdots & m_{nn} \end{bmatrix}$$

that is,

$$M^2 = M^1 + \Omega_2[M_2 + \Omega_1 M_{12}]$$

$$= |M| + \sum_{i=1}^{2} \Omega_i M_i + \Omega_1 \Omega_2 M_{12} \tag{A3}$$

Next,

$$M^3 = M^2 + \begin{bmatrix} \Omega_1 + m_{11} & m_{12} & m_{13} & \dots & m_{1n} \\ m_{21} & \Omega_2 + m_{22} & m_{23} & \dots & m_{2n} \\ 0 & 0 & \Omega_3 & \dots & 0 \\ \vdots & & & & \vdots \\ m_{n1} & m_{n2} & m_{n3} & \dots & m_{nn} \end{bmatrix}$$

$$= |M| + \sum_{i=1}^{3} \Omega_i M_i + \sum_{i=1}^{2} \sum_{j=i+1}^{3} \Omega_i \Omega_j M_{ij} + \Omega_1 \Omega_2 \Omega_3 M_{123} \qquad \text{(A4)}$$

Applying the lemma successively to $M^4, M^5, \dots, M^n$

$$M^n = |M| + \sum_{i=1}^{n} \Omega_i M_i + \sum_{i=1}^{n-1} \sum_{j=i+1}^{n} \Omega_i \Omega_j M_{ij} + \sum_{i=1}^{n-2} \sum_{j=i+1}^{n-1} \sum_{k=j+1}^{n} \Omega_i \Omega_j \Omega_k M_{ijk}$$

$$+ \dots + \sum_{i=1}^{3} \sum_{j=i+1}^{4} \dots \sum_{p}^{n-1} \sum_{q=p+1}^{n} \Omega_i \Omega_j \dots \Omega_p \Omega_q \Omega_r M_{ijk \dots pq}$$

$$+ \sum_{i=1}^{2} \sum_{j=i+1}^{3} \dots \sum_{q}^{n-1} \sum_{r=q+1}^{n} \Omega_i \Omega_j \dots \Omega_p \Omega_q \Omega_r M_{ijk \dots pqr} + \Delta$$

$M_{ijk \dots pq}$ is the matrix with $(n-1)$ rows and columns deleted, that is, it is one of the diagonal elements of M. Also,

$$\Omega_1 \Omega_2 \dots \Omega_{i-1} \Omega_{i+1} \dots \Omega_n = \frac{\Delta}{\Omega_i}$$

Hence,

$$\sum_{i=1}^{2} \sum_{j=i+1}^{3} \dots \sum_{q}^{n-1} \sum_{r=q+1}^{n} \Omega_i \Omega_j \Omega_k \dots \Omega_p \Omega_q \Omega_r M_{ijk \dots pqr} = \sum_{i=1}^{n} \frac{m_{ii} \cdot \Delta}{\Omega_i}$$

Recalling the definition of $\overline{M}_{ij}$,

$$\sum_{i=1}^{3} \sum_{j=i+1}^{4} \dots \sum_{p}^{n-1} \sum_{q=p+1}^{n} \Omega_i \Omega_j \dots \Omega_p \Omega_q M_{ijk \dots pq} = \sum_{i=1}^{n-1} \sum_{j=i+1}^{n} \frac{\overline{M}_{ij}}{\Omega_i \Omega_j} \cdot \Delta$$

Now we can rewrite

$$|\Omega + M| = M^n = |M| + \sum_{i=1}^{n} \Omega_i M_i + \sum_{i=1}^{n-1} \sum_{j=i+1}^{n} \Omega_i \Omega_j M_{ij}$$

$$+ \sum_{i=1}^{n-2} \sum_{j=i+1}^{n-1} \sum_{k=j+1}^{n} \Omega_i \Omega_j \Omega_k M_{ijk} + \ldots$$

$$+ \sum_{i=1}^{n-1} \sum_{j=i+1}^{n} \frac{\overline{M}_{ij} \cdot \Delta}{\Omega_i \Omega_j} + \sum_{i=1}^{n} \frac{m_{ii} \cdot \Delta}{\Omega_i} + \Delta$$

This proves the theorem.

Closed Loop Characteristic Polynomial:

$$|sI - \Lambda + BKC|$$

This is a special case of the theorem with

$$\Omega_i = (s - \lambda_i), \quad i = 1, 2, \ldots, n \quad \text{and} \quad M = BKC$$

9. References

[1] Davison, E. J., 1970, *I.E.E.E. Trans. Auto. Control*, Vol. 15, p. 348.
[2] Fallside, F. and Seraji, H., 1971, *Proc. Inst. Elec. Engrs.*, Vol. 118, p. 1648.
[3] Godbout, L. F., 1974, M.S. Thesis, Univ. of Connecticut.
[4] Jordan, D. and Sridhar, B., 1973, *I.E.E.E. Trans. Auto. Control*, Vol. 18, p. 292.
[5] Kalman, R. E., 1971, Ordinary Differential Equations, Ed., L. Weiss (Academic Press), p. 348.
[6] Munro, N. and Vardulakis, A. I., 1973, Univ. of Manchester Control Systems Center, Report No. 205.
[7] Retallack, D. G. and McFarlane, A. G. J., 1970, *Proc. Inst. Elec. Engrs.*, Vol. 117, p. 1037.
[8] Rosenbrock, H. H., 1962, *Chem. Eng. Prog.*, Vol. 58, p. 1962.
[9] Rosenbrock, H. H., 1965, *Electronic Letter*, Vol. 1, p. 278.
[10] Sankaran, V., 1974, NASA TM X-71, 986.
[11] Sridhar, B. and Lindorff, D. P., 1973, *Int. J. Control*, Vol. 18, p. 993.
[12] Staib, J. H., 1969, An Introduction to Matrices and Linear Transformations. (Addison–Wesley Pub. Co., Inc.) Chap. 4.

Multivariable System Zeros

W. A. WOLOVICH
Division of Engineering
Brown University
Providence, Rhode Island
U.S.A.

Abstract. The notion of a "numerator" of a multivariable system characterized by a rational transfer matrix is defined. The equivalence of any two numerators of the same transfer matrix is formally established and employed in the development of a number of equivalent definitions of the zeros of a rational transfer matrix. The fact that all of the defined zeros of a proper linear multivariable system can be "cancelled" (rendered unobservable) by an appropriate linear state variable feedback control law is constructively established. A matrix rank test is developed for directly determining the zeros of a multivariable system in state–space form.

1. Introduction

In the case of a scalar (single input/output) system characterized by a rational transfer function,

$$t(s) = \frac{r(s)}{p(s)} \tag{1}$$

with $r(s)$ and $p(s)$ relatively prime polynomials in the Laplace operator s; the *zeros* of the system [or $t(s)$] are defined as those scalars s_i belonging to the complex field $\mathscr{C}$ which "zero" $t(s)$; i.e., s_i is a zero of $t(s)$ if, and only if,

$$t(s_i) = \frac{r(s_i)}{p(s_i)} = 0 = r(s_i) \tag{2}$$

It is thus clear that the zeros of $t(s)$ are equal to the zeros of its *numerator* $r(s)$. Physically speaking, the zeros of a scalar system represent those dynamical "modes" of the system that will not appear at the system output when an appropriate set of initial conditions is placed on the internal state of the system and an appropriate input is applied. These points will be clarified and extended to the multivariable case in our subsequent discussions.

It is of general interest to extend the notion of the zeros of a scalar system to include the multivariable (multi-input/output) case and while some recent results [1, 2] have essentially resolved this extension via "different" definitions of the zeros of a rational transfer matrix, some rather significant questions remain unresolved regarding not only the equivalence of these definitions but also alternative definitions and methods that can be employed to determine the zeros of a multivariable system. The primary purpose of this report will be therefore to resolve these questions, and we will begin by defining a "numerator" of a rational transfer matrix and formally establishing the "equivalence" of any two numerators of the same transfer matrix.

2. The Numerators of $T(s)$

We first note that any $(p \times m)$ rational transfer matrix $T(s)$ can be factored in either of two (nonunique) ways [1–3]; i.e.,

$$T(s) = R(s)P_c^{-1}(s) = P_0^{-1}(s)Q(s) \tag{3}$$

with $R(s)$ and $P_c(s)$ *relatively right prime* (RRP), [1, 3] $P_0(s)$ and $Q(s)$ *relatively left prime* (RLP) polynomial matrices of the appropriate dimensions and $P_c(s)$ ($P_0(s)$) nonsingular over $\mathscr{R}$, the field of rational functions in s.

Definition. Any $(p \times m)$ polynomial matrix $R(s)$ or $Q(s)$ that satisfies (3) will be called a *numerator* of $T(s)$.

Theorem 1. *Any two numerators of a $(p \times m)$ rational transfer matrix are equivalent; i.e., if $R(s)$ and $Q(s)$ are both numerators of $T(s)$, then*

$$U_L(s)R(s)U_R(s) = Q(s) \tag{4}$$

for an appropriate pair $\{U_L(s), U_R(s)\}$ of unimodular matrices†.

Proof. If $T(s) = R(s)P_c^{-1}(s) = \bar{R}(s)\bar{P}_c^{-1}(s)$, both RRP factorizations, then $R(s)$ and $\bar{R}(s)$ are both numerators of $T(s)$ with

$$R(s) = \bar{R}(s)\bar{P}_c^{-1}(s)P_c(s) \tag{5}$$

Since $\bar{R}(s)$ and $\bar{P}_c(s)$ are RRP, there exists [1, 3] a polynomial matrix pair $\{M(s), N(s)\}$ such that

$$M(s)\bar{R}(s) + N(s)\bar{P}_c(s) = I_m \tag{6}$$

If we now represent $\bar{P}_c^{-1}(s)$ as the quotient of its *adjoint* $\bar{P}_c^{+}(s)$ and its *determinant* $|\bar{P}_c(s)|$ and then postmultiply (6) by $\bar{P}_c^{+}(s)P_c(s)$, we obtain

$$M(s)\bar{R}(s)\bar{P}_c^{+}(s)P_c(s) + N(s)\bar{P}_c(s)\bar{P}_c^{+}(s)P_c(s) = \bar{P}_c^{+}(s)P_c(s) \tag{7}$$

Since $\bar{R}(s)\bar{P}_c^{+}(s)P_c(s) = R(s)|\bar{P}_c(s)|$ in view of (5) and $\bar{P}_c(s)\bar{P}_c^{+}(s) = |\bar{P}_c(s)|I_m$, it is clear that $|\bar{P}_c(s)|$ divides both left side members of (7) and, therefore, that $|\bar{P}_c(s)|$ must divide the right side, $\bar{P}_c^{+}(s)P_c(s)$, as well; i.e.

$$\bar{P}_c^{+}(s)P_c(s) \div |\bar{P}_c(s)| = \bar{P}_c^{-1}(s)P_c(s) = G_R(s) \tag{8}$$

† A polynomial matrix U(s) is a unimodular matrix [1, 2] if, and only if, $|U(s)| = \alpha$, a nonzero scalar belonging to the real field R.

a nonsingular, polynomial matrix, *right divisor*[3] of both $R(s)$ and $P_c(s)$. Therefore, in view of (8), $P_c(s) = \bar{P}_c(s)G_R(s)$ and in view of (5), $R(s) = \bar{R}(s)G_R(s)$. Since $R(s)$ and $P_c(s)$ are RRP however, any common right divisor must be a unimodular matrix, i.e. $G_R(s) = U_R(s)$, thus establishing the (*column*) *equivalence*[3] of the two numerators $R(s)$ and $\bar{R}(s)$. By "duality" (by transposing matrices and essentially repeating the above arguments), it now follows that if $T(s) = P_0^{-1}(s)Q(s) = \bar{P}_0^{-1}(s)\bar{Q}(s)$ with both $P_0(s)$ and $Q(s)$ and $\bar{P}_0(s)$ and $\bar{Q}(s)$ relatively left prime (RLP), then $Q(s) = P_0(s)\bar{P}_0^{-1}(s)\bar{Q}(s)$, with $P_0(s)\bar{P}_0^{-1}(s) = U_L(s)$, a unimodular matrix, an observation which clearly establishes the (*row*) *equivalence*[3] of the two numerators, $Q(s)$ and $\bar{Q}(s)$.

To establish the equivalence of any $R(s)$ and any $Q(s)$ that satisfy (3), we first let q denote the rank of $T(s)$ over $\mathscr{P}$, i.e., $q = \rho\{R(s)\}$ and then reduce $T(s)$ to (unique) *McMillan form*[1, 4] via an appropriate unimodular pair $\{U_L(s), U_R(s)\}$. In particular, if $U_L(s)$ and $U_R(s)$ are chosen appropriately,

$$U_L(s)T(s)U_R(s) = U_L(s)R(s)P_c^{-1}(s)U_R(s) = U_L(s)P_0^{-1}(s)Q(s)U_R(s) \tag{9}$$

a $(p \times m)$ matrix which is identically zero except for its first q diagonal elements which will be of the form, $\dfrac{\epsilon_i(s)}{\psi_i(s)}$, with $\epsilon_i(s)$ and $\psi_i(s)$ relatively prime for all $i = 1, 2, \ldots q$, $\epsilon_i(s)$ a monic divisor of $\epsilon_{i+1}(s)$ for $i = 1, 2, \ldots, q-1$, and $\psi_i(s)$ a monic divisor of $\psi_{i-1}(s)$ for $i = 2, 3, \ldots, q$; i.e. the $(q \times q)$ matrix consisting of the first q rows and columns of $U_L(s)T(s)U_R(s)$, namely

$$[U_L(s)T(s)U_R(s)]_q = \text{diag}\left[\frac{\epsilon_i(s)}{\psi_i(s)}\right] = \begin{bmatrix} \frac{\epsilon_1(s)}{\psi_1(s)} & & & 0 \\ & \frac{\epsilon_2(s)}{\psi_2(s)} & & \\ & & \ddots & \\ 0 & & & \frac{\epsilon_q(s)}{\psi_q(s)} \end{bmatrix} \tag{10}$$

In view of (10), it thus follows that we can "factor" the McMillan form of $T(s)$ in either of two (unique) ways; i.e.

$$U_L(s)T(s)U_R(s) = \mathscr{E}(s)\psi_c^{-1}(s) = \psi_0^{-1}(s)\mathscr{E}(s) \tag{11}$$

with the $(p \times m)$ polynomial matrix $\mathscr{E}(s)$ identically zero except for its first q diagonal elements, which equal $\epsilon_i(s)$, $\psi_c(s) = \begin{bmatrix} \text{diag}\,[\psi_i(s)], & 0 \\ 0 & , \; I_{m-q} \end{bmatrix}$ and $\psi_0(s) = \begin{bmatrix} \text{diag}\,[\psi_i(s)], & 0 \\ 0 & , \; I_{p-q} \end{bmatrix}$ By now combining (9) and (11), we find that

$$U_L(s)R(s)P_c^{-1}(s)U_R(s) = U_L(s)P_0^{-1}(s)Q(s)U_R(s) = \mathscr{E}(s)\psi_c^{-1}(s) = \psi_0^{-1}(s)\mathscr{E}(s), \tag{12}$$

which clearly implies that

$$U_L(s)R(s)P_c^{-1}(s)U_R(s)\psi_c(s) = \psi_0(s)U_L(s)P_0^{-1}(s)Q(s)U_R(s) = \mathscr{E}(s) \tag{13}$$

In light of the relative primeness of all of the factorizations in (12), it now follows from (8) that $P_c^{-1}(s)U_R(s)\psi_c(s)$ ($\psi_0(s)U_L(s)P_0^{-1}(s)$) represents a unimodular matrix which we denote as $\bar{U}_R(s)$ ($\bar{U}_L(s)$). Equation (13) thus implies that

$$U_L(s)R(s)\bar{U}_R(s) = \bar{U}_L(s)Q(s)U_R(s) = \mathscr{E}(s), \tag{14}$$

which clearly establishes the equivalence of the numerators, $R(s)$ and $Q(s)$, as well as the theorem.

3. The Zeros of $T(s)$

Now that the equivalence of any two numerators of a rational transfer matrix $T(s)$ has been formally established, the zeros of a linear multivariable system characterized by $T(s)$ can be defined in a number of equivalent ways.

Definition 1 (Rosenbrock [1]). The *zeros* of any $(p \times m)$ rational transfer matrix, $T(s)$, are those scalars, s_i, in $\mathscr{C}$ which zero the individual transfer functions, $\frac{\epsilon_i(s)}{\psi_i(s)}$, which comprise the McMillan form of $T(s)$; i.e. the *zeros* of $T(s)$ are defined as all of the zeros of the $(q = \rho\{T(s)\})\epsilon_i(s)$. The number of zeros is therefore equal to the degree of the polynomial, $\prod_{1}^{q} \epsilon_k(s)$.

Definition 2. Since $\mathscr{E}(s)$, as given by (11), represents the (unique) *Smith form* [1, 5] of the numerator of $T(s)$, it is clear in light of Definition 1 that the *zeros* of $T(s)$ are also equal to the zeros of each of the (q) diagonal elements, $\epsilon_i(s)$, of the Smith form of any numerator of $T(s)$.

Definition 3 (Desoer and Schulman [2]). We now note that for any scalar $s^* \in \mathscr{C}$, with the exception of the zeros, s_i, of $T(s)$, $\rho\{\mathscr{E}(s^*)\} = q$ over $\mathscr{C}$; i.e. $\mathscr{E}(s)$ is a polynomial matrix of *normal rank* q, [2, 6] and

$$\rho\{\mathscr{E}(s_i)\} < q \tag{15}$$

if and only if s_i is a zero of $T(s)$. Since any numerator of $T(s)$ is equivalent to $\mathscr{E}(s)$ and the normal rank of a unimodular matrix is always equal to its dimension, regardless of s, it follows that the *zeros* of $T(s)$ are also equal to those s_i which reduce the normal rank, q, of any numerator of $T(s)$. It might be noted that this definition actually generalizes the one given in [2].

Definition 4. In light of the previous definition, it now follows that the *zeros* of $T(s)$ are those zeros which are common to all of the nonzero, q-order minors of any numerator of $T(s)$.

Definition 5. In view of Definition 4, we now note that if any numerator of $T(s)$ is reduced to *upper right* (when $q \leqslant m \leqslant p$) (*lower left* (when $q \leqslant p \leqslant m$)) *triangular* *form* [7] through an appropriate sequence of *elementary row* (*column*) *operations*; i.e. by premultiplying (postmultiplying) the numerator by an appropriate unimodular matrix, then only one $(q \times q)$ minor of the equivalent numerator will be nonsingular (over $\mathscr{P}$) and its zeros, given by the zeros of the diagonal elements of the triangular portion of the equivalent numerator, will represent the *zeros* of $T(s)$.

Definition 6. Let $\tilde{R}(s) \triangleq R(s)$ whenever $\rho\{R(s)\}$ is equal to the number (m) of system inputs. Otherwise (when $\rho\{R(s)\} = q < m$) we will define $\tilde{R}(s)$ as the $(p + m - q)$ matrix obtained by appending to $R(s)$ any set of $(m - q)$ real row vectors, k_i, so that

$$\rho \left\{ \tilde{R}(s) \triangleq \begin{bmatrix} R(s) \\ k_1 \\ k_2 \\ \vdots \\ k_{m-q} \end{bmatrix} \right\} = m \tag{16}$$

It now follows directly from Definition 5 that the zeros of the determinant of any *greatest* (*common*) *right divisor*, [3, 8] $D(s)$, of (the rows of) $\tilde{R}(s)$ will represent the zeros of the system, $T(s) = R(s)P(s)^{-1}$. More specifically, *if*

$$\tilde{R}(s) = \begin{bmatrix} R(s) \\ k_1 \\ k_2 \\ \vdots \\ k_{m-q} \end{bmatrix} = \hat{R}(s)D(s), \tag{17}$$

with $D(s)$ a greatest right divisor of $\tilde{R}(s)$, then the zeros of the system are, by definition, the zeros of $|D(s)|$. Since any polynomial matrix of full rank can be reduced to column proper form via elementary column operations; i.e. since $\hat{R}(s)U(s)$ is column proper for some unimodular matrix $U(s)$, the factorization, $\hat{R}(s)D(s)$, can always be chosen so that $\hat{R}(s)$ is column proper and, for reasons which will soon become apparent, we will restrict our attention to these cases. We further note that $D(s)$, as given by (17) is also a right divisor of $R(s)$; i.e. if $\hat{R}_p(s)$ is defined as the first p rows of $\hat{R}(s)$, then

$$R(s) = \hat{R}_p(s)D(s) \tag{18}$$

While all of the preceding uniquely and equivalently define the zeros of any system characterized by a rational transfer matrix $T(s)$, it should be noted that Definition 5 perhaps represents the most direct means of computationally determining the zeros of $T(s)$ when $p \neq m$. If $\rho\,[R(s)] = p = m$, $D(s) = R(s)$ and the zeros of $|R(s)|$ are clearly the system zeros.

Definition 6 will now be employed to establish the fact that all of the zeros of a multivariable system characterized by a *proper transfer matrix* ($\lim_{s \to \infty} T(s)$ finite) can be "cancelled" through the employment of an appropriate linear state variable feedback (l.s.v.f.) control law.

4. State Feedback Preliminaries

As noted in Section 2, the $(p \times m)$ transfer matrix $T(s)$ of a linear, time-invariant, multivariable system can always be factored as the product

$$T(s) = R(s)P_c(s)^{-1}, \tag{19}$$

where $R(s)$ and $P_c(s)$ are relatively right prime polynomial matrices in the Laplace operator s, and $P_c(s)$ is *column proper* (defined as the condition that the real matrix consisting of the coefficients of the highest degree s-term or terms in each column of $P_c(s)$ be of full rank). Furthermore, it is also well known[3] that if $T(s)$ is a proper transfer matrix, then the degree of each column of $R(s)$ will be no greater than the degree of each corresponding column of $P_c(s)$; a relation which we succinctly express as

$$\partial_c[R(s)] \leqslant \partial_c[P_c(s)] \tag{20}$$

It is of interest to note that (20) holds for any factorization, $R(s)P(s)^{-1}$, of the proper transfer matrix $T(s)$; i.e. whether $P_c(s)$ is column proper or not.

In view of the results given in [3], we now remark that the net consequence of employing a l.s.v.f. control law to compensate a system characterized by the proper transfer matrix $T(s) = R(s)P_c(s)^{-1}$ is that of replacing $P_c(s)$ by $P_F(s) = [P_c(s) - F(s)]$ in the factorization, where $F(s)$ can be chosen to be any arbitrary $(m \times m)$ polynomial matrix of column degress less than that of $P_c(s)$; i.e. *under l.s.v.f.*†

$$T_F(s) = R(s)P_F^{-1}(s) = R(s)[P_c(s) - F(s)]^{-1} \tag{21}$$

where $F(s)$ can be chosen to be any arbitrary polynomial matrix which satisfies the relation

$$\partial_c[F(s)] < \partial_c[P_c(s)]. \tag{22}$$

5. Zero Cancellation by State Feedback

In view of Definition 6 (Section 3) and the results of Section 4 we can now formally establish

Theorem 2. *Consider any system characterized by a proper rational transfer matrix $T(s) = R(s)P_c^{-1}(s)$, with $R(s)$ and $P_c(s)$ relatively right prime and $P_c(s)$ column proper. If $R(s)$ and $D(s)$ are as defined via Definition 6, then an $F(s)$ which satisfies (22) can be found such that*

$$P_c(s) - F(s) = G(s)D(s) \tag{23}$$

† If $\{A, B, C, E\}$ is a minimal state–space realization of $T(s)$ (see Section 6) then l.s.v.f. would be defined as the control law $u(t) = Fx(t) + v(t)$.

Proof. In order to formally establish this result, we first define $\hat{R}_m(s)$ as any nonsingular column proper matrix obtained by eliminating all but m ordered rows of $\hat{R}(s)$, and $\tilde{R}_m(s)$ as the $(m \times m)$ matrix consisting of these same ordered rows of $\tilde{R}(s)$. In light of [17], it therefore follows that

$$\tilde{R}_m(s) = \hat{R}_m(s)D(s) \tag{24}$$

which in turn implies that

$$\hat{R}_m(s)^{-1} = D(s)\tilde{R}_m(s)^{-1} \tag{25}$$

Since $\hat{R}_m(s)$ is column proper $\hat{R}_m(s)^{-1} = D(s)\tilde{R}_m(s)^{-1}$ is a proper transfer matrix and, consequently,[3]

$$\partial_c[D(s)] \leqslant \partial_c[\tilde{R}_m(s)] \leqslant \partial_c[\tilde{R}(s)] \tag{26}$$

Since $\tilde{T}(s) = \tilde{R}(s)P_c(s)^{-1}$ is also a proper transfer matrix,

$$\partial_c[\tilde{R}(s)] \leqslant \partial_c[P_c(s)], \tag{27}$$

which in turn implies that

$$\partial_c[D(s)] \leqslant \partial_c[P_c(s)] \tag{28}$$

If we now (uniquely) express $P_c(s)D(s)^{-1}$ as the sum of its *quotient*,[3] $G(s)$, and its *strictly proper part,* [3] $F(s)D(s)^{-1}$; i.e. if

$$P_c(s)D(s)^{-1} = F(s)D(s)^{-1} + G(s) \tag{29}$$

then

$$P_c(s) - F(s) = G(s)D(s) \tag{30}$$

with $\partial_c[F(s)] < \partial_c[D(s)] \leqslant \partial_c[P(s)]$, thus establishing the theorem.

It is now clear in view of (18), (21), and (23) that if $F(s)$ as given by (23) defines a particular l.s.v.f. control law, then

$$T_F(s) = R(s)[P_c(s) - F(s)]^{-1} = \hat{R}_p(s)D(s)D(s)^{-1}G(s)^{-1} = \hat{R}_p(s)G(s)^{-1} \tag{31}$$

or that *this particular l.s.v.f. control law results in complete cancellation of all of the defined zeros of* ($|D(s)|$) *the given multivariable system.*

We have now shown that all of the zeros of a proper multivariable system can be cancelled through the employment of an appropriate linear state variable feedback control law. Furthermore, any zeros, thus cancelled, will represent unobservable system modes which lower the "apparent order" of the system, a fact which follows directly from the results given in [3]. In light of these observations, it therefore follows that if the system is driven by a nonzero input equivalent to that which would result, via linear state variable feedback, due to nonzero initial conditions on only these potentially unobservable system modes, then the output will remain identically zero for all time. This observation, which is analogous to one made in [2], extends the well known scalar result, noted in the Introduction, to the multivariable case.

6. State–Space System Zeros

In this section we show that the zeros of a controllable and observable (minimal) multivariable system can be determined directly from any state–space representation of the form

$$\dot{x}(t) = Ax(t) + Bu(t);\ y(t) = Cx(t) + E(D)u(t) \tag{32}$$

with $D = d/dt$, the differential operator. To begin, we note that the $(p \times m)$ rational transfer matrix $T(s)$ of (32) is given by

$$T(s) = C(sI - A)^{-1}B + E(s) \tag{33}$$

Conversely, given any rational $(p \times m)$ transfer matrix $T(s)$, any least order ($n =$ dimension of A) state–space system of the form (32) which satisfies (33) is called a *minimal state–space realization* of $T(s)$. In view of these observations, the notion of the zeros of (a system characterized by) $T(s)$ can now be readily extended to include minimal state–space systems as well; i.e. s^* is a *zero* of (32) if and only if it is a zero of $T(s)$, as given by (33). In view of the above, we can now formally establish

Theorem 3. *Any s^* in $\mathscr{C}$ is a zero of a minimal state–space system of the form* (32) *if and only if*

$$\rho\left\{\begin{bmatrix} -s^*I + A, & B \\ C\ , & E(s^*) \end{bmatrix}\right\} \text{over } \mathscr{C} < \rho\left\{\begin{bmatrix} -sI + A, & B \\ C\ , & E(s) \end{bmatrix}\right\} \text{over } \mathscr{P}. \tag{34}$$

Proof. The proof of this theorem follows rather easily in light of (3) and the following lemma which is due to Rosenbrock.[1]

Lemma. *If* (32) *is a minimal realization of $T(s)$, as given by* (33) *and* (3), *then*

$$\begin{bmatrix} -sI + A, & B \\ C\ , & E(s) \end{bmatrix}, \begin{bmatrix} I_{n-m}, & 0\ , & 0 \\ 0\ , & P_c(s), & I_m \\ 0\ , & R(s)\ , & 0 \end{bmatrix} \text{ and } \begin{bmatrix} I_{n-p}, & 0\ , & 0 \\ 0\ , & P_0(s), & Q(s) \\ 0\ , & I_p\ , & 0 \end{bmatrix}$$

are all unimodular equivalent.

Proof. See [1], Theorem 2.1, Chapter 3, Section 2.

By Rosenbrock's Lemma, it now follows that over $\mathscr{P}$

$$\rho\left\{\begin{bmatrix} -sI + A, & B \\ C\ , & E(s) \end{bmatrix}\right\} = n - m + \rho\left\{\begin{bmatrix} P_c(s), & I_m \\ R(s), & 0 \end{bmatrix}\right\}, \tag{35}$$

or that

$$\rho\left\{\begin{bmatrix} -sI + A, & B \\ C\ , & E(s) \end{bmatrix}\right\} = n + \rho\{R(s)\}; \tag{36}$$

i.e. the rank of the minimal system matrix $\begin{bmatrix} -sI + A, & B \\ C, & E(s) \end{bmatrix}$ is solely dependent on the rank of a numerator of $T(s)$. Since s^* is a zero of (32) if and only if $\rho\{R(s^*)\}$ over $\mathscr{C} < \rho\{R(s)\}$ over $\mathscr{P}$, it is clear in view of (36) that s^* is a zero of (32) if and only if (34) holds, thus establishing the theorem.

A number of remarks are now in order.

Remark 1. We first note that *if $\rho\{B$ and $C\} \geqslant \min(p, m) \triangleq r$ over $\mathscr{R}$, then the normal rank of* $\begin{bmatrix} -sI + A, & B \\ C, & E(s) \end{bmatrix}$ *will be $n + r$*, an observation which directly follows from the results given in [3], although the details associated with the formal establishment of this fact will not be presented here. Under these conditions, the zeros of a minimal state–space system can be found by simply determining those s^* which reduce the normal rank $(n + r)$ of $\begin{bmatrix} -s^*I + A, & B \\ C, & E(s^*) \end{bmatrix}$. To demonstrate, let us consider the following minimal state–space system of the form (32), with

$$A = \begin{bmatrix} 0 & 1 & 0 \\ 1 & -1 & 2 \\ 0 & 1 & -3 \end{bmatrix}, \quad B = \begin{bmatrix} 0 & 0 \\ 1 & 2 \\ 0 & 1 \end{bmatrix}, \quad C = \begin{bmatrix} 1 & 1 & -2 \\ 1 & 0 & 1 \end{bmatrix}, \quad \text{and } E(D) = \begin{bmatrix} 0 & 0 \\ 0 & 0 \end{bmatrix}.$$

Since B and C are both of rank $r = 2$, the normal rank of $\begin{bmatrix} -sI + A, & B \\ C, & E(s) \end{bmatrix}$ is $5 = n + r$, and the zeros of this system are given by those s^* for which the system matrix

$$\begin{bmatrix} -s^*I + A, & B \\ C, & E(s^*) \end{bmatrix} = \begin{bmatrix} -s^* & 1 & 0 & 0 & 0 \\ 1 & -s^* - 1 & 2 & 1 & 2 \\ 0 & 1 & -s^* - 3 & 0 & 1 \\ 1 & 1 & -2 & 0 & 0 \\ -1 & 0 & 1 & 0 & 0 \end{bmatrix}$$

is singular. Therefore, since the determinant of the system matrix is equal to $-s^* - 3$, we conclude that the system has a single zero at $s = -3$. To verify this observation in light of the results given in Section 3 we first note that $T(s) = C(sI - A)^{-1}B + E(s)$ can be factored as $R(s)P(s)^{-1}$ with, for example, $R(s) = \begin{bmatrix} s + 1 & -2 \\ 1 & 1 \end{bmatrix}$ and $P_c(s) = \begin{bmatrix} s^2 + 3s - 1, & -2s - 8 \\ -s, & s + 3 \end{bmatrix}$. Since $|R(s)| = s + 3$, $s = -3$ is the only scalar in $\mathscr{C}$ which reduces the normal rank of the numerator, $R(s)$, which confirms the fact that -3 is the only zero of the system.

Remark 2. In view of Remark 1, it is now clear that *if* $\rho\{B$ *and* $C\} \geq r$, *then the minimal system* (32) *has a zero at the origin* ($s^* = 0$) *if and only if*

$$\rho\left\{\begin{bmatrix} A & B \\ C & E(0) \end{bmatrix}\right\} < n + r \tag{37}$$

It is of interest and importance to note that the determination of the rank of $\begin{bmatrix} A & B \\ C & E(0) \end{bmatrix}$ (usually with $E(s) = E$, a constant matrix) is equivalent to the determination of the presence or absence of any system zeros at the origin of the complex plane. The importance of locating system zeros at $s = 0$ has already been demonstrated in a variety of applications, e.g., in step disturbance elimination studies,[9] static decoupling,[10] the design of integral feedback and feedforward regulators,[11] and in classifying multivariable systems according to "type".[12]

Remark 3. We finally note that if a given state–space system is uncontrollable, unobservable, or both, then the uncontrollable and/or unobservable "modes" of the system will appear as "cancellable" pole–zero terms in the transfer matrix of the system.[3] Rosenbrock defines any such uncontrollable (unobservable) system modes as *input (output) decoupling zeros*,[1] although we prefer to call these modes *non-minimal zeros* or *non-minimal poles* since they occur only in non-minimal systems and "cancel out" of both the numerator and denominator of the transfer matrix of the system. In view of this observation, we now note that *any non-minimal zeros of a system do not correspond to the defined (minimal) zeros which characterize the transfer matrix of the system*, although both the minimal and non-minimal zeros of a system can be shown to reduce the normal rank of a general (not necessarily minimal) state–space system matrix, $\begin{bmatrix} -sI + A, & B \\ C\ , & E(s) \end{bmatrix}$. While the formal establishment of this latter fact is relatively straightforward and not unlike the proof of Theorem 3, it does involve certain additional steps and notions which would significantly lengthen this report. Furthermore, a more general result can actually be obtained; i.e. by combining the results given in [1] and [3], in view of the proof of Theorem 3, it is not difficult to show that *the minimal and non-minimal zeros of any general differential operator representation:* $P(D)z(t) = Q(D)u(t)$; $y(t) = R(D)z(t) + W(D)u(t)$ *are equal to those* s^* *in* $\mathscr{C}$ *which reduce the normal rank of the system matrix,* $\begin{bmatrix} -P(s) & Q(s) \\ R(s) & W(s) \end{bmatrix}$.

7. Conclusions

The numerator of any system characterized by a ($p \times m$) rational transfer matrix $T(s)$ was defined as any $R(s)(Q(s))$ in a relatively right (left) prime factorization, $R(s)P_c^{-1}(s)\,(P_0^{-1}(s)Q(s))$, of $T(s)$. The fact that any two numerators of $T(s)$ are equivalent was then formally established and employed to define the zeros of the system in a number of alternative but equivalent ways. A constructive proof of the fact that all of the defined zeros of a proper linear multivariable system can be cancelled via an appropriate linear state variable feedback control law was then presented. It was observed that any zeros, thus cancelled, will represent unobservable system modes which, in turn, implies an identically zero output for certain initial conditions and nonzero inputs. It was then shown that the zeros of a multivariable system in state–space form could be directly determined via a matrix rank test. The significance of this state–space matrix rank test when $s^* = 0$ was noted, and an example was presented to illustrate the procedure. The distinction between minimal and non-minimal system zeros was also discussed.

We finally note that this paper represents an almost verbatim compilation of the results presented in three earlier notes[13–15] which were published in the I.E.E.E. Transactions on Automatic Control. These are copyright (1973 and 1974), The Institute of Electrical and Electronics Engineers, Inc and their material is reprinted, by permission, from the I.E.E.E. Transactions on Automatic Control.

8. References

[1] Rosenbrock, H. H., 1970, *State–Space and Multivariable Theory*, New York: Wiley.

[2] Desoer, C. A. and Schulman, J. D., "Zeros and poles of matrix transfer functions and their dynamical interpretation", *Electron. Res. Lab.,* Univ. California, Berkeley, Tech. Memo. ERL-M366, Oct. 1972.

[3] Wolovich, W. A., 1974, *Linear Multivariable Systems*, New York: Springer–Verlag.

[4] McMillan, B., "Introduction to formal realizability theory, II", *Bell Syst. Tech. J.*, Vol. 31, pp. 541–600, May 1952.

[5] Turnbull, H. W. and Aitken, A. C., 1961, *An Introduction to the Theory of Canonical Matrices*. New York: Dover.

[6] Belevitch, V., 1968, *Classical Network Theory*. San Francisco, Calif.: Holden-Day.

[7] Gantmacher, F. R., 1960, *The Theory of Matrices*. New York: Chelsea.

[8] MacDuffee, C. C., 1956, *The Theory of Matrices*. New York: Chelsea.

[9] Davison, E. J. and Smith, H. W., "Pole assignment in linear, time-invariant, multivariable systems with constant disturbances", *Automatica*, Vol. 7, pp. 489–498, July 1971.

[10] Wolovich, W. A., "Static Decoupling", *I.E.E.E. Transactions on Automatic Control*, October 1973, pp. 536–537.

[11] Smith, H. W. and Davison, E. J., "Design of industrial regulators: Integral feedback and feedforward control", *Proc. Inst. Elec. Eng.*, Vol. 119, pp. 1210–1215, Aug. 1972.

[12] Sandell, N. Jr. and Athans, M., "On 'type L' multivariable linear systems", *Automatica*, Vol. 9, pp. 131–136, Jan. 1973.

[13] Wolovich, W. A., "On Determining the Zeros of State–Space Systems", *I.E.E.E. Transactions on Automatic Control*, Oct. 1973, pp. 542–544.

[14] Wolovich, W. A., "On the Numerators and Zeros of Rational Transfer Matrices", *I.E.E.E. Transactions on Automatic Control*, Oct. 1973, pp. 544–546.

[15] Wolovich, W. A., "On the Cancellation of Multivariable System Zeros by State Feedback", *I.E.E.E. Transactions on Automatic Control*, June 1974, pp. 276–277.

Subject Index